Understanding and Teaching **Arithmetic**

in the Elementary School

Understanding and Teaching

in the

NEW YORK

Arithmetic

Elementary School

E. T. McSWAIN
School of Education, Northwestern University

RALPH J. COOKE

HOLT, RINEHART AND WINSTON

Library of Congress Catalog Card Number: 58–6306

September, 1960

25638–0118

Printed in the United States of America

Preface

THIS BOOK has been written, primarily, for teachers in service and students preparing to teach in the elementary school. The purpose of the authors has been to prepare a teaching guide which may be helpful to teachers and prospective teachers who desire to improve their understanding of the meanings, vocabulary, and mathematical operations that constitute the language and science of arithmetic and who want to present instructional methods and materials in the classroom that may motivate and assist pupils in experiencing purpose, meaning, interests, and satisfactions from their study and use of arithmetic.

The concepts that underlie the content of chapters may be so stated:

1. Arithmetic is a language and a number system which is universally adopted to identify, to record, and to communicate ideas about form and amount of quantity and relationship which may exist among quantities.

2. Children, during the elementary school years, should discover and should develop meanings and skills which form the foundation of their mental abilities in arithmetic.

3. Each pupil should have the opportunity to find in the classroom professional guidance and resource materials and situations on which he may rely in developing a mental system and language of arithmetic that is consistent with the meanings, computational operations, and principles in the Hindu-Arabic system of numbers and mathematical thinking.

4. The mathematical sequence in curriculum and teaching procedures affects the processes in quantitative thinking and the number system created and developed in the mind of each pupil.

5. Teachers render an important service to children and society by observing curriculum and teaching methods which motivate and assist pupils in building a mental foundation in arithmetic to sustain further study in mathematics in high school and to meet the mathematical requirements in various occupational fields.

The design of presentation for each chapter includes: an introductory statement, a list of exploratory questions, an interpretation of certain mathematical meanings and computational operations, suggestions concerning teaching procedures, exercises, a list of questions for self-evaluation, and a list of selected references. The topic or topics are developed in a language that may arouse mental inquiry, may facilitate quantitative thinking, and may contribute to improved professional competency in understanding and teaching arithmetic. The authors have considered each chapter as an opportunity to think with teachers about the topics which are found in a typical curriculum in arithmetic.

The book is dedicated to the many teachers who are rendering an indispensable service to American society through their daily effort to guide and enrich the learnings in arithmetic of millions of future adults who will need a meaningful foundation in the language and science of elementary mathematics in dealing realistically and effectively with the numerous opportunities which will characterize the nation's future.

March 15, 1958

E.T.McS.
R.J.C.

Contents

1

Importance of Arithmetic in the Elementary School

"Arithmetic is the foundation of all mathematics, pure and applied. It is the most useful of all sciences, and there is probably no other branch of human knowledge which is so widely spread among the masses."—Tobias Dantzig[1]

Introduction

American children are under the professional guidance of elementary school teachers for about 1000 hours each year for six or eight years, depending on the organizational pattern of the school system. The quality of learning each pupil experiences during these 6000-8000 hours in the classroom will have a continuing effect on maturing interest in and understanding of education as a process in developing strength in personality and mind. The psychological methods used in learning will condition the child's understanding of each subject and its value in his personal and social living.

Teachers in the elementary school have the opportunity to provide instruction, learning situations, and materials that motivate and assist pupils in learning the meanings and terms in arithmetic and

[1]Tobias Dantzig, *Numbers: The Language of Science,* New York: The Macmillan Company, 1930, pp. 36-37.

the thought processes required in mathematical computation. To the degree that teachers are successful in helping pupils to understand the meanings and operations in arithmetic and to appreciate the value of foundational mathematics in modern society, these young citizens may be personally motivated to continue their study of more advanced mathematics in high school. Also, they will develop understandings, values, and skills by which to comprehend more fully the indispensable service that mathematics has rendered to man in his great achievement during the past century in research, industry, commerce, agriculture, and the professions.

Exploratory Questions

Questions or problems may be useful in motivating mental curiosity and exploration. The authors suggest to teachers and prospective teachers that they consider the response they may give to each question before reading this chapter and subsequent chapters in the book. A re-examination of the reader's interpretation of arithmetic, its importance in the curriculum, the nation's shortage of creative manpower in mathematics and other sciences, and the purpose in teaching mathematical meanings may stimulate thought and action to improve curriculum and instruction.

1. How may an understanding of the language and meanings in arithmetic help pupils to find personal motivation and reason to pursue the study of mathematics in high school?
2. What has been the role of arithmetic and mathematics in advancing the standards of employment, production, and living in modern society?
3. What conditions and trends reveal the demand for more persons prepared in mathematics and in one or more of the other sciences?
4. How may the elementary school help to reduce the shortage of mathematicians and other scientists?
5. What do you interpret to be the meaning and function of foundational mathematics or arithmetic?
6. How may the teacher's understanding of arithmetic affect the pupils' interest in and understanding of arithmetic?
7. Where do the language vocabulary and operations in arithmetic have meaning and value for pupils?
8. How may the curriculum and instruction be used to assist pupils

to develop psychological sequence when learning meanings and developing mental skills in arithmetic?

Arithmetic's Contribution to the Progress of Society

The American people are living in an industrial or technological society. The transition from an agrarian pattern to the technological pattern in industry, employment, and economics has been achieved largely in the past one hundred and fifty years. Research and the application of the discoveries in research that have been made in industry, agriculture, commerce, and the military forces have produced a variety of new inventions and methods to accelerate societal change, to introduce many opportunities in occupational employment, and to increase the nation's productivity. These advances in industry, commerce, and the professions have made available to a greater number of people higher standards of work and living than can be found in any other nation of the world. This unprecedented achievement of human endeavor would have been impossible without arithmetic, the science of mathematics, and the other sciences. Mathematics has become a universal language and science.

Reasonable is the hypothesis that continued change can be expected in all fields of human enterprise during the second half of this century. The billions of dollars invested annually by industry and the federal government in research will open the way for further advance in production, health, education, communication, and transportation. Teachers have the opportunity to observe the conditions and trends of social change so that they may envisage the probable developments in the next few decades and study the implications for improvements in the curriculum and instruction in the schools. The yesterdays cannot be relived, but people may learn from their cultural heritage information and ideas that are useful in better understanding the resourceful, dynamic present. From the values, thought, and action of people who live and work in the present are fashioned the plans, hopes, and probable achievements of the nation's next fifty years.

Some of the salient conditions and trends to be observed and which offer the potential for accelerated change in many areas of society in the next few decades are: (1) The recent rise in the nation's population because of the annual number of births and the number of persons living beyond the age 65; (2) the increase in speed and range of modern transportation, especially in aviation; (3) the exchange of ideas and information through radio, press, and television among the people of this nation and peoples of the world; (4) the application of electronics and automation in industry and business; (5) the discovery and control of nuclear fission as a new source of mechanical power; (6) the amount of money invested in private and public research; (7) the realization that another world war would bring mass destruction of people and property; and (8) the growth in interdependence among nations for raw materials, economic trade, and conditions to bring about world peace. The changes that came during the first half of this century were unprecedented. The dynamic potential in existing conditions and trends at midcentury can be expected to produce greater change in the second half of the century. Mathematics will be a major instrument and process in the implementation of societal advance.

The Obligation of the Elementary Schools

A survey of the historical record shows that the elementary schools served the children and the nation well during the past fifty-year period of tremendous societal change. Teachers of that period deserve high commendation for their leadership. The changing times place a heavier obligation upon teachers and administrators. Emphasis should be directed to the educational needs of an expanding society and the improvements that must be made in the program and instruction of the schools so that young people may better prepare themselves for higher requirements to be encountered in adult occupations and community citizenship.

Children draw heavily upon curriculum and instructional methods for resource assistance in discovering and refining interests, meanings, and values in all subjects. Each pupil follows his unique biological and psychological rate of growth patterns in developing from year to year the content and meaning of his maturing personality and mind. Differences in ability and progress among pupils in each classroom reveal a normal situation. A reasonable goal for teachers is that they take time to plan activities, to select materials, and to use methods that will help each pupil to experience maximum development from year to year in each subject. All children in attendance in the nation's elementary schools will face in a relatively few years the opportunities and duties of early adulthood. They will need, and employment will demand of them, functional competence in their understanding and use of arithmetic as a language and a thought process. Teachers should reach agreement regarding the knowledge pupils should possess about arithmetic and its social value upon completion of the elementary school.

An Interpretation of Arithmetic

Arithmetic includes more than personal figuring or business calculation. The meanings, principles, and computational concepts were formulated as creative minds struggled to develop a mathematical language and system to use in dealing with practical affairs and also theoretical inquiry. In early civilization scholars made no effort to differentiate between practical arithmetic and the science of mathematics. Their concern and their objective were to invent and refine, based on experimentation and critical thinking, a logical system and language that would be useful in identifying the concrete, in recording quantitative thinking, in exploring the unknown in their environments, and in dealing meaningfully and effectively with practical situations. Many years were devoted to mental inquiry into and observation of the development of words and symbols to identify concrete objects and groups of objects, a system of numerical notation, the mathematical theories and generalizations involved in mental computation with integers, fractions, and decimal fractions. The language and structure of arithmetic, and the foundation of the science of mathematics were reaching a level of tentative completion by the seventeenth century. Universal recognition was rapidly given to such foundational meanings as: (1) one-to-one relationship between objects, man's idea of objects, and symbols to represent ideas of objects; (2) the numerical value of digits 1, 2, 3, 4, 5, 6, 7, 8, and 9; (3) the principle and function of place value, the quantitative meanings to be identified with integers, common fractions, decimal fractions, and percents; (4) the numerical functions of the symbol zero (0); (5) the properties related to geometric lines and forms; and (6) the mathematical meanings required in accurate mental computation. The man-invented ideas, symbols, and computational process illustrate only a small but essential part of the mathematical heritage that has become universal in application and that has been so useful in man's efforts to know more about his world, to improve his living and working conditions, to advance a theory of numbers, and to effect expansion and efficiency in industry and trade. Arithmetic has become the foundation, and advanced mathematics the superstructure, in man's most important of all the sciences, the science of mathematics.

The record and content of man's mathematical heritage can be found by reference to books, articles, and textbooks. These resource media may be used by teachers to discover, organize, and refine their understanding of the content and structure of arithmetic. The theory, nature, and structure of arithmetic are found in the cumulative writing of scholars who shared in creating and refining a language and number system that has become universal. Further developments will become accepted when supported by research. Arithmetic, therefore, may be interpreted to be: (1) a science of numbers, (2) a language system for quantitative thinking and communication, (3) a system of notation, and (4) a system of meanings and operations useful to man in finding answers to quantitative questions and in seeking solutions to quantitative problems. When a person wants to record an amount he uses a number. When he desires to compare two numbers he uses subtraction. When he wants to change a number into equal component numbers he divides. The meanings and structure of arithmetic are used in mental thought. The results of mental thought are identified by number. Arithmetic is a man-made language and number system that is used in mental or mathematical thought and communication.

The Teacher's Understanding of Arithmetic

Each has learned through mental interaction with instructors, courses, textbooks, and library references his own interpretation of the meanings, terminology, and computational principles that constitute the substance of arithmetic. In the degree to which teachers have discovered, interpreted, and refined through mental processes the meanings, vocabulary, and computational procedures consistent with the logical structure system and language in arithmetic, they experience personal understanding and satisfaction in their use of arithmetic. They also find professional satisfaction from the sharing and guidance given to pupils who are engaged in the mental process leading to the discovery, interpretation, and acceptance of similar mathematical meanings, vocabulary, and operational procedures.

The nature and uniqueness of learning prevents teachers from imparting or transferring to pupils their knowledge of arithmetic. A pupil may memorize the mathematical statement $3 + 4 = 7$ by frequent repetition of the teacher's oral instruction. The meanings involved in the statement are learned, however, only when he derives a mathematical interpretation from concrete situations assisted by the mature friendly guidance of the teacher. Teachers who have gained an abstract knowledge of arithmetic from memorizing rules and performing rote drills may experience some difficulty in interpreting properly mathematical meanings and vocabulary and in providing situations, material, and guidance by which pupils may discover and properly understand these important learnings in arithmetic.

An examination of the response given to these questions may reveal the difference between abstract learning and meaning learning as related to some mathematical meanings and principles.

1. What is the meaning of an integer? A common fraction?
2. What is the mathematically correct interpretation of subtraction?
3. What does the multiplicand represent in a multiplication example?
4. What change in thought is required when in dividing common fractions the divisor is inverted and multiplication is then used?
5. What is the mathematical function of the divisor in division?
6. What meaning is involved in the abstract rule, "To change a common fraction to lower terms, divide the denominator and numerator by the same number"?
7. What mathematical meaning can be applied to an integer, a common fraction, and a decimal fraction?
8. Why is the quotient in division always less than one when the dividend is a number smaller than the number used for the divisor?

One purpose of the authors when writing this book was to present questions, to give an interpretation of mathematical meanings and operations consistent with the system and language of arithmetic, and to provide illustrations of mathematical meanings and computational thought processes that may be useful to persons who desire to examine and to refine their understandings in arithmetic. The mathematical meanings have been expressed in language easy for pupils to interpret and consistent with the accuracy of the meanings in arithmetic. An emphasis has been given to meaningful interpretation and explanation rather than to abstract analysis and theory of numbers. The authors accept the view that the primary objective in teaching arithmetic in the elementary school is to assist pupils in discovering and understanding meanings, vocabulary, and computational operations, so that they may use these learnings with reasonable speed and accuracy and through such use develop interest and understanding of the value of arithmetic in personal life and in modern society.

Pupils Create Their Mental Interpretations of Arithmetic

Thought is a process involving the behavior of the whole organism. Learnings are discovered, examined, refined, and used only in the thought process. Research supports the generally accepted idea that each pupil is biologically, psychologically, and emotionally a unique individual. The child calls into play one or more of the five senses to obtain impressions of objects, persons, and situations in his interacting environment. Previous learnings are used, as needed, to create mental interpretations of the sensory impressions. What he accepts for use he learns. He may borrow through memory and unexamined acceptance the words, statements, explanations, and information conveyed in oral or written communication from other persons. He must, however, through his use of the thought process, create his own meanings, values, and skills. The value of each classroom experience depends on the quality of meaningful interpretations and learnings created, appraised, and accepted during each mental experience.

While pupils may engage in a physical act with little conscious planning, the learnings created or refined in this kind of situation are affected by the quality of the thought process. When interacting with teacher, peer associates, parents, concrete situations, and resource material, each pupil creates, appraises, refines, and organizes his interpretation of the meanings, vocabulary, and mathematical operations that are the structure and substance in arithmetic. As the pupil experiences sequential development in learning meanings, terms, and computation principles consistent with those found in arithmetic he builds, mentally, an understanding of the meaning and use of arithmetic in personal living and a meaningful interpretation of the value and use of arithmetic in contemporary society.

Easy and practical situations that involve arithmetic may be quickly interpreted and solved. The mental use of counting or adding in simple practical situations presents no difficulty for children. Large numbers and abstract computation present a more complex thought process. Time, guidance, encouragement, and concrete situations and materials are required if pupils are to comprehend properly the meanings and terms involved in abstract computation. Arithmetic is a logical, sequential system. Each pupil needs guidance and the means to discover and to build mentally a logical and sequential system that is consistent with the man-made and universally used language and system in arithmetic.

The difficulties that many pupils experience in their learning of and work in arithmetic are not to be found in the language and system of foundational mathematics. They are learned difficulties. They emerge from meaningless exercises or incorrect learning and in many instances from classroom situations that stress memorization of abstract rules, abstract drill, and rote learning. The important meanings, vocabulary, and operations in arithmetic are not difficult to learn, provided means are given to develop a logical and sequential thought system. More maturity in learning in arithmetic is required to compute the answer to the mathematical question $24 \times 36 = ?$ than is required to find the answer to the question $3 \times 2 = ?$ or $5 \times 6 = ?$ A program and teaching methods that recognize the logical sequence in arithmetic will reduce, if not eliminate, the causes of difficulties and negative attitudes learned by some pupils during their work in arithmetic.

Pupils who show progress in reading, language, or other subjects should experience no difficulty in learning the meanings and thought processes involved in mental arithmetic. Differences in the developmental pattern and growth rate among children may cause some pupils to be more rapid achievers in arithmetic than other pupils. All pupils, or most of the pupils, when given the means and guidance to motivate mental observation, to foster interpretation of relationship between ideas and symbols, to stimulate mental imagination and inquiry, to illustrate mathematical meanings, and to apply learnings to social situations should possess a meaningful knowledge of the foundation in mathematics when they complete the elementary school. The quality of instruction, situations, and resource materials does affect mental understanding and use of arithmetic. The need for an extensive program in remedial arithmetic may have its roots in the curriculum and instruction rather than in the ability and mental behavior of pupils.

Teaching Meanings in Arithmetic

Teaching pupils to understand the meanings in the number system is not a new method. Many teachers who have understood the nature and operational structure of arithmetic have for years adopted teaching procedures and have used selected materials thought to be effective in helping pupils to learn the mathematical meanings and to develop mental processes required for use of these meanings with accuracy. They have emphasized a program in the classroom that gave proper emphasis to instructional guidance, meaningful and sustaining practice, and the application of mathematical meanings and principles in personal and community activities.

Instructional methods used to help pupils to learn with meaning the nature and structure of arithmetic and to develop thought processes consistent with the number system are based upon established concepts. One recognizes arithmetic to be a language and numerical system that man has created and refined through years of study and experimentation. There are universally accepted meanings and principles, such as: (1) The numerical value of a digit depends upon its notated place in the decimal system; (2) a number may show a collective meaning or a position in a number series; (3) the sum in addition is a number that is the total amount of the units represented by the addends; (4) only like value fractions can be grouped by addition or multiplication; (5) when one component number of a given number is known, the other component number can be found by finding the difference between the given number and its component; (6) the principles governing computation are found in arithmetic, but the actual computation is a thought process; and (7) the zero is a symbol used in notation to show the absence of units in any value position (304). Each pupil's interpretation of these and other mathematical meanings and principles and of mathematical terms and symbols depends on the thought process. Counting is governed by mathematical principles, but its meaning and use are in the thought process. The example, 24 ft $\div$ 6 ft $=$?, asks a specific mathematical question. The answer may be found by applying certain mathematical meanings during the thought process and then notating it.

An abstract rule may be memorized as a verbal statement, such as, "Only digits with like place value may be added." The rule may be useful in abstract addition, but it offers pupils little, if any, understanding of the mathematical meanings and place value that justify the rule. Pupils who memorize abstract rules and achieve computation skills through much drill are able to show a degree of competence in abstract computation, but may be unable to explain the mathematical meanings used in mental computation and to give a correct interpretation of the answer. An abstract rule has no meaning in the mind of the pupil. A rule to be meaningful must be formulated in the thinking of the pupil as he derives its meaning in concrete situations. Pupils who are deprived of the means to discover and understand mathematical meanings and operations can easily learn to dislike arithmetic and refrain from further study in mathematics when permitted to elect another subject.

Teaching for meanings in arithmetic involves methods that make use of: (1) concrete materials and practical situations; (2) questions and problems to arouse mental curiosity, experimentation, and verification; (3) application of imagination and inquiry to different ways to solve examples and problems; (4) illustration and explanation of a new mathematical meaning or principle by the teacher; (5) definite instruction periods; (6) time for reteaching; (7) diagnostic procedures and instruments to determine the needs and progress of pupils; (8) properly designed and spaced practice periods; (9) time for pupils to summarize and re-examine previous learnings; (10) audiovisual teaching and learning aids; (11) flexible grouping of pupils; (12) the use of persons and situations in the community to enrich the classroom curriculum; (13) special assignments for rapid achievers in arithmetic; and (14) field trips and resource materials to help pupils to understand the contribution made by foundational mathematics to societal progress.

A Sequentially Developed Curriculum

If not properly interpreted and designed, an experience curriculum may result in incidental, accidental, and faulty learnings. Teachers, by their professional preparation, are expected to know the meanings and thought processes in arithmetic that are to be learned by pupils in the primary grades, in the intermediate grades, and in the junior high school. They are more effective as teachers when they select appropriate situations and materials and use teaching methods that assist pupils to learn in psychological sequence these mathematical meanings and thought processes.

Teachers may determine the appropriateness and effectiveness of instruction and work in arithmetic by examining their answers to such questions as these:

1. Have I prepared a summary of the meanings and thought processes I expect pupils to learn during the year in arithmetic?

2. Have I obtained materials to be used by pupils in discovering and understanding the different meanings and thought processes?

3. Is sufficient time allowed for pupils to think about what they are learning and how they are learning it?

4. Do I provide instructional periods with the definite purpose of sharing with pupils my understanding as means to foster self-discovery and self-learning of arithmetical meanings, terms, and computational operations on the part of all pupils?

5. Have I obtained audiovisual aids and supplementary materials to motivate curiosity, exploration, and meaningful learning?

6. Do I use diagnostic instruments and interviews to determine each pupil's interpretation and understanding of the different meanings, terms, and computation processes?

7. Are pupils given the opportunity to use the textbook to stimulate thoughtful reading and discovery of mathematical meanings through examination of illustrative pictures and diagrams, and to use purposeful practice to improve mental computational problem solving?

8. Do I use field trips and resource persons to foster interest in and awareness of the importance of applied arithmetic in the modern world?

9. Have I prepared a list of the mathematical terms that pupils should be expected to understand and to use correctly in written and oral work?

10. Do I strive to correlate the pupils' learnings in arithmetic with their work in other subjects?

11. Do I find interest, enjoyment, and satisfaction in the methods and materials I use to help pupils to learn meanings and to develop mental skills in arithmetic?

12. Do I invite parents to my room to help them better to understand my objectives, methods, and materials in teaching arithmetic?

Also, do I offer suggestions that may assist parents to supplement the classroom curriculum?

Teachers may find useful such questions as these in appraising the results of their instruction:

1. Do the pupils show interest in and curiosity about their work in arithmetic?

2. How frequently do pupils ask questions concerning the meaning and value of their work in arithmetic?

3. Are pupils able to give an illustration or to construct a drawing to show the meaning and accuracy of an answer in computation?

4. Can the pupils give a mathematically correct interpretation of the meaning and use of different terms and symbols?

5. Do pupils understand the principle of the one-to-one relationship?

6. Do pupils understand the meaning of place value in notation and computation?

7. How often do pupils bring to the classroom problems and materials to illustrate meanings they have learned in arithmetic?

8. Do pupils understand that computation is a thought process and written numbers are used to show the progress and result of their thinking?

9. Do the pupils interpret the textbook as a source where they can obtain explanation and illustrations of mathematical meanings, or do they think only practice examples and problems are to be found in the textbook?

10. What do diagnostic procedures reveal to be the weaknesses and strengths of individual pupils in their use of arithmetic?

11. What materials are to be found in the classroom to aid individual pupils or small groups in improving their interpretation of arithmetical meanings and principles?

12. Do the pupils understand the relationship between the universally adopted language and system in arithmetic and the language and system they create and organize in their mind?

Summary

Arithmetic is a language and a number system. It is the foundation of high school and college mathematics. The technological advance in modern society would have been impossible without the use of arithmetic and higher mathematics.

Conditions and trends in present-day society offer the potential for and indicate the probability of continued progress in all areas of human endeavor in the second half of the twentieth century. Teachers have the opportunity to examine the implications in these societal changes for improvement in the curriculum and instruction in all subjects, and especially in arithmetic and science. There is a crucial shortage of properly prepared mathematicians and scientists. The quality of learning experienced by pupils in arithmetic will affect ability and desire to pursue their study of mathematics in high school.

Arithmetic has been developed through the centuries by creative scholars. The results of their research and experimentation may be found in library references and textbooks. Each teacher, however, has learned his interpretation of the meaning and value of this heritage. Teachers who possess an understanding of the meanings and operations in arithmetic find means and satisfaction in helping pupils to learn mathematical meanings and operations consistent with universal arithmetic. Time, resource materials, and professional guidance are essential in helping pupils to develop meaningful understanding of arithmetic and its application in quantitative thought and problem solving. Textbooks and concrete visual aids can be most effective in supplementing the teacher's instruction in the classroom.

School people can be more productive in serving the needs of pupils and the needs of a dynamic society when curriculum and instruction provide young people the means to learn the meanings in arithmetic and to develop abilities in using the language and number system in dealing with situations and problems in everyday life. Teachers should examine frequently their understandings in arithmetic. The needs and progress of pupils can be diagnosed by teacher-constructed questions and instruments, supplemented by standardized tests. Teaching meanings in arithmetic cannot be left to children's interests and activities. Teachers who understand the language and meanings in arithmetic are successful in helping pupils to comprehend the meaning and value of arithmetic in modern society. The survival of technology and American democracy is dependent in a large measure on the success of elementary schools in helping pupils to acquire the foundational preparation for continued study in mathematics and in the other sciences.

SELECTED REFERENCES

1. Allen, Frederick, *The Big Change*. New York: Harper & Brothers 1952.

2. Dantzig, Tobias, *Numbers: The Language of Science*. New York: The Macmillan Company, 1930.

3. Drucker, Peter F., *America's Next Twenty Years*. New York: Harper, 1957.

4. Educational Policies Commission, *Manpower and Education*. Washington, D. C.: National Education Association, 1956.

5. Kramer, Edna E., *The Main Stream of Mathematics*. London: Oxford University Press, 1950.

6. Sanford, V. A., *A Short History of Mathematics*. Boston: Houghton Mifflin Company, 1930.

7. Sarnoff, David, *et al.*, *The Fabulous Future*. New York: E. P. Dutton & Co., Inc., 1956.

2

The Meaning of Numbers and Number Systems

Introduction

Arithmetic is an invented language and structured system of quantitative concepts and numbers. Number concepts and the structure of computation were developed to deal logically with practical situations. Arithmetic is a science and theory of numbers. The concepts of numbers and computation are in the minds of individuals. The symbols that are generally referred to as numbers are convenient devices used to record or to communicate ideas of quantity and relationship of quantity.

The historical story of man's struggle to create and structure a logical system of notation and computation covers many centuries. The thought process has evolved from direct contact with objects, to mental perception, and then to names and number symbols. The number or mathematical meanings of numbers does not reside in the number symbols and computation. They are the product of mental perception and quantitative thinking. The meaning of numbers and computation has been expanded from earlier ideas about counting numbers to more complex concepts of magnitude, such as fractions, denominate numbers, irrational and literal numbers.

Exploratory Questions

The content of this chapter has been designed to assist individuals in developing mathematical concepts consistent with the nature and structure of numbers and the decimal number system used in notation and computation. Teachers may find it helpful to appraise their interpretation of numbers and the decimal number system by considering what they think is an appropriate answer to each of the following questions.

1. What is the meaning of a number? What is the relation between number concepts and number symbols?

2. What method did primitive man use to count and to do computation?

3. What number concepts and notation symbols were used by the Greeks? The Romans? The Hindus? The Arabs?

4. What revolutionary step was achieved by the creation of the meaning and application of zero?

5. What features of the Hindu-Arabic system of numbers and notation caused it to be accepted as a universal number system?

6. What thought process is involved in the one-to-one correspondence between objects, number concepts, and notated numbers?

7. What is the cardinal meaning of a number? The ordinal meaning of a number?

8. What is the meaning and function of place value and digits in the decimal number system?

9. What is a group? Where is the numerical meaning of a group of objects to be found? How does a number identify a group?

10. How may teachers help pupils to learn number concepts and the mathematical structure of the decimal number system?

Before Numbers

Primitive man did not possess a concept of numbers. He devised a system of one-to-one relationship between objects and pebbles or marks. He could not count or write numbers. The herdsmen identified objects or animals by relating one pebble or mark to each object or animal. In a similar way, chiefs were able to account for warriors. This method became inadequate as man's practical need to know *how many* expanded.

Simple Number Concepts

From the stage of one-to-one correspondence between objects and pebbles or marks, the idea of the amounts of one, two, three, four, and five began to emerge. The idea of a small group of objects opened the way for the idea and symbol for a group of two objects, of three objects, of four objects, or of five objects. A word and then a symbol were invented to record or to communicate the concept of two objects, three objects, four objects, and five objects. The historical record supports the view that the human fingers were used in a one-to-one relation process and were the foundation for the idea of the digit one, the concept of five, and the concept of ten. When there were more objects than four or five, a concept of the amount of objects required counting. When there were ten or more objects, there arose a need for substituting one symbol for a group of ten objects.

Counting

Counting is a thought process used to find how many in all. Man could perceive the form of a few objects, but he was unable to know how many objects until he developed the ability to think of one object and one object as a group of two objects and a group of two objects and another object as a group of three objects. Counting of a number of objects by 1's, 2's, etc., was the thought process used in developing the concept of such amounts as six, seven, eight, nine, and ten. The five fingers of the two hands served as a convenient abacus. In time, words and symbols were patterned for the quantitative concept of 1, 2, 3, 4, 5, 6, 7, 8, 9. As the need arose for symbols to stand for number concepts larger than nine, different systems for writing numbers and simple computation were developed. Since all individuals possessed a common element, ten fingers, the idea of ten was applied, in some form, in the different systems.

Early Number Systems

The formation of a number system by the people living in the region of the Mediterranean Sea was a difficult and long endeavor.

A description of the background of each system can be obtained from one or more books dealing with the history of arithmetic and mathematics. A brief statement concerning the features of a few of these earlier number systems is presented to indicate similarity and difference in thinking and patterning by the early Greeks, Romans, Hindus, and Arabs. Each system reveals the application of the concept of one, many in a group, and symbols to notate the number concepts.

The Greeks structured a number system that required 24 letters and three additional symbols. Each letter or symbol was assigned a number meaning or value. Nine of these were used as symbols for 1, 2, 3, 4, 5, 6, 7, 8, 9. Another nine were used for the numbers 10, 20, 30, 40, 50, 60, 70, 80, and 90. Still another nine were used to write the numbers 100, 200, 300, 400, 500, 600, 700, 800, and 900. This system did not have a structured place-value order. The writing of numbers was based on the required letters. The Greeks did not use or have a symbol for zero. The dependence on so many different symbols presented great difficulty for learning and writing numbers.

The Romans designed a somewhat superior system of numbers and notation. The primary letters used were I, V, X, L, C, D, and M. A process of repeating a symbol was employed to write numbers, i.e.,

I,	II,	III,	IIII,	V,	VI,	VII,	VIII,	VIIII,	X,	XI,	XII,	XIII,	XIIII,
1	2	3	4	5	6	7	8	9	10	11	12	13	14

etc. Later the Romans introduced a technique of subtraction to reduce the number of symbols in writing certain numbers; IV was substituted for IIII, IX was substituted for VIIII, and XL was easier to write than XXXX. The symbol I, when written to the right of V, X, and so forth, added one (VI, XII, LI) or the symbol X written to the left of a symbol like L or C reduced it by ten (XL, XC). Larger numbers were difficult to read and computation involved a complex process. The use of the Roman number system can be found today on watches, clocks, chapters in books, and cornerstones of buildings. The trade activities, fortunately, did not call for the application of large numbers.

Read the equivalent decimal number for: XXXIV, XLII, CCLIV, CCLVII, DCLXXIV, MDCCCXV, MCDLVI.

The Universal Number System

The Hindus invented a number system that had these distinct characteristics: (1) There was a separate symbol (number) for each of the number concepts 1, 2, 3, 4, 5, 6, 7, 8, 9; (2) a place-value structure of ten and powers of ten; and (3) the meaning and use of zero (0). The zero was used to show the void or absence of a digit in any place-value position. In the number 805, the zero shows that there are no tens; however the tens place must be kept so that the digit 8 can be written in the hundreds place. The zero has been interpreted as a symbol that holds a place-value position. It is a place holder in a number. This system is called the Hindu-Arabic number system because it was invented by the Hindus and carried by means of trade to Italy and Spain by the Arabs. The use of a separate symbol for numbers 1 to 9, the zero as a place-value holder, and the place-value of ten and multiples of ten, made it easy to write large numbers. It proved to be a valuable aid in mental and written computation. The Hindu-Arabic or decimal system has become a universal system for notation and computation.

This decimal system can be readily interpreted by examining each number written in the grid and the accompanying explanation of its numerical value.

$(10)^3$ thousand 1000	$(10)^2$ hundred 100	$(10)^1$ ten 10	$(10)^0$ one 1	
	1	1	1	$1(100) + 1(10) + 1$ or 111
9	0	8	2	$9(1000) + 0(100) + 8(10) + 2$ or 9082
4	4	4	4	$4(10)^3+4(10)^2+4(10)^1+4(10)^0$ or 4444.

Other Number Systems

A variety of number systems of notation have been developed and used for a period of years. However the decimal system has supplanted other systems for reason of the radix, ten, the nine separate digits, and the zero.

Teachers may assist rapid achievers in arithmetic to stimulate curiosity and interest by investigating and notating in systems other than the decimal system. Pupils may find how a decimal number can be notated in one or more of these number systems.

Number System	Radix or Place Value	Digits Required in Notation
Binary	2	1 and 0
Ternary	3	1, 2, and 0
Quinary	5	1, 2, 3, 4, and 0
Senary	6	1, 2, 3, 4, 5, and 0
Octonary	8	1, 2, 3, 4, 5, 6, 7, and 0
Decimal	10	1, 2, 3, 4, 5, 6, 7, 8, 9, and 0
Duodecimal	12	1, 2, 3, 4, 5, 6, 7, 8, 9, *T*, *E*, and 0.

An analysis of these number systems will reveal that the smaller the radix or place value, the fewer the digits and the more often digits are used to notate numbers. Each system requires the use of the symbol for zero as a place holder.

The notated number for 24 objects in each system is:

Binary	11000	$1(2)^4 + 1(2)^3 + 0(2)^2 + 0(2)^1 + 0(2)^0$
Ternary	220	$2(3)^2 + 2(3)^1 + 0(3)^0$
Quinary	44	$4(5)^1 + 4(5)^0$
Senary	40	$4(6)^1 + 0(6)^0$
Octonary	30	$3(8)^1 + 0(8)^0$
Decimal	24	$2(10)^1 + 4(10)^0$
Duodecimal	20	$2(12)^1 + 0(12)^0$

Many persons advocate the adoption of the duodecimal number system for the reason that 12 is divisible by more factors than is 10. Twelve may be divided evenly by 1, 2, 3, 4, 6, but 10 can be divided evenly only by the factors 1, 2, 5.

EXERCISE

1. Use the *binary* number system and write the number for each:

(*a*) Five
(*b*) Ten
(*c*) Fifteen
(*d*) Fifty
(*e*) One hundred
(*f*) One hundred eleven
(*g*) One hundred twenty-five
(*h*) Two hundred eighty-four
(*i*) Five hundred

2. Use the *quinary* number system and write the number for each:

(*a*) Five
(*b*) Ten
(*c*) Twenty
(*d*) Twenty-five
(*e*) Fifty
(*f*) Seventy-five
(*g*) One hundred
(*h*) Five hundred
(*i*) One thousand five hundred ten

3. Use the *duodecimal* system and write the number for each:

(*a*) Five
(*b*) Ten
(*c*) Twelve
(*d*) Twenty-four
(*e*) One hundred
(*f*) One hundred forty-four
(*g*) Two hundred fifty-six
(*h*) Five hundred
(*i*) Two thousand twenty-five

The Number Line

Pupils may find the number line a useful aid in discovering and understanding the quantitative concept to be associated with a number and its symbol.

0 1 2 3 4 5 6 7 8 9 10 11 12

The number line shows continuous magnitude. It is based on a linear segment that is 1. This is the distance from 0 to 1. The number 2 represents the length from 0 to 2 or 1 + 1. The number 12 represents the length from 0 to 12 or 1+1+1+1+1+1+1+1+1+1+1+1. The magnitude of a number line is unlimited, therefore its potential length is expressed by the symbol N.

The number 2 is written above the second dot. It is to be interpreted to show the value of 1 + 1 or the length from 0 to 2, or the length of two segments each with the length of whatever segment 1 is. The number 12 is written above the twelfth dot, and the value of 12 is the sum of the segments from 0 to 12. An examination of a foot ruler or a yardstick will show the numerical principle and structure of the number line.

Two Important Concepts of a Number

A number and its corresponding symbol may identify a specific number or amount of objects or units in a group. A pupil may have a bag of marbles. When asked, "How many marbles in the bag?" he may have to count the marbles before answering. If he says, "Nine marbles," the answer shows a group of nine objects. The number 9 is the symbol to notate the concept of a group of 9 ones. This concept represents the cardinal meaning of a number. Counting is a mental process to determine the amount of objects or units in a group to be notated by a number. The number 34 pounds is a way to express the concept of an amount that has the collective weight of 34 one pounds. A cardinal number identifies, therefore, the mental concept of total amount, total collection, or how many in all.

A number may also represent the idea of one object or position in an established magnitude series. This ordinal meaning of a number is most useful in many situations in modern society. Tickets purchased for the theater or sport events have a letter and/or number to indicate a specific seat in a certain row in a prearranged serial plan. The engine of an automobile is assigned a serial number. Many commercial firms use the ordinal meaning of a number to identify and record each item of production or sale.

The words such as "first," "second," "third," "fourth," communicate the idea of ordinal or serial position. An additional symbol may be attached to a number to show ordinal position, for example, 8th, 25th, 150th.

Record keeping may involve the use of both the cardinal and ordinal meaning of numbers. In a classroom library there are 35 reading books on the second shelf. The number, 35, indicates how many books and the word, "second," shows what shelf.

The abstracting of the cardinal or ordinal meaning of a number is a thought process. Pupils should be given the opportunity to learn these mathematical meanings through experiencing practical situations in the school and in the community. A survey may be made by the pupils to determine the application of the cardinal and ordinal concept of numbers in the community.

Place Value

In the Hindu-Arabic number system the base or radix of place value is ten. The center position is one. The first position or order place to the left of the ones place is assigned a value of 10. The second position or order place to the left of the ones place is assigned a value of $(10)^2$ or 100. The place-value series may continue for an indefinite number of place value or order positions to the left of the ones place, thus the use of the symbol $(10)^N$.

The first place or order position to the right of the ones place is assigned the value of one-tenth of one or tenths. The second place to the right of the ones place is assigned a place value of one-hundredth of one or hundredths. There is no limit to the number of place value or order positions that may be used to the right of the position one.

Illustration of Decimal Place Value or Order Position

10,000	1,000	100	10	1	.1	.01	.001	.0001
$(10)^4$	$(10)^3$	$(10)^2$	$(10)^1$	$1(10)^0$	$(10)^{-1}$	$(10)^{-2}$	$(10)^{-3}$	$(10)^{-4}$
Ten-thousand	Thousand	Hundred	Ten	One	Tenth	Hundredth	Thousandth	Ten-thousandth

Writing Numbers

The concept of a number may be communicated in two forms. Words may be used to write the idea of a number, such as fifty-three, ten thousand eight hundred, or one hundred nine thousand fifty-six. This form is called numeration. Use words to write these numbers: 50; 185; 5046; 100; 750; 405.

The other form that may be used to write or notate the idea of a number requires the use of one or more of the nine digits, 1, 2, 3, 4, 5, 6, 7, 8, 9, and the symbol (0) for zero. The place value of each digit depends on the place value position in which it is written. In the number 568, the digit 8 indicates ones, the digit 6 identifies tens, and the digit 5 identifies hundreds.

Pupils may see a magnitude of books in a school library. Counting is the thought process used to determine how many on one or more of the shelves and how many in all in the library. A number is written to record the result of the counting. If the number 5475 has been notated, it shows the total number of books in the school library.

Large numbers are easier to read when a comma is used to punctuate the number into periods of three, beginning with the ones, such as 463,845,972. The name of the period, 972 is hundred; the name of the period 845, is thousands; the name of the third period is millions.

Substitution in Notation

Writing numbers in the Hindu-Arabic or decimal number system involves the thought process of substituting a digit in the next higher place value for ten units of any given place value. The reason for the use of this thought process of substitution is that there are only nine digits (1, 2, 3, 4, 5, 6, 7, 8, 9) in the decimal system. In writing a number to show the idea of a group of objects larger than nine, a digit in the next higher place value is substituted for the idea of ten units in any place-value position.

Pupils may see many pencils in a box. To determine how many in all they have to think 1 + 1 are 2, 2 + 1 are 3, 3 + 1 are 4, 4 + 1 are 5, 5 + 1 are 6, 6 + 1 are 7, 7 + 1 are 8, 8 + 1 are 9, and 9 + 1 are a group of ten ones. Since there is no digit for 10 ones then 1 ten must be substituted for the 10 ones. Counting may then be continued by thinking 1 ten + 1, 1 ten + 2, 1 ten + 3, 1 ten + 4, 1 ten + 5, 1 ten + 6, 1 ten + 7, 1 ten + 8, 1 ten + 9, and 1 ten + 9 + 1, which requires pupils again to substitute 1 ten for the ten ones, which is interpreted as 2 tens. This counting process continues until all pencils have been counted and a thought organization has given the number to show how many pencils. If there were one hundred pencils in the box, the thought number to notate is 100. Counting and notating numbers becomes a somewhat difficult process as the magnitude of objects becomes larger. An understanding of the thought process used in substitution is essential in the application of addition, subtraction, multiplication, and division.

Kind of Numbers

The expansion in industry and commerce presented the need for other meanings of a number. The more frequently used meanings or kinds of numbers are:

Natural or counting numbers.

Each number shows one or more objects or units of common likeness: 12 pennies, 36 books, 45 boys, 10 dollars.

Fractions.

A fraction is a number to show units less in magnitude than the integer 1 ($\frac{1}{4}$ lb, $\frac{2}{3}$ ft, $\frac{5}{6}$ yd, .3 mile). A fraction may also be a number to show one or more objects or units of a given group of similar objects or units ($\frac{2}{5}$ of a package of chewing gum, $\frac{3}{8}$ of a bag of 16 marbles).

Literal number.

This is a number notated with letters: $a + b = c$, $a \times b = c$, $\frac{a}{b} = c$, $\frac{c}{a} = b$.

Denominate numbers.

This is a number to show the result of measurements such as 10 feet or 3 pounds. The magnitude of the measure is an approximation rather than discrete.

Negative number.

The extension of the number line to the left of zero enabled man to show the amount or number of units in a negative direction by introducing the symbol, $-$, to be written to the left of a number (-1, -3, -5).

$$\underline{-5 \quad -4 \quad -3 \quad -2 \quad -1 \quad 0 \quad 1 \quad 2 \quad 3 \quad 4 \quad 5}$$

The thermometer reading may be notated -10 degrees. This communicates the idea that the measurement of the temperature is 10 degrees below zero.

The Responsibility of the Teacher

The responsibility for helping pupils develop correct ideas of numbers and the number system and of the vocabulary and accepted means of recording the ideas is the responsibility of the teacher. The steps in teaching should guide the pupil from physical manipulation of objects, to observation of quantities, to mental perception, to the use of number names, to arithmetical symbols.

The number system itself determines the ideas pupils need to develop, but teachers must reach the decision as to when and how the material will be presented. Suggestions for helping pupils develop an understanding of the meaning of numbers and the number system and facility in using them are given in the following paragraphs.

Rote Counting

Many of the children know the number names when they come to school. Their classmates learn the number names through imitation and practice. Various stories, rhymes, and songs are helpful to pupils lacking in experience with saying the number words. What teacher is not familiar with and what pupil does not enjoy the number rhymes: "One little, two little, three little Indians," "One, two, buckle my shoe," and so forth? The "Three Bears," "Three Little Pigs," and "Chicken Little Counts to Ten," should be part of each teacher's repertoire.

Visualizing Groups and Numbers

The ability to recognize groups of five or less can be developed by most children. This ability is helpful because it enables a child to form a mental picture of the two-ness of 2, three-ness of 3, four-ness of 4, and five-ness of 5, using a variety of objects such as chairs, picture cutouts, flannel squares on a flannel board, etc., so that pupils develop the idea that they can see without counting, *how many* regardless of the physical characteristics of the objects themselves.

After numerous experiences with groups of five or fewer, pupils can be helped to visualize groups larger than five. As a result of their experiences they may construct a chart similar to the one on the following page.

Rational Counting

An individual flannel board about 9 inches × 12 inches made of heavy cardboard or wallboard and covered with a pillowcase of gray cotton flannel is an excellent piece of equipment for pupils to use in developing their ideas of rational counting and in demonstrating their ideas of counting. As the teacher displays one object, the pupil may put one small square on the flannel board. As two objects are displayed, the pupil displays two objects. The process continues until the pupil has a complete display as follows:

x	(Observe the small space between 5 and 1, 5 and 2, etc. An arrangement of this type permits teacher and pupil alike to check on the accuracy of the arrangement without taking time to count.)
xx	
xxx	
xxxx	
xxxxx	
xxxxx x	
xxxxx xx	
xxxxx xxx	
xxxxx xxxx	

In later lessons the pupils may use a 12-inch felt strip to separate their flannel board into two sections, which may be labelled *tens* and *ones*. When the tenth object in a group is counted, the pupils may put one marker in the tens place to represent 1 ten.

A simple abacus constructed by inserting three thin dowel rods in a wooden base and then cutting each dowel rod to a length to hold

NUMBER CHART

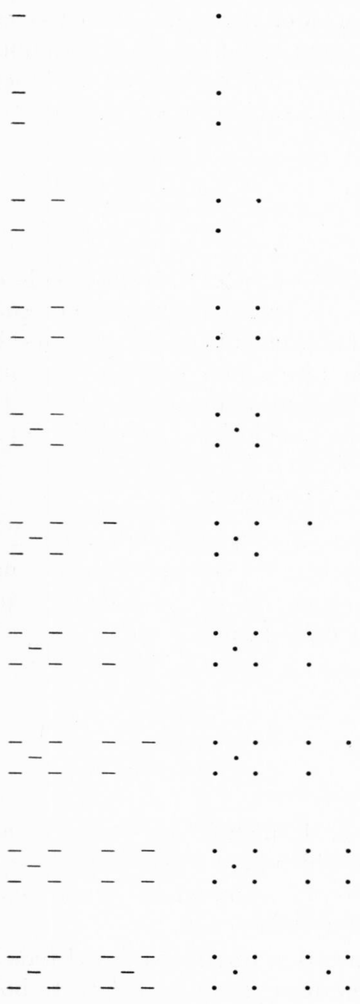

Column 1 (*Pictures or plastic objects arranged as indicated*)	Column 2 (*Large dots arranged as indicated*)	Column 3 *Words*	Column 4 *Numbers*
		one	1
		two	2
		three	3
		four	4
		five	5
		six	6
		seven	7
		eight	8
		nine	9
		ten	10

exactly nine spools is a piece of objective material that pupils may use when demonstrating their answers to questions such as these:

1. How many girls in the class?
2. How many boys in the class?
3. How many pupils in the class?
4. How many books on the shelf?
5. Etc.

A decimal guide as shown at the right can take the place of the abacus. Most pupils can soon progress to the point where no aids are needed to help them understand counting.

Tens	*Ones*

However, teachers may find it helpful to have pupils construct a number chart for class display and reference. Observe the chart below:

	1	2	3	4	5	6	7	8	9
10	11	12	13	14	15	16	17	18	19
20	21	22							

Providing Opportunities for Using Ideas

The list of situations in which pupils use the skills of counting, using ordinal numbers, and reading and writing numbers could be extended to great lengths. The following lists are representative:

Counting

1. Divide into groups for work or play.
2. Distribute supplies—1 item to each person.
3. Set the table with enough places for each one.
4. Get enough chairs for visitors.
5. Count votes.
6. Order daily milk supply.
7. Count money to be put in school bank.
8. Count packages of seeds for school gardens.
9. Know number of easels that can be used at any one time by a given number of children.
10. Construct various things. Suggestions:
    (*a*) Get 4 wheels for truck.
    (*b*) Get 2 headlights for truck.

(*c*) Get 2 wings for airplane.
(*d*) Get 1 wing for monoplane.
(*e*) Get 6 or 7 stanchions for barn.
(*f*) Get 5 windows for house, etc.

11. Keep records in games.
12. Count beats of stroke of clock.
13. Count in playground activities as in jumping rope, bouncing a ball, arranging equal numbers in rows for games, marching by two's, etc.
14. Count spots on dominoes.
15. Count characters for dramatizations.

Practice in Ordinal Numbers

1. Find page of book—"Turn to the seventh page, etc."
2. Follow directions—"Color the fifth balloon red."
3. Tell dates of holidays such as Fourth of July.
4. Picture study—"What is the third child doing?"

Reading and Writing Numbers

1. Numbering pages and objects in booklets.
2. Telling sizes of articles of clothing as dresses, suits, shoes, stockings.
3. Reading prices on toys in newspapers.
4. Reading weights on scales.

Diagnosing Pupil Growth

The meanings of numbers and the number system are in the minds of pupils. Answers written in computation do not reveal the meaning and operation of the thought process used in computation. Teachers find valuable information about a pupil's maturing understandings in arithmetic from teacher and pupil interviews and from teacher-constructed diagnostic instruments. Diagnostic tests A and B illustrate the kinds of questions and directions that may be used in diagnosing the progress and needs of pupils.

Test A

1. In the number 8052, what does the symbol 0 show?

2. Look at the number 78,943 and draw a circle around the digit that shows the most units in a place-value position.

3. What is the place value or radix in the decimal number system?

4. What is the place value or radix in the binary number system?

5. What is the place value or radix in the duodecimal number system?

6. There are how many place-value positions in the number 7543?

7. Draw a circle around the fourth number in the series 2, 4, 6, 8, 10, 12.

8. There are how many digits used to notate idea of amount in the decimal system?

9. Draw a circle and put x's in it to show the cardinal meaning of 8.

10. Draw a number line to show the meaning of positive and negative numbers.

Test B

1. Use the digits 3, 8, 5. Write the largest possible three-place-value number.

2. Use the digits 4, 2, and 0. Notate the smallest three-place-value number.

3. Use the digit 1 and 0. Notate the largest possible five-place-value number.

4. The binary number, 1110, stands for a group of how many like objects?

5. The duodecimal number, TTOE, stands for a group of how many like objects?

6. How would the decimal number 36 be notated in the binary system?

7. How would the decimal number 584 be notated in the duodecimal system?

8. How would the number 1956 be written in the Roman number system?

9. Write the number represented by $8(10)^4 + 5(10)^3 + 0(10)^2 + 3(10)^1 + 6(10)^0$.

10. Construct drawings to illustrate the difference in meaning between a cardinal number and an ordinal number.

Summary

Arithmetic is an invented language and notation system. The concepts of numbers and computation are in the mind. The notated numbers show the result of the thought process. The meaning of numbers has been expanded to include integers, fractions, denominate numbers, and literal numbers.

Primitive man was unable to count. He used a one-to-one relation method between objects and pebbles or marks. The Greeks invented a system of notation that required the use of twenty-four letters and three additional symbols. The Romans developed a number system that employed such primary letters as I, V, X, L, C, and D. This system did not use place value or a zero. The Hindu-Arabic system contained features that caused it to become a universal number system. The place value was ten and multiples of ten. There were nine separate digits and a symbol for zero. The numerical value of a digit depended upon the place or position in which it was written. Other number systems that have been invented are: the binary system, quinary system, and duodecimal system. Each system requires a radix, digits, and the symbol for zero.

The cardinal meaning of a number stands for a group or collection of similar objects or units. The number tells how many in all. An ordinal number identifies an object or place in series arrangement. Numbers may be expressed in words or figures. When large numbers are written, a comma is used to group the digits as an aid in reading.

The important meanings teachers should help pupils to learn about the decimal system of notation are: (1) place value, (2) substitution of one unit in any place-value position for ten units in the next lower place-value position, and (3) the use of zero to hold a place-value position when there are no units in the place-value position. Frequent use of diagnostic instruments will enable teachers to interpret the ideas and thought processes pupils have learned about numbers and the number system.

SUGGESTED QUESTIONS FOR TEACHER SELF-EVALUATION

1. What is your interpretation of the mathematical meaning of counting?
2. Why is it possible to record numbers of any magnitude using only 9 digits and the 0?
3. Why was the invention of the 0 of such significance to mankind?
4. What primitive societies still employ number systems other than the Hindu-Arabic system?
5. What number system is used in modern computing machines? What are the advantages of the system used?

6. Why is it necessary to think of a group of 115 ones as fewer but larger units before recording them in the number system?
7. What were the advantages of the number system used by the Romans over the number system used by the Greeks?
8. How does the invention of numbers and the number system enable man better to control his environment?
9. What has been the evolution of the Hindu-Arabic number symbols from early times to the present?
10. At what period in history did fractions come into common use?

SUGGESTED ACTIVITIES

1. Review your activities for the day and list applications you have made of (*a*) cardinal concept of numbers and (*b*) ordinal concept of numbers.
2. Examine the new textbooks in arithmetic to discover and appraise the methods used in teaching numbers and the number system.
3. Prepare a list of meanings about the number system that you think pupils should understand.
4. Make a collection of songs, stories, rhymes, and poems you might use in teaching rote counting and rational counting.
5. Preview recent filmstrips and films designed to help pupils understand numbers and the number system, and write a review of each.
6. Construct an abacus and use it in teaching place value to children or adults.
7. Prepare a diagnostic test suitable for use with pupils at the level you intend to teach.

PRACTICE EXERCISES

1. Write the number that means:
50 and 6 ______ 70 and 3 ______ 90 and 9 ______ 7 tens ______
6 tens ______ 4 tens and 3 ______ 6 thousands and 7 tens ______
80 million and 5 thousand ______

2. Write the missing numbers:
36 means ______ tens and 6 ______ 95 means 9 tens and 5 ______
357 means ______ hundreds ______ tens and 7 ______ 4500 means ______ thousands ______ hundreds ______ tens and ______ ones.

3. Write the place-value names for each digit in these numbers:
1,426,756 870,565,235,426 .097 .721564

4. Write the names of the periods into which these numbers should be separated:
17,005,698 2,718,415,276 7,400,235,676,130

5. Round to the nearest 10:
7754 9275 47.36 97,507.50

6. Write as Roman numbers:
24 97 1776 5000 1965

7. Write as decimal numbers:
LXX DCCC XCVI MMXC D

8. Write as numbers in the quinary system:
3, 5, 7, 18, 35, 156

9. Write these numbers from the quinary system as numbers in the decimal system:
10, 14, 320, 413

10. Notate the decimal number 22 in each of the following number systems:
binary, quinary, duodecimal.

SELECTED REFERENCES

1. Dantzig, Tobias, *Number: The Language of Science*. New York: The Macmillan Company, 1930.

2. Conant, L. L., *The Number Concept*. New York: The Macmillan Company, 1923.

3. Hooper, Alfred, *The River Mathematics*. New York: Henry Holt and Company, Inc., 1945.

4. Karpinski, L. C., *The History of Arithmetic*. Chicago: Rand-McNally & Company, 1925.

5. Logsdon, Mayme T., *A Mathematician Explains*. Chicago: University of Chicago Press, 1935.

6. Newman, James R., *The World of Mathematics* (4 vols.). New York: Simon and Schuster, Inc., 1956.

7. Sanford, Vera, *A Short History of Mathematics*. Boston: Houghton Mifflin Company, 1930.

8. Smith, David Eugene, *History of Mathematics* (2 vols.). Boston: Ginn & Company, 1923-1925.

9. Smith, David Eugene, *The Teaching of Elementary Mathematics*. New York: The Macmillan Company, 1902.

3

Meaning and Use of Addition: Integers

Introduction

Addition is the first of the "four fundamental operations" used to answer the question "How many in all?" The addition algorism $2 + 3$ or $\begin{array}{r} 2 \\ +\underline{3} \end{array}$ consists of two addends, and a sign + (read *and* or *plus*). It asks a question, "How many in all?" The answer to the question in the example is the sum. The sum is derived by applying quantitative thinking after mentally perceiving and visualizing the amounts represented by both addends.

Exploratory Questions

The chapter has been designed to assist teachers in determining how to help pupils develop a correct mathematical concept of addition consistent with the number system. Teachers may find it helpful to appraise their understanding of the meanings of thought processes of addition by deciding upon what they believe to be appropriate answers to the following questions.

1. What is the mathematical meaning of addition?
2. What mathematical and social problems require the use of addition?

3. How do you interpret the physical act of grouping or adding objects and the mathematical and thought process in adding numbers?

4. What are the mathematical terms related to addition that pupils should learn?

5. What mathematical principles must be observed when adding numbers notated in the decimal system? In the binary system? In the duodecimal system?

6. What is the mathematical function of the digits 1, 2, 3, 4, 5, 6, 7, 8, 9, and the symbol 0 in addition?

7. In what way is the thought process in addition more complex than in counting?

8. What may be the most effective method to be used by teachers to help pupils to learn the meaning and use of the basic addition facts with a sum less than 10? The basic addition facts with a sum of 10 or greater?

9. What developmental patterns in addition examples should be observed by teachers so pupils may develop a mathematical and psychological understanding of the sequence in addition?

10. What diagnostic procedures may teachers use to appraise the understanding, progress, and needs of pupils in addition?

The Meaning of Addition

Addition as a physical act is a process of grouping objects of the same kind together. Young children have experiences in the physical act of adding. They may pour small containers of liquid into a larger container. Another illustration is building a pile of blocks. Children frequently have reason for putting objects into a box or a bag. In each act of physical adding, the end product is something more than the original objects. Pouring cups of liquid, salt, or sand into a larger container illustrates the principle that when quantities are added, they lose their identity in a new quantity. Obviously, young children may engage in an act of physical adding long before they have a desire to know how many in all. Pupils are ready to add as a mathematical and a thought process when they have some desire to know "How many in all?" or "How many are in one group that has been formed by grouping two or more groups of like things?" or "How many in the new group?"

Addition in a mathematical sense involves a thought process rather than a physical act. Thinking replaces physical doing. Addition is the process of thinking of quantities represented by two or more numbers as being one total quantity and of thinking of the number that represents or notates the concept of the total quantity. Physically, two bags of marbles may be put together to make one bag of marbles. Addition as a process of mathematical thought requires thinking of the number of marbles in each bag and then thinking of a number that shows how many marbles there are together in one bag.

Addition is a mathematical thought process used in combining numbers to find a number that equals all the numbers together. Each number in an addition example is an addend. In thinking, the sum is a number that is substituted for or equals all addends when combined. In an addition example, both the addends and the sum are stated yet neither exist in reality. Numbers merely represent ideas of things. They are not the things themselves.

In physical addition, either the smaller quantities (addends) or the single larger quantity (sum) exist in reality but do not exist at the same time. In adding physical quantities, the quantities lose their identity as they are put into a larger quantity.

The addition fact, $3 + 4 = 7$, is a completed process. The first step in the thought process is to identify the question, "3 and 4 are how many?" The second step is to think, "7 is the number to stand for 3 and 4, after they have been thought to be combined (added). The mathematical example, $5 + 3 = ?$ asks the question, "5 and 3 are how many in all?" or "What number is the sum when 5 and 3 are added?" The sum 8 is the mathematical answer to the question $5 + 3 = ?$

Questions Answered by Addition

Addition is a thought process to answer the questions, "How many in all?" or "What is the total?" or "What is the amount?" or "What is the sum?" These questions may be answered by counting. The important value of addition as a mathematical thought process is that it provides a rapid method of thinking together numbers that stand for groups.

Groups or Objects	Possible Arrangements into Two Groups	Examples
2	x x	1 +1
3	(xx) x x (xx)	2 +1; 1 +2
4	(xx) (xxx) x (xx) x (xxx)	2 +2; 3 +1; 1 +3
5	(xxxx) (xxx) x (xx) x (xx) (xxxx) (xxx)	4 +1; 3 +2; 1 +4; 2 +3
6	(xxxxx) x (xxx) (xx) (xxxx) x (xxxxx) (xxx) (xxxx) (xx)	5 +1; 1 +5; 3 +3; 2 +4; 4 +2
7	(xxxxx) (xx) (xxxx) (xxx) (xxxxxx) x (xx) (xxxxx) (xxx) (xxxx) x (xxxxxx)	5 +2; 2 +5; 4 +3; 3 +4; 6 +1 + 1 +6
8	(xxxx) (xxxxx) (xxx) (xxxxxx) (xx) (xxxxxxx) x (xxxx) (xxx) (xxxxx) (xx) (xxxxxx) x (xxxxxxx)	4 +4; 5 +3; 3 +5; 6 +2; 2 +6; 7 +1; 1 +7
9	(xxxxx) (xxxx) (xxxxxx) (xxx) (xxxxxxx) (xx) x (xxxxxxxx) (xxxx) (xxxxx) (xxx) (xxxxxx) (xx) (xxxxxxx) (xxxxxxxx) x	5 +4; 4 +5; 6 +3; 3 +6; 7 +2; 2 +7; 1 +8; 8 +1

Relating Ideas of Groups to the Meaning of Addition

Pupils can interpret the meaning of addition when teachers help them to visualize groups. It is important that pupils learn to think of a number such as 3 as representing or notating a group of 3 ones. This idea may be represented by (xxx). The number 4 is interpreted as having a group meaning of 4 ones (xxxx). Pupils must learn to think of 5 as a group of 5 ones (xxxxx). In a similar way, they learn to think of 6 as a group of 6 ones (xxxxx/x); 7 as a group of 7 ones (xxxxx/xx); 8 as a group of 8 ones (xxxxx/xxx); 9 as a group of 9 ones (xxxxx/xxxx).

The study of groups of physical objects will help pupils to discover the smaller quantities (addends) which make the total quantity or sum. Through their study of groups smaller than 9, pupils will discover and learn to think with the examples on the facing page.

When there is a group of 2 ones, there is only one arrangement and one example. For a group of 3 ones, there are two possible arrangements and two examples. A group of 5 ones has four arrangements and four examples. The group of 9 ones has eight arrangements and eight examples. Pupils soon learn that the number of arrangements and the number of examples is less by 1 than the number of objects in a group up to and including 9. These examples with their sums are discovered to be the 36 addition facts with sums of 9 or less.

Vocabulary Terms in Addition

Pupils need to learn the ideas related to addition before the terms can be properly understood. However, they need to know the terms used in thinking with addition. Studying under teacher's guidance such examples as $\begin{array}{r} 4 \text{ addend} \\ +3 \text{ addend} \\ \hline 7 \text{ sum} \end{array}$ or $\overset{\text{addend}}{4} + \overset{\text{addend}}{3} = \overset{\text{sum}}{7}$, pupils can understand that the numbers to be added are called addends and the total amount (all together) is the sum. Essential is the idea that the sum is a number that can be substituted for or stands for all the addends together. Addition is the thought process of finding a number or sum that equals all the addends combined. Caution should be taken by teachers to prevent pupils from learning the misconception that addition means to increase. The sign + (called "plus"), when placed between two numbers, shows that the numbers are to be added. When the sign + is placed before the last number in a column of addends it shows that all numbers in the column are to be added. The sign + asks the question, "How many in all?" or "What number can be notated to stand for or be equal to all the addends together?"

The example, $\begin{array}{r} 3 \\ +4 \\ \hline ? \end{array}$ or $3 + 4 = ?$ asks a mathematical question. The 3 and the 4 tell how many in each group and the sign + asks, "How many in all?" Pupils should be taught from the beginning that when they see or read an example they should think, "It tells something," "It asks a question," "It calls for thinking to find the answer."

The sign = is called "equals." It is used to complete a mathematical question or to express a mathematical statement. So $5 + 4 = ?$ is read or thought, "5 and 4 are how many in all?" $5 + 4 = 9$ is read or thought, "5 and 4 together equal 9."

Addition Combination Facts with Sums of 10 or More

The principal difference between addition combination facts with sums of 10 or more and those with sums of 9 or less is in the notation of the sum. Each addend causes the pupil to think "How many?" The addition sign + motivates the thought question, "How many in all?" When the sum of an addition fact is 10 or more, pupils have to think of 10 ones as 1 ten and substitute in their thinking, 1 ten for 10 ones. The largest number of units that can be notated or shown in any decimal place is 9.

The use of the grid for addition combination facts with sums of 10 or more may be helpful to pupils in learning how to think and to notate sums of 10 or more.

(*a*)

$$\begin{array}{|c|c|} \hline & 6 \\ + & 4 \\ \hline 1 & 0 \\ \hline \end{array} \text{ or } \begin{array}{r} 6 \\ +4 \\ \hline 10 \end{array}$$

(*b*)

$$\begin{array}{|c|c|} \hline & 7 \\ + & 8 \\ \hline 1 & 5 \\ \hline \end{array} \text{ or } \begin{array}{r} 7 \\ +8 \\ \hline 15 \end{array}$$

(*c*)

$$\begin{array}{|c|c|} \hline & 9 \\ + & 9 \\ \hline 1 & 8 \\ \hline \end{array} \text{ or } \begin{array}{r} 9 \\ +9 \\ \hline 18 \end{array}$$

In example (*a*) the first step is "Think 6 + 4 are 10 ones." Second step is to substitute 1 ten for 10 ones and write 1 in the tens' place in the sum. Since no ones are left, the symbol (0) is written in the one's place. Thus 6 + 4 = 1 ten and 0 ones.

In example (*b*) the thought process is, "7 and 8 equal 15 ones; substitute 1 ten for 10 ones; write the 5 in the ones' place in the sum and write 1 in the tens' place in the sum." (7 + 8 = 15 ones or 1 ten and 5 ones or 15.) What is the thought process to be used by pupils in finding the sum for: 9 + 9 = ?; 7 + 4 = ?; 5 + 5 = ?; 8 + 8 = ?; 7 + 9 = ?; 9 + 8 = ?.

Below is a chart showing the 45 addition examples with sums of 10 or more. Observe that there are 9 facts with the sum of 10, 8 facts with a sum of 11, 7 facts with a sum of 12, and so forth. These examples with their sums are discovered to be the 45 addition facts with sums of 10 or more.

Sum	*Addition Examples*								
10	9 1 — ?	1 9 — ?	8 2 — ?	2 8 — ?	7 3 — ?	3 7 — ?	6 4 — ?	4 6 — ?	5 5 — ?
11	9 2 — ?	2 9 — ?	8 3 — ?	3 8 — ?	7 4 — ?	4 7 — ?	6 5 — ?	5 6 — ?	
12	9 3 — ?	3 9 — ?	8 4 — ?	4 8 — ?	7 5 — ?	5 7 — ?	6 6 — ?		
13	9 4 — ?	4 9 — ?	8 5 — ?	5 8 — ?	7 6 — ?	6 7 — ?			
14	9 5 — ?	5 9 — ?	8 6 — ?	6 8 — ?	7 7 — ?				

Sum	*Addition Examples*			
15	9 6 — ?	6 9 — ?	8 7 — ?	7 8 — ?
16	9 7 — ?	7 9 — ?	8 8 — ?	
17	9 8 — ?	8 9 — ?		
18	9 9 — ?			

Pupils who do not learn the thought processes for the addition combination facts will count or guess. Accuracy and speed in thought addition depends on a meaningful mastery of the 81 combination facts.

The Computing of Sums Under 10 in Column Addition

The basic facts can be used in adding columns of three or more addends. Observe the column at the right. The two basic facts used in finding the sum are $3 + 2$ and the $5 + 4$. The 5 is not notated so it must be remembered mentally.

$$\begin{array}{r} 3 \\ 2 \\ +4 \\ \hline ? \end{array}$$

Diagnosing Pupil Growth

Because future progress in addition is based first upon an understanding of what has been taught and second upon the thoroughness with which the addition facts have been memorized, time should be taken to diagnose progress. Teacher questions and teacher-made pencil and paper tests are as effective as any instrument can be. One of the most satisfactory ways to determine a child's understanding of arithmetic is to let him tell what he thinks when confronted with addition examples and how he goes about finding the answer. He may be encouraged to reconstruct a situation that an addition example represents. Questions which the teacher may raise are:

1. What question does an addition example ask?

2. What two addition facts do you use in finding the answer to the example $3 + 2 + 4$?

3. What addition fact do you use in finding the answer to the example $4 + 0 + 3$?

Test items such as the following may be included on pencil and paper tests.

Part I—The Meaning of Addition

Put a circle around the correct answer.

1. Which addition example could you make by looking at the dots on the card at the right?

5	3	5
+4	+2	+3
?	?	?

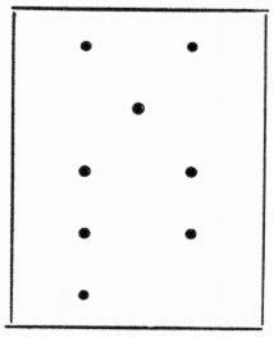

2. Which number tells "How many in all?" in the example $4 + 5 = 9$? (5, 4, 9)

3. Which question can be answered by adding? (How many in all? How many in each group? How many do you see?)

Part II—Mathematics Vocabulary

Put a circle around the correct answer.

1. What are the addends in the addition fact, $4 + 3 = 7$? (4 and 7, 3 and 7, 4 and 3)

2. What is the sum in the example in exercise 1? (4, 7, 3)

3. Which of these signs asks a question? (+, =, ¢)

Part III—Computation

Write the answer to each of these examples.

1.	1	3	2	5	7	3	6	4	3	4
	+8	+6	+5	+4	+2	+4	+3	+4	+3	+2
	?	?	?	?	?	?	?	?	?	?

2.									
5	8	7	5	8	4	8	6	7	5
+8	+3	+6	+9	+8	+8	+9	+7	+3	+7
?	?	?	?	?	?	?	?	?	?

3.									
6	2	1	3	5	4	1	5	2	3
2	3	4	5	4	3	1	1	3	3
+1	+4	+3	+1	+0	+2	+7	+3	+3	+1
?	?	?	?	?	?	?	?	?	?

Adding One-Place and Two-Place Numbers

Observe how the basic facts are used in finding the sum in examples such as that at the right. Custom decrees that the smaller units, ones, be added first. The sum of the ones is thought to be 7. There are no tens to add to the 2 tens. The complete sum is 27 (2 tens and 7 ones). Many children can think the sum directly without isolating the ones and tens. This is a mature response that may well be encouraged.

```
 24
+3
---
 ??
```

The basic facts are also used in finding the sum to examples such as that at the right. The sum of 8 + 7 cannot be notated in the ones place.

```
 38
+7
---
 ??
```

The example with its sum may be written on the decimal grid chart as shown at the right. Observe that a small 1 is written above the 3 in the tens column. This serves as a reminder that 1 ten was substituted for 10 of the 15 ones. Observe that there is no "carrying." The process is one of substituting 1 ten for 10 ones. The final step is that of writing the example without the decimal grid chart. As soon as children can dispense with the small figure in the tens place, they should be encouraged to do so.

Tens	*Ones*
1	
3	8
+	7
4	5

or

```
 38
+7
---
 45
```

The children need considerable experience with examples such as these:

24	72	53	67	45	31	19	86	98
+ 7	+ 9	+ 8	+ 4	+ 5	+ 9	+ 2	+ 6	+ 3
?	?	?	?	?	?	?	?	?

With direction from the teacher the children will see that they are using what they learned about basic addition facts when finding answers to examples such as those in the preceding exercise.

Preparing for Column Addition Involving Changing to Tens (Adding by Endings)

Children need to develop the skill of thinking the sum to examples such as 17 + 9 in a single step. Examine the addition example at the right. To find the answer, the child must learn to think: 17, 26 without taking time to add 9 + 8 = 17; 17 + 9 = 1 ten + 16 ones = 2 tens + 6 ones.

$$\begin{array}{r} 9 \\ 8 \\ +9 \\ \hline ? \end{array}$$

To help children think the number that represents the total quantity, the teacher may wish to present examples such as these: 5 + 6 and 15 + 6; 6 + 7 and 16 + 7; 7 + 9 and 27 + 9. The teacher will discuss with the children the idea that 15 + 6 is 1 ten more than 5 + 6; 16 + 7 is 1 ten more than 6 + 7; 27 + 9 is 2 tens more than 7 + 6. The children may need considerable practice in using the addition facts in these so-called "higher decade additions." Since there are 45 addition facts with sums of 10 or more, there must be 45 higher decade additions with sums in the twenties, 45 with sums in the thirties, etc.

The Finding of Sums in Column Addition When the Sum Is 10 or More

The same kind of thinking is required in solving examples such as 6 + 6 + 5 = ? as in examples such as 3 + 2 + 3 = ? However, the notation of the sum requires the writing of tens and ones. The numbers may be put on a decimal grid chart as indicated on the preceding page. Children may need some guidance before they can see that 6 + 6 + 5 is really a situation where they use their basic facts together with higher decade addition: 6 + 6 = 12; 12 + 5 = 17.

Tens	*Ones*		
	6		6
	6	or	6
	5		+5
1	7		17

Some children are helped in solving addition examples with three addends if, in the initial steps of learning, they are permitted to cover the third addend until they have thought the sum of the first two addends. Then they use this sum and add to it the remaining addend.

The children's attention may be called to examples such as the example at the right, which may be notated on the decimal grid. They can be helped to see how to apply knowledge learned in previous examples. First, ones are added and there are 18 ones, or 1 ten and 8 ones. The 1 ten is added to the tens in tens place and the sum is seen to be 58.

	Tens	*Ones*		
46	1	6		46
5	4	5	or	5
+7	+	7		+7
?	5	8		58

Adding Two-Place Numbers with No Changing to Tens

Children can quickly learn that tens can be added in the same way as ones because of their experience with higher decade addition. However, they will need to be encouraged to think about the addition of examples such as $43 + 52 = ?$

The example may be written on a decimal grid as indicated previously. From their experience children can see that they can find *how many in all* when they think about tens, just as they find *how many in all* when they think about ones. As a final step the example is written without using the decimal grid.

Tens	*Ones*		
4	3		43
+5	2	or	+52
9	5		95

From their experience with adding ones and tens, children should have developed these understandings:

1. Each addend represents a quantity. Each digit in each addend tells the frequency of the units in its decimal position, i.e., 4 represents the frequency of units in the tens' place and 3 represents the frequency of ones in the first addend; 5 represents the frequency of the tens and 2 represents the frequency of the ones in the second addend.

2. The digits in each decimal place are added, with the ones being added first.

3. The sum, 95, is a number equal to the total amount of the combined addends.

Many children may be helped by using the decimal grid to find the sums in these examples:

14	36	43	25	52	81	67	46	20
+74	+23	+52	+43	+36	+18	+30	+52	+65
??	??	??	??	??	??	??	??	??

Adding Two-Place Numbers Substituting Tens for One

Substituting 1 ten for 10 ones is a previously learned skill used in examples such as 37 + 9 = ? Some children have difficulty in applying this skill to examples such as 48 + 37 = ?

The example may be put on the decimal grid as shown earlier. The small "1" at the top of the tens column is used as a means of helping children to think to add the 1 ten substituted for 10 ones. Observe again the accuracy of the term "substitute" as contrasted to the usual term "carry." Nothing is carried from ones to tens, so the word *carry* is misleading.

Tens	*Ones*	
1		
4	8	48
+3	7	= +37
8	5	85

As a final step, the example and its sum are written. Pupils may be helped in finding the sums for these examples by using the decimal grid.

43	37	21	54	62	15	88	79	25
+28	+56	+69	+18	+29	+77	+13	+14	+45
??	??	??	??	??	??	??	??	??

Adding Larger Addends

The principles learned about column addition, adding ones and then adding tens, and substituting 1 ten for each 10 ones can be applied to examples in which there are larger addends. The principle of substituting 1 hundred for each 10 tens is similar to the process of substituting tens for ones.

Diagnosing Pupil Growth

As suggested earlier in this chapter, one of the best ways to discover the thought processes a child uses is to ask him to work orally with the teacher. Representative questions teachers may ask pupils include:

1. How can you tell when you are to add to find the answer to an example?

2. What does a 0 in any addend tell you?

3. In how many ways can you find the answer to the example $34 + 3 = ?$

4. What do you do when the sum in any place is 10 or more?

5. In what way is adding tens like adding ones?

Test items such as the following may be included on pencil and paper tests.

Part I—The Meaning of Addition

Draw a line under the correct answer.

1. You add to answer the question ("How many in each group?" "How many in all?" "How many numbers are to be added?").

2. The sign that asks you to add is ($=$, $-$, $+$).

3. Each addend in an addition example represents (tens, a digit, a quantity).

4. Each digit in a two-place addend tells (how many tens or how many ones, how many in all, how many ones).

5. When adding the digits in a three-place number first add the (hundreds, tens, ones).

6. The sum in addition equals (the sum of all of the digits, the total amount represented by all of the addends, the sum of the ones).

7. When the sum of the digits in ones place is 10 or more (carry 1 ten, change 10 ones to 1 ten, add the tens).

Part II—Vocabulary

Fill the blanks using one of these words or signs: sum, addend, $+$, $=$, adding.

1. When you know how many in each group and want to find how many in all, you find the answer by ____________ .

2. The sign read *and* or *plus* is ____________ .

3. The sign read *equals* is ____________.

4. Finding the sum is called ____________.

5. The total quantity or amount equal to the combined quantities or amounts represented by all the addends is the ____________.

Part III—Computation

1.

4	3	3	8	63	12	41	8	9
+2	4	0	+7	+4	+8	3	2	6
	+2	+5				+2	+3	+45

2.

45	61	39	47	98	89	68	93	88
+33	23	+48	25	+6	8	+71	+37	97
	+14		+16		+7			+52

Summary

Addition is one of the so-called "fundamental" operations of arithmetic used to answer the question, "How many in all?" Each of the addends represents a quantity equal to the cardinal value of the number itself. The plus sign asks a question, "How many in all?" To answer the question, the person doing the adding must think of another number that represents the total quantity called the sum.

In teaching addition, the teacher will show how objects can be used to represent either the addends or the sum but not both because the objects used to represent the addends lose their identity in the sum. For this reason the teacher recognizes the limitations of the objects even as they are being used as teaching tools. The thinking required to find the equality between addends and the sum differs from the thinking required to push groups of objects together. On paper, the addends do not move. They merely represent ideas. Teachers will want to be certain that numbers representing *ones* stimulate specific mental pictures in the minds of the viewers. To illustrate, 4 can be seen as · · / · · 5 as · · / · / · · etc.

Two-place numbers should also stimulate specific mental pictures in which both tens and ones are visualized as separate kinds of units, each with its own specific place. The ideas learned in adding ones can be used in adding tens because the figures that represent tens are identical to those that represent ones.

No quantity greater than nine can be represented in any place-value position in the decimal system. Thus when there are ten units, a single unit ten times greater in decimal value must be substituted. There is no "carrying" involved. Substituting is a much more descriptive word to use in indicating the thought process used before notating sums of ten or more of any units.

Since the 0 represents the absence of frequency, there are no addition facts in which 0 is an addend. A 0 in any place in an addend simply tells the person doing the adding that there are no ones, no tens, etc., to add.

Pupils must learn the 81 addition facts and need help in understanding that these same facts are used over and over again in the various addition examples. Sometimes they are used in adding ones, sometimes in adding tens, sometimes in adding hundreds, and so forth. This is true because adding tens, hundreds, and larger units is like adding ones.

Addition examples follow a specific developmental pattern determined by the complexity of the examples themselves. Simplest of the examples are those with sums of 9 or less. The more complex examples require substituting 1 unit with a decimal value ten times as large for ten units in any decimal place, when the sum of the units is greater than 9.

Teachers need to learn to listen to children to find out the thinking they use when solving addition examples. When the thinking is faulty, reteaching must be done because successful work in addition is based upon understanding. Where children cannot express their thought processes, teachers will want to ask skillful questions to help them think about what they are doing. There is a place for pencil and paper diagnostic tests. Tests that measure computational skill should follow a regular developmental pattern dictated by the number system itself. With tests like this, the teacher can quickly find the kinds of difficulties encountered by the children and can conserve time by being specific in the kind of reteaching that is done.

SUGGESTED QUESTIONS FOR TEACHER SELF-EVALUATION

1. What mathematical questions are answered by addition?
2. In what ways does the notation of an addition example differ from its representation with objects?
3. What steps might be taken to help pupils make the transition from working with objects to working with addends?
4. What does each digit in the addend 435 represent?
5. How would you help a child understand the reason for adding ones before adding tens in two-place addends?
6. Why is the word "substitute" a more descriptive word than "carry" when used in connection with sums greater than 9 in any value position?
7. What are the advantages of using the decimal grid?
8. What do the addends and the sum represent in any addition combination fact?
9. How many addition facts have sums less than 1 ten?
10. How many addition facts have sums of 10 to 18 inclusive?
11. What is the use of the symbol 0 in column addition?
12. What developmental pattern do the addition examples follow?
13. How does the thinking required for column addition differ from the thinking required in adding two addends?
14. How would you help a child who notates the example 33 + 24 + 4 as shown at the right?

$$\begin{array}{r} 33 \\ 24 \\ +4\ \\ \hline \end{array}$$

15. How would you help a child who wrote the answer to the example 39 + 9 as shown at the right?

$$\begin{array}{r} 39 \\ +9 \\ \hline 318 \end{array}$$

SUGGESTED ACTIVITIES

1. Prepare an addition combination fact chart that shows the sum to each of the 81 addition facts.
2. Examine the new textbooks in arithmetic to appraise the meanings and methods presented about addition.
3. Prepare a summary of mathematical meanings related to addition that teachers should help pupils to understand.
4. Prepare diagnostic tests to help determine: (*a*) mathematical understandings (*b*) computational ability (*c*) vocabulary development.

PRACTICE EXERCISES

Addition of integers. (*Note:* All the addition facts are used in the examples in the following exercise.)

1.	54	10	33	71	81	94	40	65	94	90
	72	98	86	78	53	51	90	43	25	71

2.	82	21	72	67	51	82	92	85	30
	25	96	41	82	94	84	63	61	71

3.	73	52	76	65	91	30	46	86	90
	65	57	81	64	12	92	83	32	77

4.	72	60	45	82	50	91	60	44	68
	32	74	72	46	83	35	56	64	91

5.	77	84	91	23	83	51	70	93	90
	51	93	47	81	72	61	95	93	84

Column Addition

220	403	180	981	116	904	159	797
113	234	241	782	309	318	204	486
401	810	271	920	113	424	267	575
224	142	304	805	325	542	308	938

1102	5013	1131	4801	1271	1280	4005	5261
1120	2301	3110	6713	2152	2550	2851	2730
4021	8103	2862	2430	3596	7031	1270	8592
1203	2452	1513	7013	2040	3146	1923	7685

20,830	21,305	17,354	127,586	3,567,254
16,079	10,057	25,026	349,275	4,850,775
17,987	36,892	17,603	975,850	5,962,347
24,753	12,675	36,020	632,489	9,875,500

Problems

1. There are 975 pupils in McKinley School, 769 in Franklin School, and 509 in Jefferson School. What is the total enrollment in all three schools?

2. Jane spent $9.75 for shoes, $8.79 for a dress, and $17.98 for a coat. How much did she spend in all?

3. Mr. Brow's sales for each month in the year 1956 were:

January	$ 8,410.62	February	$12,429.14	March	$10,960.75
April	$ 9,700.45	May	$11,875.20	June	$13,005.85
July	$10,200.75	August	$ 9,003.50	September	$11,325.80
October	$18,500.20	November	$21,005.96	December	$22,014.25

What was the total amount of the sales in 1956?

4. The check stubs in Mrs. Jones's checkbook showed these amounts: $25.75, $30.45, $125.36, $80.36, and $20.50. What was the total amount of the five checks she had written?

5. There are five elementary schools in Mapleville. The enrollment in each school is: 875 pupils, 1025 pupils, 670 pupils, 983 pupils, and 945 pupils. How many pupils are enrolled in the elementary schools?

6. Find the sum for these examples which are notated in the quinary system:

(*a*)	(*b*)	(*c*)	(*d*)
204	100	400	300
431	243	320	220
140	400	344	444
+423	+324	+102	+323

7. Find the sum for these examples which are notated in the duodecimal system:

(*a*)	(*b*)	(*c*)	(*d*)
2 5	TE	9 0E	3 2T
1 0T	TE	3 7T	T 9 9
4TE	TE	2T 9	7TE
9 0T	TE	TTT	8TT

SELECTED REFERENCES

1. Brownell, William A., *The Development of Children's Number Ideas in the Primary Grades.* Chicago: University of Chicago Press, 1928.

2. Brueckner, Leo J., and Grossnickle, Foster E., *How to Make Arithmetic Meaningful.* Philadelphia: John C. Winston Company, 1947.

3. Buckingham, B. R., *Elementary Arithmetic, Its Meaning and Practice.* Boston: Ginn & Company, 1947.

4. Clark, John R., and Eads, Laura K., *Guiding Arithmetic Learnings.* Yonkers, N. Y.: World Book Company, 1954.

5. Morton, Robert Lee, *Teaching Children Arithmetic.* Morristown, N. J.: Silver Burdett Company, 1953.

6. Reckzeh, John, "Addition and Subtraction Situations." *The Arithmetic Teacher,* April, 1956.

7. Spencer, Peter Lincoln, and Brydegaard, Marguerite, *Building Mathematical Concepts in the Elementary School.* New York: Henry Holt and Company, Inc., 1952.

8. Spitzer, Herbert F., *The Teaching of Arithmetic,* 2d ed. Boston: Houghton Mifflin Company, 1954.

9. Wheat, Harry G., *The Psychology and Teaching of Arithmetic.* Boston: D. C. Heath and Company, 1937.

4

Meaning and Use of Subtraction: Integers

Introduction

Subtraction is the second of the "four fundamental operations" and is used to find the mathematical difference between two notated numbers. The subtraction algorism, $9 - 5$ or $\begin{array}{r} 9 \\ \underline{-5} \end{array}$ consists of two numbers and a sign $-$ (read "minus"). The larger of the numbers, the minuend 9, tells how many in one group. The number to be subtracted, the subtrahend 5, tells how many in another group. The difference between two numbers is derived by comparing the subtrahend with the minuend. The addition fact, $5 + 4 = 9$, helps in finding the difference for the reason that since $5 + 4 = 9$, then $9 - 5 = 4$ and $9 - 4 = 5$.

Teachers may find it helpful to appraise their understanding of the mathematical meanings and structure of subtraction of integers by deciding upon what they believe to be appropriate answers to the following questions. They may also wish to determine answers which, they believe, they should help pupils to discover and understand.

1. What is the mathematical meaning of subtraction?
2. What mathematical and social questions are answered by using subtraction?

3. How may the meanings and basic facts related to addition be used in subtraction?
4. What is the difference between subtraction when using concrete materials and when using numbers to represent ideas of quantity?
5. What is the mathematical meaning that teachers should help pupils to learn for: (*a*) the minuend, (*b*) the subtrahend, (*c*) the difference?
6. What are the developmental patterns in subtraction examples that teachers should help pupils to discover and understand?
7. What methods should be used in verifying the accuracy of the answer?
8. Why is correctness in the thought process used by pupils in subtraction as important as accuracy in computation?
9. What diagnostic procedures may teachers use to determine the understanding, progress, and needs of pupils in subtraction of integers?

The Meaning of Subtraction

Subtraction in a physical sense is removing a portion of a whole object or a portion of a group of objects from a larger group of the same kind of objects. When this is understood, it is easy to see the accuracy of the statement, "We subtract like units," i.e., a piece of ribbon from a spool of ribbon, some oranges from a bag of oranges. The idea of subtracting like things can easily be extended to subtracting like decimal units such as: ones from ones, tenths from tenths. Subtraction in earlier civilizations consisted of calculating with counters or counting boards. From this early primitive method of calculation we have inherited such words as "subtraction," which can be illustrated by actually taking, subtracting, from a specified group representing the whole (the minuend) a smaller group (the subtrahend) leaving the remaining small group (remainder). Borrowing as applied to this type of subtraction can be understood because it is descriptive of what is actually done. These words, "subtraction," "minuend," "borrow," and "remainder" are descriptive of earlier calculation practice but are not descriptive of the subtraction that is done mathematically.

In mathematics, subtraction is the mathematical and thought process of finding how much one number exceeds another number, or of finding the difference between two numbers. The difference may be determined by visualizing the cardinal value of the minuend and the subtrahend and then visualizing the amount by which one exceeds the other. Subtraction may also be interpreted as the mathematical process of finding the component of a number which, when added to the given component, equals the number ($13 = 7 + 6$; $13 - 7 = 6$; $13 - 6 = 7$).

Observe what happens in the social situation where a child has a 32-inch board and knows he is to cut off a 15-inch piece, and wants to know how much is left. To find how much is left he could measure the piece remaining and find it to be about 17 inches long. The subtraction consists in the cutting off of one piece 15 inches long. Finding the answer consists in looking at, and in this situation, measuring what is left.

In a mathematical situation, thinking replaces the physical act. Let us see what we actually do when finding the answer to the example at the right. We know that the whole quantity was 32 inches and that the quantity removed was 15 inches. We must find the length of the quantity that is left. To find the answer, we must first subtract the ones and then the tens. There are not enough ones to subtract so we:

$$\begin{array}{r} 32 \text{ in.} \\ -\underline{15} \text{ in.} \\ ?? \end{array}$$

(*a*) Take one of the 3 tens and for it substitute 10 ones and add these ones to the 2 ones in the minuend.

(*b*) Rewrite the minuend as 2 tens and 12 ones.

(*c*) Think, "The difference between 12 ones and 5 ones is 7 ones," or "12 ones − 5 ones = 7 ones."

Next we subtract the tens, We think, "2 tens − 1 ten = 1 ten."

Observe that in a mathematical situation, no subtraction was performed, at least not to the extent that anything was taken away. Nothing was borrowed. Except for writing the answer, only thinking was required, with numbers used to record the results of the mental processes employed in comparing 32 and 15 to find by how much 32 exceeds 15. The 17 represents the difference between the two numbers. It can be thought of as the unknown addend which, when added to 15, equals 32. This is true because the 15 inches was originally a part of the 32 inches. The amount removed plus the amount left must equal the original quantity. There is a relationship between subtraction and addition. Pupils who understand this relationship can use their understandings of the basic facts in addition when finding the answer to subtraction examples.

Social and Mathematical Questions Answered by Subtraction

There are a number of social situations in which we use the subtraction process. If the social situation is dramatized, we can usually see clearly that the answer to each question can be determined by using either addition or counting. Some social situations are given to show the kind of question answered by subtraction. In each case, once the example has been determined, the computation consists of finding the unknown quantity. This is done by finding the difference between the larger and smaller known quantities.

1. Mary had 21 stamps. She gave 8 stamps to Judy. How many stamps did she have left?

In dramatizing this situation, the child can see that the stamps left (the unknown quantity) equal 13. The minuend, 21, represents all the stamps. The subtrahend, 8, represents the known component part or number. The number of stamps left, 13, represents the unknown component part or number, which in subtraction is called the difference. The example would be properly notated as shown at the right. The difference between 21 and 8 represents the answer to the question, "How many left?"

$$\begin{array}{rl} 21 & \text{minuend} \\ -8 & \text{subtrahend} \\ \hline ?? & \text{difference} \end{array}$$

2. Jerry caught 32 fish. Dick caught 19. How many more fish were caught by Jerry than by Dick?

In dramatizing this situation, the child could count from 19 to 32 with the result of his count being the answer to the question in the problem. The example should be notated as shown at the right. The unknown number equals the difference between 32 and 19. Observe that the notation is similar to the notation for the example in problem 1, even though the question in the problem is entirely different.

$$\begin{array}{r} 32 \\ -19 \\ \hline ?? \end{array}$$

3. Nancy had 25¢. After buying some stamps she had 10¢ left. How much did she spend for stamps?

The unknown number equals the difference between 25¢ and 10¢. The more usual way to notate the example is shown at the right. The answer to the question represents the difference between 25¢ and 10¢.

$$\begin{array}{r} 25¢ \\ -10¢ \\ \hline ??¢ \end{array}$$

4. Joan is 51 inches tall. Sally is only 39 inches tall. What is the difference between their heights?

In this situation, Joan can be seen to be as tall as Sally, (39 in. tall) + an unknown number of inches. In the social situation, this distance can be measured. In mathematics, the example is notated as shown at the right. The unknown number represents the difference between the two numbers.

$$\begin{array}{rl} 51 & \text{in.} \\ -39 & \text{in.} \\ \hline ?? & \end{array}$$

A number of other questions can be answered by finding the difference between the whole quantity (minuend) and a given number (subtrahend), which represents part of the minuend. Representative questions include, How many fewer? How much change did he receive? How much more money will he need?

After analyzing each of the problems commonly solved by subtraction, one can easily see that the subtraction example, such as that at the right, can be used to represent a wide variety of social situations. The minuend, 41, is equal to the subtrahend, 17, plus the difference. The minuend is a sum and the subtrahend and difference are addends of that sum. The minuend can be thought of as the larger number given, the subtrahend as the smaller number given, and the missing number or unknown addend as the difference. Each subtraction example then is understood to have numbers that represent a situation and to ask a question, "What is the difference between two numbers?"

$$\begin{array}{r} 41 \\ -17 \\ \hline ?? \end{array}$$

Subtraction of Numbers with Minuends of Less than Ten

There are 36 subtraction facts with minuends of 9 or less. There are also 9 facts where there is *no* difference between the minuend and the subtrahend. The examples are:

1	2	2	3	3	3	4	4	4	4
−1	−1	−2	−1	−2	−3	−1	−2	−3	−4
5	5	5	5	5	6	6	6	6	6
−1	−2	−3	−4	−5	−1	−2	−3	−4	−5
6	7	7	7	7	7	7	7	8	8
−6	−1	−2	−3	−4	−5	−6	−7	−1	−2
8	8	8	8	8	8	9	9	9	9
−3	−4	−5	−6	−7	−8	−1	−2	−3	−4
9	9	9	9	9					
−5	−6	−7	−8	−9					

When the minuend and subtrahend are notated as in the above examples, then the minus sign asks the question, "What is the difference between two numbers?" The question can be answered by using what was learned in addition. Since $4 + 2 = 6$, then $6 - 4 = 2$, and $6 - 2 = 4$.

Teaching Subtraction Facts with Minuends of Less Than Ten

A class demonstration in which the children observe the various arrangements of pupils in a group and the numbers used to represent the various arrangements will help pupils understand subtraction. To illustrate, a group of seven children may be asked to come to the front of the room and the number 7 may be written on the chalkboard to represent the idea of seven children. Then two of the children may be asked to sit down and a 2 is written beneath the 7 to represent the idea of the children who sat down. Then ask, "how many are left?" The answer, 5, is written beneath the 2. The demonstration illustrates that $7 - 2 = 5$. The example $7 - 2 = ?$ illustrates a particular situation in which the known ideas are: (1) There are seven children in a group, and (2) two children sat down. The minus sign asks the question, "How many are left?"

Either as a cooperative class exercise or by working individually the children can discover the various ways in which seven can be separated into component parts. The various examples may be written on a page or chart with the title, "The Story of 7." The children can see that the known component is written beneath the 7 to form each of the examples.

In teaching pupils to compare two numbers to find the difference between them, a procedure such as the following may be used. Step 1: Ask seven children to stand in a row in the front of the room and write 7 on the chalkboard to represent the idea of seven children. Step 2: Ask two children to make a second row in front of the original row. One is to stand in front of the first child and the other in front of the second child in the row of seven. Then write a 2 on the chalkboard to represent the idea of the two children in the front row. Step 3: Ask: "Which group is larger?" "How much larger?" and write 5 beneath the 2 to represent the idea of the difference in size between the groups.

The difference between any two numbers can be determined by using objects to represent the cardinal value of each of the numbers and by telling how much one group exceeds the other. The children may be asked to use objects in making discoveries about the relationship between two numbers and may be asked to use pictures and numbers to represent situations used in making the discoveries.

Indicate the addition fact that would be used in finding the answer to the following pairs of subtraction facts:

EXERCISE

4	4	7	7	5	5	6	6	8	8
−1	−3	−3	−4	−1	−4	−2	−4	−1	−7

Basic Subtraction Facts with Minuends More Than Ten

There are 45 subtraction facts with two-place minuends of 18 or less. These examples are:

10	10	10	10	10	10	10	10	10
−1	−2	−3	−4	−5	−6	−7	−8	−9
11	11	11	11	11	11	11	11	12
−2	−3	−4	−5	−6	−7	−8	−9	−3
12	12	12	12	12	12	13	13	13
−4	−5	−6	−7	−8	−9	−4	−5	−6
13	13	13	14	14	14	14	14	15
−7	−8	−9	−5	−6	−7	−8	−9	−6
15	15	15	16	16	16	17	17	18
−7	−8	−9	−7	−8	−9	−8	−9	−9

Each of the above examples asks the question, "What is the difference between the minuend and the subtrahend or the difference between the two numbers?" The difference may be found by using the addition facts. To illustrate, since $9 + 7 = 16$, then $16 - 9 = 7$, and $16 - 7 = 9$.

Teaching Subtraction Facts with Minuends of More Than Ten

A review of the use of place value for recording the number value of groups greater than nine will assist pupils in recalling that 10 ones may be recorded as 1 ten and that 1 ten = 10 ones. To illustrate the preceding statement, ten children may be arranged in a row in the front of the room. If a one were used to represent each child, there would be 10 ones. If a ten were used to represent all the children there would be 1 ten.

Ten children can be used in demonstrating the "how many left" idea in a subtraction situation where the minuend is 10. The number 10 is written on the board to represent the 10 children. Three children may be asked to be seated and a 3 written beneath the 0. Then ask the pupils to look at the children still standing and ask, "How many are left?" The answer, 7, is written beneath the 3. Then ask, "Did you think of the 10 as 1 ten and no ones or as 10 ones when you answered the question, "How many are left"? The pupils can see that it was necessary to think of 1 ten as 10 ones.

At the concrete level, the minuend and subtrahend must both be thought of as ones before it is possible physically to find the difference between them or to answer the question "How many are left"? Many pupils may need the experience of physically separating a group of 10 ones, 11 ones, 12 ones, etc., into two component parts. Three-inch by five-inch library cards may be considered as ones and may be distributed to pupils to use in constructing a table of subtraction facts. To illustrate, if they start with 12 cards and arrange them in two groups each of nine or less, they may have a group of 7 cards and a group of 5 cards. Twelve is seen to equal two component groups. If the 12 and one component group are known, the other can be easily thought. As the pupils discover subtraction facts, they may write them on small cards to be used as flash cards in drill situations.

Generalized Rule

To find the difference between two numbers, one may use the corresponding addition facts.

EXERCISE

Indicate the two subtraction facts in which the difference can be found by using the following addition facts:

6	6	9	4	5	7	9	7	8
+5	+4	+3	+8	+8	+6	+6	+9	+7

Subtracting Larger Numbers with No Substitution Required

The generalization that we compute with like units applies in subtraction as in addition. If the minuend represents feet, then the subtrahend, which is either a part of the minuend or which is to be compared with the minuend, must also represent feet. Explain why this must be true.

But the number that represents the quantity of feet may consist of different sized units: i.e., ones, tens, hundreds, etc. The generalization of comparing like units extends to the units represented by the figures in the minuend and subtrahend. Consider the examples below:

(*a*)

T	*O*	
4	8	48
	6	− 6
4	2	42

(*b*)

T	*O*	
5	6	56
3	2	−32
2	4	24

(*c*)

H	*T*	*O*	
9	6	5	965
	3	3	−33
9	3	2	932

(*d*)

H	*T*	*O*	
5	8	6	586
3	3	4	−334
2	5	2	252

In example (*a*), the question asked is "What is the difference between 4 tens and 8 ones (48) and 6 ones"? The ones can be compared because they are like units. Think $8 - 6 = 2$. Write 2 in the ones place in the answer. The second step is to observe that there are no tens to compare. The difference between 48 and 6 is seen to be 42.

In example (*b*), there are enough tens and enough ones to compare. The question can be considered, "What is the difference between 5 tens and 6 ones (56) and 3 tens and 2 ones (32)?" Ones can be compared with ones and tens with tens. The difference between the ones and the difference between the tens is written in the proper place value position in the answer. The difference between 56 and 32 is seen to be 24.

In examples (*c*) and (*d*), the thinking required is similar to that used in finding the answer to the question in examples (*a*) and (*b*). It can be seen that tens are subtracted in the same way as ones. Hundreds and decimal units larger than hundreds are also subtracted in the same way as ones and tens. In example (*c*), what is the difference between 5 and 3? What is the difference between 6 tens and 3 tens? Why is 9 written in the hundreds' place of the difference? In example (*d*), what is the difference between 6 ones and 4 ones? What is the difference between 8 tens and 3 tens? What is the difference between 5 hundreds and 3 hundreds?

EXERCISE

Find the answer to each example and explain the thinking required.

38	57	95	158	164	796	985	678
−4	−42	−91	−35	−60	−432	−934	−673

Subtracting Larger Numbers with Substitution Required

The ideas developed in learning to subtract integers when each digit in the minuend is larger than the corresponding digit in the subtrahend can be used in subtracting numbers where this may not be true. Some of these ideas are:

1. Subtract only numbers that express like decimal units.
2. Compare figures in each decimal place to find the difference between them.
3. To find the difference in each decimal place, compare the two numbers.
4. Subtract the smaller units before subtracting the progressively larger units.

Examples That Require Rewriting the Minuend Before Subtracting

Consider the example at the right. Ones must be compared with ones but there are more ones in the subtrahend than in the minuend. The first step is to take 1 of the 8 tens, substitute for

$$\begin{array}{r} 83 \\ -7 \\ \hline ?? \end{array}$$

it 10 ones, and add them to the 3 ones. The minuend can then be thought of as 7 tens and 13 ones and the example can be rewritten on a place-value chart as shown at the right. The second step is to find the difference between 13 ones and 7 ones (13 − 7 = 6). The third step is to observe that there are no tens to compare. The difference between 83 and 7 is seen to be 76.

T	*O*
7	13
8̸	3̸
	7
?	?

Subtraction by Endings

When thought processes are understood, short cuts may be encouraged. Observe the examples at the right: The subtraction fact, 15 − 7, is used in finding the answer to each. In each case there is 1 less ten in the difference than in the minuend. What subtraction fact is used in finding the answer to each example below?

15	25	35	45	55	65
−7	−7	−7	−7	−7	−7

83	47	51	64	75	93	26	38
−5	−9	−3	−9	−6	−7	−8	−9

Generalized Rule

To find the difference when subtracting by endings:

a. Use the appropriate subtraction fact.

b. Write one less ten in the difference than in the minuend.

Consider the examples below.

(*a*)

T	*O*		
6	13		
7̸	3̸		73
		or	
4	8		−48
2	5		25

(*b*)

T	*O*		
3	15		
4̸	5̸		45
		or	
3	8		−38
	7		7

(*c*)

T	*O*		
5	10		
6̸	0̸		60
		or	
2	7		−27
3	3		33

In example (*a*), the first step is to rewrite the minuend by taking one of the 7 tens, substituting for it 10 ones and adding them to the 3 ones. The minuend can then be thought of as 6 tens and 13 ones. The second step is to subtract (13 − 7 = 6) the ones. The third is to subtract the tens (6 tens − 4 tens = 2 tens or 6 − 4 = 2). The difference between 73 and 48 is seen to be 25.

Consider example (*b*). Explain how the minuend was rewritten. What thinking was required to find the difference between 15 and 8? Is there any difference between 3 and 3? Why is it unnecessary to write a zero in tens' place in the difference of example (*b*)?

In example (*c*), the first step is to take 1 of the 5 tens, substitute for it 10 ones in the ones place. What is the second step? What is the third step? What is the difference between 60 and 27?

All the above examples are similar in that in each there are fewer ones in the minuend than in the subtrahend. Observe that there was no carrying or borrowing. Mathematically, it is only necessary to think of one of the larger units as being changed to 10 of the smaller units, which in turn are substituted for the larger unit. Then the minuend is rewritten to represent the new situation in which there is 1 fewer ten and there are 10 more ones.

The principle of substituting 10 smaller units for a larger unit can be applied to subtraction of larger numbers as shown in examples (*d*) to (*f*).

(*d*) *H T O*		(*e*) *H T O*		(*f*) *H T O*		(*g*) *H T O*		(*h*) *H T O*	
4 16		6 13		13		9		9	
5̸ 6̸ 8	568	6 7̸ 3̸	673	5 3̸ 15		7 1̸0̸10		3 1̸0̸11	
				6̸ 4̸ 5̸	645	8̸ 0̸ 0̸	800	4̸ 0̸ 1̸	401
8 2	−82	3 5	−35	7 9	−79	6 4	−64	3 6	−36
4 8 6	486	6 3 8	638	5 6 6	566	7 3 6	736	3 6 5	365

In example (*d*) there are enough ones but not enough tens in the minuend to subtract. The first step is to take one of the 5 hundreds, substitute for it 10 tens and add them to the tens. How is the minuend rewritten? The second step is to find the difference between the ones. The third step is to find the difference between the tens. The fourth step is to observe that there are no hundreds to compare. The difference between 568 and 82 is 486.

Examine example (*e*) and answer these questions. Are there enough ones to subtract? Are there enough tens to subtract? How is the minuend rewritten? What steps are followed in finding the difference? What is the difference?

In example (*f*) there are too few ones and too few tens in the minuend to subtract. Before rewriting the minuend, take 1 of the 4 tens, substitute for it 10 ones and add them to the ones. Then take 1 of the 6 hundreds, substitute for it 10 tens and add them to the 3 tens. What steps are used in finding the difference in each value position? What is the difference between 645 and 79?

The thought process used in finding the answer to the example 800 − 64 [example (*g*)] is first to observe that there are no ones and no tens in the minuend. The minuend can be rewritten by taking 1 of the 8 hundreds, substituting for it 10 tens and then taking 1 of the 10 tens and substituting for it 10 ones. The rewritten minuend becomes 7 hundreds, 9 tens, and 10 ones. What is the difference between 10 ones and 4 ones? What is the difference between 9 tens and 6 tens? Are there any hundreds to compare? The difference between 800 and 64 is 736.

The thought processes used in finding the answer to the example 401 − 39 [example (*h*)] differ but slightly from those used in finding the answer to example (*g*). The minuend can be rewritten by taking 1 of the 4 hundreds, substituting for it 10 tens, and by taking 1 of the 10 tens, substituting for it 10 ones and adding them to the 1 in ones' place. The minuend then becomes 3 hundreds, 9 tens, and 11 ones. What steps are taken in finding the difference in each value position? The difference between 401 and 36 is 365.

Generalized Rule

When there are more units in any decimal place in the subtrahend than in the corresponding place in the minuend, rewrite the minuend by taking 1 of the next larger units, substituting for it 10 smaller units and adding them to the figure in the place to the right.

EXERCISE

Find the answer to each example. Explain the thought process required to find the answer.

689	995	874	500	702	456	300	204
−95	−26	−87	−48	−59	−238	−143	−198

Verifying the Answers in Subtraction

The answer in subtraction examples represents the difference between the minuend and one of its component parts (the subtrahend). Consequently, the difference must be the other component part. Checking subtraction consists of adding the difference and the subtrahend. The resulting sum should equal the minuend. Observe the example at the right. The minuend in the subtraction example equals the sum in the example used as a check. Therefore, the example is solved correctly.

Subtraction	Verification
605	209
−396	+396
209	605

Generalized Rule

When checking the answer in subtraction, add the difference and the subtrahend. The sum should equal the minuend.

Diagnosing Pupil Growth

As suggested in the chapter on addition, one of the best ways to discover thought processes is to ask the pupil to work orally in conference with the teacher. Representative questions teachers may ask pupils include the following.

Part I—Meanings

1. How can you tell when you are to subtract to answer the question in a problem?

2. What does each number in a subtraction example tell?

3. What question is asked by the minus sign in a subtraction example?

4. When will you need to write a 0 in any place in the answer?

5. In how many ways can you find the answer to the example 46 − 8?

6. What do you do to find the answer in ones place when there are enough ones to subtract?

7. What do you do to find the answer in tens place when there are not enough tens to subtract?

8. In what way is subtracting tens like subtracting ones?

Suggestions for Diagnostic Paper and Pencil Tests

Part I—Meanings

1. You subtract to find (how many in all, how many left, which one).

2. The sign that asks you to subtract is (+, −, ÷).

3. The minuend in a subtraction example is (the larger number, the smaller number, the answer).

4. The subtrahend in a subtraction example may represent (a number larger than the minuend, a number smaller than the minuend, a difference between two numbers).

5. The difference in a subtraction example may represent (a number larger than the minuend, a difference between the minuend and subtrahend, a number to be subtracted from the minuend).

6. In subtracting a three-place number, first subtract (the ones, the tens, the hundreds).

7. In subtracting a two-place number with too few ones to subtract (substitute for 1 ten 10 ones; borrow 1 ten).

Part II—Vocabulary

Fill the blanks using one of these words or signs: subtrahend, minuend, difference, remainder, minus, −, =, subtracting.

1. When you know how many in a group and want to find how much larger it is than a smaller group, you find the answer by ______.

2. The sign read *minus* is ______.

3. In a subtraction example the smaller number is the ______.

4. The amount left may be called the ______.

5. The number in a subtraction example that represents how many in all is the ______.

Part III—Computation

Write the answer to each example below and be ready to explain your thinking.

A.	8	6	4	9	7	**B.**	17	13	15	16	12
	−3	−5	−2	−6	−4		−9	−6	−7	−8	−5
	___	___	___	___	___		___	___	___	___	___

C.	68	86	57	75	94	D.	46	78	77	84	25
	−3	−5	−4	−2	−1		−24	−76	−53	−42	−14
E.	53	95	71	80	64	F.	52	85	73	46	64
	−9	−7	−6	−8	−5		−28	−67	−49	−37	−56
G.	875	796	653	484	327	H.	561	983	374	600	801
	−65	−54	−31	−43	−16		−80	−65	−96	−74	−95

Summary

Subtraction is another of the so-called "fundamental operations" of arithmetic, used to find the difference between two numbers. One of the numbers, the minuend, tells how many in a group. The other, the subtrahend, tells how many in the other group. The missing number, the difference, is found by comparing the two numbers to find the number or quantity representing the numerical difference between the minuend and the subtrahend.

In a physical sense, subtraction consists of removing a part of a whole quantity and in finding how much is left. The part removed is contained in the whole quantity. The excess of the whole quantity over the part removed is the difference between them. The mathematical and thought process in subtraction is one of finding the difference between two numbers (the minuend and the subtrahend). All notated or written subtraction requires finding the difference between the minuend and the subtrahend. In physical subtraction and in subtraction as done on paper, only units of like things and like decimal value can be compared.

In subtracting two-place or larger numbers, like decimal units are compared. Smaller units are compared first and the larger units compared in sequence: i.e., first ones, then tens, then hundreds, etc. Should there be a smaller figure in any decimal place of the minuend than in the corresponding decimal place in the subtrahend, one of the next larger decimal units is taken and for it are substituted 10 smaller units in the place at its right.

Subtraction examples follow a specific developmental pattern determined by the complexity of the examples themselves. The examples become more complex as the number of substitutions of smaller for larger units increases.

SUGGESTED QUESTIONS FOR TEACHER SELF-EVALUATION

1. What is your interpretation of the mathematical meaning of subtraction?

2. What are the three types of questions that subtraction asks about the relationship of numbers?

3. What meanings should the teacher help children to discover and to understand for the terms: minuend, subtrahend, difference, addends?

4. What methods would you use to help pupils to discover and to understand: subtraction facts with minuends less than 10; subtraction facts with two-place minuends of 18 or less.

5. How may you help pupils to discover the relationship between subtraction and addition facts?

6. How may the addition facts chart be used as a subtraction facts chart?

7. What are the developmental levels or types of subtraction examples that teachers should observe when teaching subtraction?

8. What are the psychological steps and mathematical meanings involved in the following examples:

9	29	14	37	\$1.00	\$4.32	4000	500
−3	−13	−9	−28	−.75	−2.69	−1397	−499
?	?	?	?	?	?	?	?

9. How many subtraction facts have a minuend less than 10?

10. How many subtraction facts have two-place minuends of 18 or less?

SUGGESTED ACTIVITIES

1. Prepare a subtraction fact chart that could be used to find the answer to each basic subtraction fact.

2. Examine the new textbooks in arithmetic to discover and appraise the various methods used in teaching subtraction.

3. Prepare a summary of mathematical meanings related to subtraction that teachers should help pupils to understand.

4. Prepare representative diagnostic tests to help determine (*a*) mathematical understandings, (*b*) computational ability, (*c*) vocabulary development.

5. Preview a number of filmstrips or films and evaluate them in terms of how they might be used to help children learn subtraction.

PRACTICE EXERCISES

Subtraction of whole numbers. (*Note:* All of the subtraction facts are used in the examples in the following exercise.)

1.	989	457	7897	7865	6786	78,249	1897	53,949
	38	135	5796	6832	1355	41,232	1272	13,543

2.	63,879	423,586	57,969	95	76	232	941	811
	21,616	212,546	47,441	6	8	15	96	77

3.	645	812	5252	6960	9341	7527	5124
	77	14	753	984	8693	4729	3396

4.	205	490	700	8076	9807	7530	6207
	24	81	485	3764	4362	4989	3784

5.	79,711	86,312	913,426	7,541,414	976,502,001
	8,724	29,769	388,559	2,867,959	497,386,925

Problems

1. Dick had $10. He spent $8.69. How much money was left?

2. Enrollment is 1078 at Lincoln High School and 1426 at Roosevelt High School. How many more pupils are in Roosevelt than in Lincoln High School?

3. The Johnsons drove 1006 miles in March and 845 miles in April. How many less miles did they drive in April than in March?

4. Mr. Hansen had $1110 in his checking account. After paying his bills he had $289 left. What was the total amount of his bills?

5. A total of 22,000 tickets was printed for a game. If 18,575 were sold, how many were unsold?

6. A large car weighed 5270 pounds and a smaller car weighed 4185 pounds. What was the difference between the weights of the two cars?

7. A treasurer collected $15.75 in dues, $18.98 from a bake sale, and $25 as a gift to the club. Club expenses were $29.85. What was the balance?

6. Subtraction in the quinary number system. Compute the answer for each example:

(a)	(b)	(c)	(d)
302	400	3402	42,000
−114	−244	−1430	−24,304

7. Subtraction in the duodecimal number system. Compute the answer for each example.

(a)	(b)	(c)	(d)
80*E*	5*TT*	8900	8*TE*09
−247	−2*EE*	−3*TE*9	−3*E*57*E*

8. Subtraction in the binary number system. Compute the answer for each example.

(a)	(b)	(c)	(d)
100	111	10,100	11,101
− 10	− 11	− 1,011	1,110

SELECTED REFERENCES

1. Brownell, William A., *The Development of Children's Number Ideas in the Primary Grades.* Chicago: University of Chicago Press, 1928.

2. Brueckner, Leo J., and Grossnickle, Foster E., *How to Make Arithmetic Meaningful.* Philadelphia: John C. Winston Company, 1947.

3. Buckingham, B. R., *Elementary Arithmetic, Its Meaning and Practice.* Boston: Ginn & Company, 1947.

4. Clark, John R., and Eads, Laura K., *Guiding Arithmetic Learnings.* Yonkers, N. Y.: World Book Company, 1954.

5. Morton, Robert Lee, *Teaching Children Arithmetic.* Morristown, N. J.: Silver Burdett Company, 1953.

6. Reckseh, John, "Addition and Subtraction Situations." *The Arithmetic Teacher*, April, 1956.

7. Spencer, Peter Lincoln, and Brydegaard, Marguerite, *Building Mathematical Concepts in the Elementary School.* New York: Henry Holt and Company, Inc., 1952.

8. Spitzer, Herbert F., *The Teaching of Arithmetic*, 2d ed., Boston: Houghton Mifflin Company, 1954.

9. Wheat, Harry G., *How to Teach Arithmetic.* Evanston, Ill.: Row, Peterson Company, 1951.

5

Meaning and Use of Multiplication: Integers

Introduction

Multiplication is another of the "four fundamental operations" and is used to answer the mathematical question how many in all, which is the question answered by counting or by addition. Multiplication is more complex than either counting or addition. The multiplication algorism 2×3 or $\begin{array}{r} 3 \\ \underline{\times 2} \end{array}$ consists of one number, the multiplicand 3, which tells the size of the groups to be multiplied; the multiplier, 2, which tells the number of groups, and a sign $\times$ (read "times"). The answer to the question in the example is the product. The product is derived by thinking of a number equal to two groups with a quantity size of three each.

Exploratory Questions

The chapter has been designed to help teachers develop their own understanding of multiplication to enable them more successfully to guide pupils to discover and understand the mathematical concept of multiplication consistent with the number system. Teachers may find it helpful to appraise their understanding of the mathematical meanings and structure of multiplication by answering the following questions.

1. What is the mathematical meaning of multiplication?
2. What is the mathematical relationship between multiplication and addition?
3. What is the mathematical meaning that teachers should help pupils to learn for: (*a*) the multiplicand, (*b*) the multiplier, (*c*) the partial product, (*d*) the product?
4. What kinds of mathematical and social questions are answered by using multiplication?
5. What is the relationship between the thought process and written computation in multiplication that teachers should help pupils to learn?
6. What is the mathematical meaning and function of zero in multiplication?
7. How many of the basic facts in multiplication have a product less than ten? How many facts have a product of ten or more?
8. What are the developmental patterns in multiplication examples that teachers should help pupils to discover and understand?
9. What method should be used in verifying the accuracy of computation in multiplication?
10. What change is made in the meaning of a multiplication example if the multiplicand and multiplier are reversed?
11. Why is the correct comprehension in the thought process used by pupils in multiplication as important as accuracy in computation?
12. What diagnostic procedures may teachers use to determine the understandings, progress, and needs of pupils in multiplication of integers?

The Meaning of Multiplication: Integers

The multiplication of integers is the thought and computation process used to find the product of two or more numbers which notate groups of equal size. The product is, in fact, a sum for the reason that it represents the answer to the question, "How many in all?" The product is a notated number that shows the total amount when a given number of equal size groups of like units have been combined or are thought to be combined in one group.

The principle of computing with like units is essential in multiplication. Consider the situation where an individual has 15 books,

15 chairs, and 15 pencils. The notated number, 15, is identical, but the objects are dissimilar. The question, "How many in all?" could not be answered in terms of the same objects or units. However if there are 15 chairs in one row, 15 chairs in another row, and 15 chairs in still another row, then the question, "How many chairs in all?" can be answered by multiplication. The thought question is, "What number identifies the total number of chairs in the three rows?" (3×15 chairs = ? chairs). Each number (15) consists of one decimal unit of ten and 5 decimal units of one. There are, therefore, three decimal units of 5 ones each or 15 ones (1 ten and 5 ones) and three decimal units of 1 ten each or 3 tens. One ten and 5 ones together with 3 tens equal 4 tens and 5 ones or 45. The product shows that the notated number, 45, is the total of three equal groups of 15 chairs.

Multiplication involves a more complex thought process than addition. In addition, numbers are used to identify each of the addends. If three addends are to be added, all are written ($15 + 15 + 15 = ?$). However, in multiplication, one number is used to notate the number of objects represented by only one of the addends. Another number is used to notate the number of equal size or like addends ($3 \times 15 = ?$).

Historically, multiplication was an advanced process and developed only in those nations that had a high degree of civilization. Smith in *History of Mathematics* tells us that the Babylonians had such tables centuries before Christ. If one studies numerals in use by various peoples, he will discover that Hindu numerals lend themselves much more readily to multiplication than the numerals in use by the Egyptians, Romans, and Greeks. However, the Greeks did have a form of multiplication table, which appeared in an arithmetic textbook written about A. D. 100. Both Greeks and Romans seem to have depended upon the abacus to perform repeated additions in lieu of multiplication.

Social and Mathematical Questions Answered by Multiplication

Whenever it becomes necessary to combine the smaller groups of equal size into a single larger group, multiplication is the shortest process. Multiplication, rather than addition, is probably the most used process today. By dramatizing the social situation in which multiplication can be used, the children can usually see that there will be a definite number of equal size groups and a question that means, "Find how many in all." Following are given some social situations and representative questions answered by multiplication. In each case, once the example has been determined, the computation consists of finding the unknown sum (product). This is done by using the multiplication facts, by addition, or by counting.

Consider the following problems, which are representative of social situations:

1. Bonnie put 6 stamps on each of 4 pages. How many stamps did she use?

After dramatizing this situation, the learner can see that Bonnie used 24 stamps. The answer to the question in the problem may be determined by counting, 1, 2, 3, 4, 5, 6 on the first page and continuing the count on succeeding pages until all the stamps are counted. The answer may be determined by adding 6 + 6 + 6 + 6. The fastest thought and computation process used to find how many stamps in all is to multiply. Observe that the question asked in the problem is, "How many stamps did Bonnie use?" The answer is found by thinking, "What number equals 4 groups of 6 each?"

6 multiplicand	6
×4 multiplier	×4
? product	? product

2. Nancy bought 5 candy bars that cost 6¢ each. What was the total cost?

To answer the question, units representing money value must be added (6¢ + 6¢ + 6¢ + 6¢ + 6¢ = ?), or multiplied (5 × 6¢ = ?). Multiplication is a faster thought process to use to find the total cost. The multiplicand, 6, shows the cost of one candy bar; the multiplier, 5, shows the number of candy bars purchased. The product, 30, shows the total cost. It is important that teachers help pupils learn to identify and understand the mathematical meaning and function of the multiplicand, the multiplier, and the product.

After analyzing easy problems solved by multiplication, pupils can discover and understand that multiplication examples such as the examples at the right can represent a variety of social situations. The *product* is understood to be the number equal to the total of all of the equal addends, i.e., the product, 90, is equal to 6 groups of 15 each. The correct way of thinking and expressing the example is, "Six 15's equal what number?" or "Six times 15 equals

15		15
× 6	or	× 6
?		90

what number?" The multiplicand shows the amount of each equal addend. The multiplier shows how many equal size groups or addends. The mathematical symbol, ×, asks the question, "How many in all?" or "What number is equal to all the addends when they are combined or thought to be combined in one group?"

EXERCISE

Write several original problems to illustrate questions answered by multiplication. In each case, explain how to determine which number tells, "How many in an equal group?" and which tells, "How many equal groups?"

Multiplication of Numbers with Products Less Than Ten

There are 23 multiplication facts with products less than 10.

1	1	1	1	1	1	1	1	1
×1	×2	×3	×4	×5	×6	×7	×8	×9
2	2	2	4	3	3	3	4	4
×1	×2	×3	×4	×1	×2	×3	×1	×2
5	6	7	8	9				
×1	×1	×1	×1	×1				

Basic Multiplication Facts with Products of More Than Ten

There are 58 multiplication facts with products of 10 or more.

2	2	2	2	2	3	3	3	3	3
×5	×6	×7	×8	×9	×4	×5	×6	×7	×8
3	4	4	4	4	4	4	4	5	5
×9	×3	×4	×5	×6	×7	×8	×9	×2	×3
5	5	5	5	5	5	6	6	6	6
×4	×5	×6	×7	×8	×9	×2	×3	×4	×5

6	6	6	6	7	7	7	7	7	7
×6	×7	×8	×9	×2	×3	×4	×5	×6	×7
7	7	8	8	8	8	8	8	8	8
×8	×9	×2	×3	×4	×5	×6	×7	×8	×9
9	9	9	9	9	9	9	9		
×2	×3	×4	×5	×6	×7	×8	×9		

The Meaning and Use of Zero

Observe that in none of the basic facts do you see a 0. Considering zero as either a multiplicand or multiplier in one of the basic facts violates the principle of multiplication because it is impossible to answer such questions as, "How many in all the equal groups of none (0) each?" or "How many in no (0) groups of, for example, 6 each?" However, zero does have an important role in multiplication. A zero in any decimal value place in the multiplicand tells that there are no decimal units of that particular value to multiply. A zero in ones place in the multiplier indicates that there are 10 or more equal groups and that the first step in the multiplication will be by units greater than one. A zero in any place in the product indicates there are no decimal value units in the place it occupies.

Multiplication of Integers—Multiplier an Integer—One Value

(*a*)

T	*O*
2	3
	3
	9
6	
6	9

(*b*)

H	*T*	*O*
	8	2
		4
		8
3	2	
3	2	8

(*c*)

H	*T*	*O*
	5	0
		6
		0
3	0	
3	0	0

(*d*)

H	*T*	*O*
	2	7
		3
	2	1
	6	
	8	1

(*e*)

H	*T*	*O*
	6	5
		5
	2	5
3	0	
3	2	5

(*f*)

Th	*H*	*T*	*O*
	3	5	6
			7
		4	2
	3	5	
2	1		
2	4	9	2

(*g*)

Tth	*Th*	*H*	*T*	*O*
	7	8	2	9
				8
			7	2
		1	6	
	6	4		
5	6			
6	2	6	3	2

In example (*a*), 3 × 23, the question asked and to be answered is, "What number equals 3 groups of 23?" The first step is to observe that 23 = 2 tens and 3 ones. The second step is to think, "What number equals 3 groups of 3 ones each?" ($3 \times 3 = ?$). The answer is 9. The third step is to think, "What number equals 3 groups of 2 tens each?" (3×2 tens = ?). The answer is 6 tens. The product in example (*a*) is the sum of 6 tens and 9 ones or 69.

In example (*b*), 4×82, the question asked is, "What number equals 4 groups of 82 each?" By thinking of 82 as 8 tens and 2 ones and using the principle of computing with like units, first ones and then tens, the steps are: Step 1—think, "What number equals 4 groups of 2 ones each?" The answer is 8. Step 2—think, "What number equals 4 groups of 8 tens each?" The answer is 32 tens or 3 hundreds and 2 tens. The product in example (*b*) is the sum of 32 tens and 8 ones and the number 328 shows 3 hundreds, 2 tens, and 8 ones.

In example (*c*), 6×50, the question asked is, "What number equals 6 groups of 50 each?" There are no ones to multiply so we use a zero in the ones' place of the product to serve as a reminder of this fact. In step 2, think, "What number equals 6 groups of 5 tens each?" The answer is 30 tens. The product in example (*c*) is 30 tens and no ones and is notated as 3 hundreds, no tens, and no ones (300).

In example (*d*), 3×27, the question is, "What number is equal to 3×27?" In answering the question, think, "Three groups of 7 ones each equal 21 or 2 tens and 1 one. Three groups of 2 tens each equal 6 tens." The product in example (*d*) is 8 tens and 1 one or 81.

In example (*e*), 5×65, the question is, "What number is equal to 5×25?" Five groups of 5 ones equal 25 or 2 tens and 5 ones. Five groups of 6 tens equals 30 tens or 3 hundreds. The product in example (*e*) is the sum of the partial products, 2 tens and 5 ones plus 3 hundreds and no tens (325).

In example (*f*), 7×356, the question is, "What number is equal to 7×356?" By computing with like units: first ones, then tens, then hundreds, the steps to find the product are; think, "What number equals 7 groups of 6 ones?" The answer or partial product is 42 ones and is notated as 4 tens and 2 ones. Step 2—think, "What number equals 7 groups of 5 tens?" The answer or partial product is 35 tens and is notated as 3 hundreds and 5 tens. Step 3—think, "What number equals 7 groups of 3 hundreds?" The answer is 21 hundreds and is notated as 2 thousands and 1 hundred. The product in example (*f*) is the sum of the notated partial products. The product is found by adding the addends in each value position of the notated partial products: 2 ones, then 4 tens and 5 tens equal 9 tens, then 3 hundreds and 1 hundred equal 4 hundreds, and 2 thousands. The product is 2492.

In example (*g*), 8 × 7829, the question asked is, "What number is equal to 8 × 7829?" (8 × 7829 = ?). By computing the like units, the thought steps in finding the product are: Step 1—think, "What number equals 8 × 9 ones?" The answer is 72 ones and is notated 7 tens and 2 ones. Step 2—think, "What number equals 8 × 2 tens?" The answer is 16 tens and is notated 1 hundred and 6 tens. Step 3—think, "What number equals 8 × 8 hundreds?" The answer is 64 hundreds and is notated 6 thousands and 4 hundreds. Step 4—think, "What number equals 8 × 7 thousands?" The answer is 56 thousands and is notated 5 ten-thousands and 6 thousands. The product is found by adding the partial products as notated in the decimal value positions. There is only one addend in the ones position. Thus 2 is written in the ones place in the product; 7 tens and 6 tens are 13 tens or 1 hundred and 3 tens. The 3 is written in the tens place in the product and the 1 hundred is combined with the addends in the hundreds place (1H + 1H + 4H = 6H). The 6 is written in the hundreds place in the product; 6 thousands plus 6 thousands equal 12 thousands or 1 ten-thousands and 2 thousands. The 2 is written in the thousands place in the product and the 1 ten-thousands is added to the 5 ten-thousands (1TTh + 5 Th = 6 TTh), and 6 is written in the ten-thousands place in the product. The notated number, 62,632, is the total product.

$$\begin{array}{r} 7829 \\ \times 8 \\ \hline 62{,}632 \end{array}$$

The product for example (*g*), 8 × 7829, may be computed by an abstract method that is illustrated at the right. The first thought step is to think, "8 × 9 = 72." Then write 2 in the ones' place and remember 7. The second thought step is "8 × 2 = 16, and 16 + remembered 7 is 23." Write 3 in the tens place and remember 2 (2 H). The third step is to think, "8 × 8 = 64 + 2 = 66. Write the 6 hundreds in the hundreds place in the product and remember 6 thousands. The fourth step is to think, "8 × 7 = 56 + 6 = 62. Write 2 in the thousands place in the product and 6 in the ten-thousands place. The product is 62,632. This method in multiplication is frequently called *the short* or *mental method.*

The authors present the point of view that the process used in multiplying, in which the partial products are left in their correct value positions before finding the total product, is more meaningful and no longer than the "short or abstract" method. Each method requires the same number of thought steps. The short or abstract method places an additional burden by requiring pupils to remember an unnotated part of each partial product. The authors recommend the use of the *Partial Products Method* for the reason it helps pupils properly to understand the meaning of each thought step required in multiplication. Pupils who have developed understanding and accurate skills in multiplication may use the short or abstract method.

Generalized Rules

Correct Place Value or Grid Method

Write the numbers for the multiplicand and multiplier in their correct decimal value positions. Find the partial products by multiplying first the smallest and then successively larger decimal units in the multiplicand by the integer that is the multiplier. Write the partial products in their correct value positions. Then add the partial products to find the total product.

Abstract Rule Method

Write the multiplier under the multiplicand. Multiply the ones. If the product is 10 or more, take each group of 10 ones and for it substitute 1 ten. Remember the tens substituted. Write the ones remaining, in the ones' place. Next multiply the tens. Add the ten remembered. If the sum is 10 or more, take each group of 10 tens and for it substitute 1 hundred. Remember the hundreds substituted. Write the tens. Proceed with multiplication of hundreds and larger decimal units as with ones and tens. The numbers written will represent the total product.

EXERCISE

Find the product for each example first by the *correct place value method or grid method* and then by the *abstract rule method*. Explain the thought process involved in finding the product.

	(*a*)	(*b*)	(*c*)	(*d*)	(*e*)	(*f*)	(*g*)
	32	93	70	29	95	587	9386
A.	×2	×3	×8	×7	×6	×4	×9

B. 4 × 22 = ? 3 × 72 = ? 6 × 45 = ? 8 × 675 = ?

C. Construct decimal grids. Compute the product for each example in row B. Beside each partial product, explain the thinking used in computing it.

Multiplication—Multiplier a Two-Value Integer—No Changes to Larger Units in Writing Partial Products

(a)			(b)			(c)			(d)			
H	*T*	*O*	*H*	*T*	*O*	*H*	*T*	*O*	*Th*	*H*	*T*	*O*
	2	0		2	4		3	0			3	2
	3	0		2	0		3	2			3	3
		0			0			0				6
	0			0			6				9	
	0			8			0				6	
6	0		4	0		9	0			9	0	
6	0	0	4	8	0	9	6	0	1	0	5	6

In example (*a*), 30 × 20, the question asked and to be answered is, "What number equals 30 (3 tens) groups of 2 tens each or 3 tens × 2 tens = ?" By thinking of 20 as 2 tens and 0 ones and applying the principle of computing with like units, first ones and then tens, the steps are: Step 1—think, "The multiplier consists of 3 tens and 0 ones. First multiply by the ones. There are no ones in the multiplier. Write 0 in the ones place in the first partial product. Write 0 in the tens place in the second partial product." Step 2—think, "Now multiply by the tens. There are no ones to multiply by 3 tens. Write 0 in the tens place in the third partial product." Step 3—think, "What number equals 30 (3 tens) groups of 2 tens each?" The answer is 60 tens. Write 6 in the hundreds place in the fourth partial product. The total product in example (*a*) is the sum of 6 hundreds, 0 tens, and 0 ones or 600.

In example (*b*), 20 × 24, the question asked is, "What number equals 20 groups of 24 each?" By thinking of 24 as 2 tens and 4 ones and using the principle of computing with like units, first ones and then tens, the steps are: Step 1—think, "There are no ones in the multiplier. Write 0 in the ones place in the first partial product and 0 in the tens place in the second partial product." Step 2—think, "Now multiply by the tens in the multiplier. What number equals

20 (2 tens) × 4 ones?" The answer is 80 or 8 tens. Step 3—and now think, "What number equals 20 (2 tens) groups of 2 tens each or 2 tens × 2 tens = ?" The answer is 40 tens or 4 hundreds and no tens. The product in example (*b*) is the sum of 40 tens + 8 tens or 48 tens which may be written 480.

In example (*c*), 32 × 30, the question asked is, "What number equals 32 groups of 30 each?" There are no ones to multiply by 2 so we put a 0 in the ones place of the first partial product. In Step 2, think, "What number equals 2 × 3 tens?" The answer is 6 tens. In Step 3 observe there are no ones to multiply by 3 tens. Write 0 in the tens place of the partial product. In Step 4, think, "What number equals 30 groups of 3 tens each? (3 tens × 3 tens = ?)." The answer is 90 tens or 9 hundreds and no ones. The product in example (*c*) is 9 hundreds, 6 tens, and 0 ones or 960.

In example (*d*), 33 × 32, the question asked is, "What number equals 33 groups of 32 each?" In Step 1, think, "What number equals 3 × 2 ones?" The answer is 6 ones. Step 2, think, "What number equals 3 × 3 tens?" The answer is 9 tens. Step 3, think, "What number equals 3 tens × 3 tens?" The answer is 90 tens or 9 hundreds, 0 tens, and 0 ones. The product is the sum of the partial products, which is 1056.

The Abstract Rule Method

$$\begin{array}{r} 20 \\ \times 30 \\ \hline 600 \end{array}$$

The abstract rule for example (*a*), 20 × 30, is illustrated at the right. The first step is to observe there are no ones in the multiplier so write 0 in the ones place in the product. The second step is to think, "There are no ones to multiply by tens so write 0 in the tens place of the product." The third step is to think, "3 (tens) × 2 (tens) = 6 hundreds so write 6 in the hundreds place." The product is 600.

$$\begin{array}{r} 32 \\ \times 33 \\ \hline 96 \\ 96 \\ \hline 1056 \end{array}$$

The abstract rule for example (*d*), 33 × 32, is illustrated at the right. To find the answer, first multiply by the ones and then by the tens. Steps 1 and 2 below concern multiplying by ones. Step 1—think, "3 × 2 = 6." Write 6. Step 2—think, "3 × 3 (tens) = 9 (tens)." Write 9 in the tens place.

Next multiply by the tens. Steps 3 and 4 concern multiplying by tens. Step 3—think, "3 (tens) × 2 (ones) = 6 (tens)." Write 6 in the tens' place. Step 4—think, "3 (tens) × 3 (tens) = 9 (hundreds)." Write 9 in the hundreds place. Step 5—add the partial products. The total product is 1056.

Generalized Rules

When multiplying by a two-place multiplier, first multiply by the ones in the multiplier. Then multiply by the tens. Then add the partial products to find the total product.

Multiplication of Integers—Multiplier a Two-Value Integer—Changes to Larger Units in Writing Partial Products

(*a*)

H	*T*	*O*
	2	3
	2	4
	1	2
	8	
	6	
4		
5	5	2

(*b*)

H	*T*	*O*
	2	4
	3	3
	1	2
	6	
1	2	
6		
7	9	2

(*c*)

H	*T*	*O*
	2	2
	3	6
	1	2
1	2	
	6	
6		
7	9	2

(*d*)

Th	*H*	*T*	*O*
		4	6
		2	3
		1	8
	1	2	
	1	2	
	8		
1	0	5	8

(*e*)

Th	*H*	*T*	*O*
		6	7
		8	2
		1	4
	1	2	
	5	6	
4	8		
5	4	9	4

In example (*a*), 24 × 23, the question asked is, "What number equals 24 groups of 23 each?" The thought process is similar to that used in finding answers to examples on the preceding pages. The first step is to think, "4 × 3 ones = 12." Write 1 in the tens place and 2 in the ones place. The second step is to think, "4 × 2 tens = 8 tens." Write 8 in the tens place. The third step is to think, "2 (tens) × 3 (ones) = 6 tens." Write 6 in the tens place. The fourth step is to think, "2 (tens) × 2 (tens) = 4 hundreds." Write 4 in the hundreds place. The total product is 552.

Study examples (*b*), (*c*), (*d*), and (*e*). In which examples is the product of ones × ones more than 9? What was done with each 10 ones? In which examples is the product of ones × tens more than 9 tens? What was done with each 10 tens? In which examples is the product of tens × ones more than 9 tens? What was done with each 10 tens? In which examples is the product of tens × tens more than 9 hundreds? What was done with each 10 hundreds?

The *abstract rule method* can be used in finding the answer to each of the examples as shown below.

(*a*)	(*b*)	(*c*)	(*d*)	(*e*)	(*f*)
23	24	22	46	67	395
×24	×33	×36	×23	×82	×45
92	72	132	138	134	1975
46	72	66	92	536	1580
552	792	792	1058	5494	17,775

In using the abstract rule method, first multiply by the ones in the multiplier. Use the procedure outlined below:

Multiply the ones in the multiplicand. If the product is 10 or more, take each group of 10 ones and for it substitute 1 ten. Remember the tens substituted. Write the ones. Next multiply the tens. Add the tens remembered. If the sum is 10 or more, take each group of 10 tens and for it substitute 1 hundred. Remember the hundreds substituted. Write the tens. Proceed with multiplication of hundreds and larger decimal units as with ones and tens.

Then multiply by the tens in the multiplier. The first number written in the partial product will be in the tens place because we are multiplying by tens. Then follow steps identical to those outlined in the preceding paragraph.

If the multiplier has a place for hundreds, the first number in the partial product will be in the hundreds place because the multiplying is by hundreds. Then follow steps identical to those outlined for multiplying by the ones.

EXERCISE

Find the product for each example first by the *correct place value method* or *grid method* and then by the *abstract rule method*. Explain the thought process involved in finding the product.

	(*a*)	(*b*)	(*c*)	(*d*)	(*e*)	(*f*)
A.	31	42	49	28	37	395
	×36	×28	×29	×72	×74	×65
	?	?	?	?	?	?

B. $42 \times 23 = ?$ $45 \times 22 = ?$ $36 \times 28 = ?$ $82 \times 35 = ?$

C. Construct decimal grids. Compute the product for each example in row B. Beside each partial product, explain the thinking used in computing it.

Verifying the Answers in Multiplication

The product in multiplication is a number (the product) that equals a specified number of groups (the multiplier) *times* a number that notates the size of each group (the multiplicand). Multiplication examples can then be checked by adding the multiplicand as many times as specified by the multiplier. See the examples at the right. This method, while effective for examples with small multipliers, is unwieldy with numbers that are larger. To verify the accuracy of multiplication examples that have a multiplier that is a two-place number or larger, pupils should repeat carefully each step taken to find the product. Pupils should be given the opportunity to ask a classmate to verify the accuracy of their computation.

	Check
	98
98	98
×3	98
294	294

As the pupils demonstrate their ability to work with abstract numbers and *after* all example types have been presented, they may check examples by reversing the multiplier and multiplicand as shown at the right.

	Check
32	85
×85	×32
160	170
256	255
2720	2720

The method of verifying answers in multiplication by reversing the multiplicand and the multiplier is based on the mathematical principle that the product is a number equal to an integer multiplied by an integer. Therefore, the reversing of the two numbers does not change the product ($4 \times 12 = 48$ and $12 \times 4 = 48$). The meaning of the multiplication example or problem is changed, however, when the multiplier and the multiplicand are reversed. *Caution.* Teachers should not introduce too early the *reversal method* in verifying accuracy in multiplication. It may cause pupils to confuse the mathematical meaning and function of the multiplier and the multiplicand when they are related to a specific economic or social situation.

Diagnosing Pupil Growth

As suggested in earlier chapters, a good way to discover thought processes is to ask the learner to work aloud. Representative questions that may be asked include:

1. How can you tell when you are to use multiplication to answer the question in a problem?

2. What does each number in a multiplication example tell?

3. What does the sign, ×, ask you to do?

4. How could you use addition to show what a multiplication example means?

5. What do you do when you see a 0 in the multiplicand? In the multiplier?

6. When multiplying by tens, why do you put the first figure in the second partial product in the tens place?

7. When using the short way of multiplying 7 × 59, what do you do with the 6 tens in the product 63 (7 × 9 ones)?

Test items such as the following may be included on pencil and paper tests:

Part I—Meanings

1. You multiply to find (how many equal groups, how many in all the equal groups, how many in each group).

2. If you forget the answer to the example, 4 × 7, you can find it by using the addition fact (4+4+4+4+4+4+4, 7+7+7+7, 4+7+4+7).

3. The sign that asks you to multiply is (×, +, −, ÷).

4. The multiplicand in a multiplication example represents (how many in each equal group, how many equal groups, how many in all the equal groups).

5. The number that tells how many equal groups is the (multiplier, multiplicand, product).

6. The product in a multiplication example is usually (larger than, smaller than, the same size as) the multiplier.

7. In multiplying a three-place multiplicand, first multiply the (tens, hundreds, ones).

8. In multiplying by a two-place multiplier, first multiply by the (ones, tens).

Part II—Vocabulary

Fill the blanks using one of these words or signs: multiplicand, multiplier, product, ×, partial product, addend, sum, =.

1. The sign that is read *times* is ______ .

2. The number in a multiplication example that tells how many equal groups is the ______ .

3. The number in a multiplication example that tells how many in all is the ______ .

4. The ______ in a multiplication example tells how many in each equal group.

5. The ______ in multiplication is like the sum in addition.

6. The multiplicand in a multiplication example is like the ______ in addition.

7. When we multiply by the ones and then the tens the numbers written are called ______ .

Part III—Computation

Write the answer to each example below and be ready to explain your thinking.

A.	3 ×2	4 ×2	2 ×3	3 ×3	2 ×4
B.	5 ×4	6 ×8	9 ×5	7 ×6	8 ×7
C.	23 ×2	32 ×3	22 ×4	14 ×2	30 ×3
D.	43 ×3	93 ×2	72 ×4	82 ×3	80 ×9
E.	46 ×2	15 ×6	24 ×4	45 ×2	27 ×3
F.	53 ×6	25 ×8	34 ×6	89 ×4	98 ×3

G.	242 ×2	701 ×8	151 ×7	980 ×4	865 ×7
H.	20 ×40	21 ×12	49 ×21	17 ×15	13 ×77
I.	83 ×13	21 ×39	65 ×18	43 ×24	49 ×29
J.	37 ×82	32 ×64	76 ×94	354 ×26	897 ×47

Summary

Multiplication is another of the so-called "fundamental operations" of arithmetic used to find the product (sum) of two or more numbers that notate equal-sized groups. The product in any multiplication example can be discovered by adding the number that notates how many in each group (multiplicand). This number, in the corresponding addition example would be an addend and it would be repeated to represent each group to be added. In multiplication the addend (multiplicand) is written only once. Another number (multiplier) notates the number of addends. Multiplication is more abstract than addition because the addends are not repeated.

A multiplication example asks a question which, when answered, equals the product. In the example, 3 × 75, the question is, "What number equals 3 groups of 75 each?" In finding the answer, first ones and then tens are multiplied. The principle of computing like units extends to multiplication. Smaller units are multiplied first and then the larger units in sequence; i.e., tens, hundreds, thousands, etc. When finding partial products, if the number of units or number in any value position equals 10 or more, then one unit of the next larger decimal value must be substituted for it. The total product is the sum of the partial products. Ideas developed in addition are used in adding partial products.

Multiplication examples follow a specific developmental pattern determined by the complexity of the examples. Pupils may be asked to learn to use one-place multipliers before using two-place multipliers. The examples become more complex as the number of substitutions of larger for smaller units increases.

SUGGESTED QUESTIONS FOR TEACHER SELF-EVALUATION

1. What is your interpretation of the mathematical meaning of multiplication?

2. What mathematical and social questions are answered by multiplication?

3. What understandings developed in the study of addition can be applied to multiplication?

4. What meanings should the teacher help children discover and understand for: multiplicand, multiplier, partial sum or product, sum or product?

5. What methods would you use to help children discover and understand: (*a*) the 23 multiplication facts with products less than 10; (*b*) the 58 multiplication facts with products more than 10.

6. What methods would you use to help children discover and understand the meaning and use of zero in: (*a*) the multiplicand, (*b*) the multiplier, (*c*) the product.

7. What are the developmental levels of multiplication examples that teachers should observe when teaching multiplication?

8. What are the psychological steps and mathematical meanings involved in the following examples:

2	2	23	24	46	23	23	43	26	48	243
×4	×7	×3	×4	×7	×32	×34	×24	×25	×96	×212

SUGGESTED ACTIVITIES

1. Prepare a *multiplication facts chart* that shows the multiplication facts in mathematical sequence.

2. Examine the new textbooks in arithmetic to appraise the meanings and methods that are presented for multiplication.

3. Prepare a summary of the mathematical meanings related to multiplication that teachers should understand.

4. Prepare representative diagnostic tests to help determine (*a*) mathematical understandings, (*b*) computational ability, (*c*) vocabulary development.

5. Preview a number of filmstrips or films and evaluate them in terms of how they might be used to help children learn multiplication.

PRACTICE EXERCISES

Multiplication of Integers

	24	20	85	64	70	67	52	43	39	42
1.	×2	×4	×3	×4	×5	×6	×7	×8	×9	×6

2.	378	725	849	793	905	923	582	679
	×4	×9	×7	×3	×4	×6	×8	×7

3.	641	580	9358	3495	4086	8201	7160
	×3	×6	×2	×2	×9	×5	×8

4.	28	407	2368	352	346	$75.75	9865
	37	25	57	132	654	225	4397

5. Multiplication in the quinary number system. Find the product for each example.

(*a*)	(*b*)	(*c*)	(*d*)	(*e*)
3	4	32	44	33
×2	×4	×2	×3	×3

(*f*)	(*g*)	(*h*)	(*i*)	(*j*)
20	34	40	103	324
×21	×14	×40	×34	×240

6. Multiplication in the duodecimal number system. Find the product for each example.

(*a*)	(*b*)	(*c*)	(*d*)	(*e*)
7	9	T	35	TE
×8	×9	×T	×T	×TE

(f)	(g)	(h)	(i)	(j)
56	340	8T	92	ETE
×7	×5	×T	×EE	×25

7. Multiplication in the binary number system. Find the product for each example.

(a)	(b)	(c)	(d)
10	11	100	111
×10	×11	×11	×101

Problems

1. At an average speed of 375 miles an hour, how far can a plane fly in 5 hours?

2. A truck was loaded with 125 bags of potatoes. Each bag weighed 60 pounds. What was the total weight?

3. If his cost for shoes is $12.75 a pair, how much will a shoe store owner pay for 25 pairs of shoes?

4. A man bought 2 dress shirts at $4.98 each and a pair of shoes for $14.75. What was his total cost?

5. How much change should a woman receive from a $20 bill if she buys 2 bath towels at $2.95 each?

SELECTED REFERENCES

1. Brueckner, Leo J., and Grossnickle, Foster E., *How to Make Arithmetic Meaningful.* Philadelphia: John C. Winston Company, 1947.

2. Buckingham, B. R., *Elementary Arithmetic: Its Meaning and Practice.* Boston: Ginn & Company, 1947.

3. Clark, John R., and Eads, Laura K., *Guiding Arithmetic Learnings.* Yonkers, N. Y.: World Book Company, 1954.

4. De Vault, M. Vere, "The Abacus and Multiplication." *The Arithmetic Teacher,* March, 1956.

5. Gunderson, Agnes G., "Teaching Multiplication and Division Facts." *Grade Teacher,* April, 1956.

6. Morton, Robert Lee, *Teaching Children Arithmetic.* Morristown, N. J.: Silver Burdett Company, 1953.

7. Spencer, Peter Lincoln, and Brydegaard, Marguerite, *Building Mathematical Concepts in the Elementary School.* New York: Henry Holt and Company, Inc., 1952.

8. Spitzer, Herbert F., *The Teaching of Arithmetic,* 2d ed. Boston: Houghton Mifflin Company, 1954.

6

Meaning and Use of Division: Integers

Introduction

Division is another of the "four fundamental operations." The division algorism, $12 \div 4$ or $4\overline{)12}$ consists of two numbers and a sign $\div$ or $\overline{)\quad}$ (read "divided by"). The larger of the numbers, the dividend 12, tells how many in one group. The smaller of the numbers, the divisor 4, tells how many in another group, which may (1) represent a quantity that is a component part of 12, (2) represent a quantity not a component part of 12, (3) represent the number of equal component parts of 12. The mathematical relationship between 12 and 4 is derived by thinking of a number which, when multiplied by 4, equals the dividend 12. This relationship indicates the ratio of 4 to 12 which is as 1 is to 3.

Exploratory Questions

Teachers may find it helpful to appraise their understanding of the mathematical meanings and the structure of division of integers by deciding upon what they believe to be appropriate answers to the following questions. They may also decide upon answers to help pupils discover and understand.

1. What is the mathematical meaning of division?

2. What is the mathematical relationship between division and multiplication?

3. What is the mathematical meaning that teachers should help pupils learn for: (*a*) the dividend, (*b*) the divisor, (*c*) the quotient, (*d*) the remainder?

4. What kinds of mathematical and social questions are answered by using division?

5. What is the relationship between the thought process and written computation in division?

6. What is the mathematical meaning and function of zero as used in division?

7. How many of the basic combinations in division have dividends and divisors less than 10? How many have dividends that are two-place numbers and divisors that are one-place numbers?

8. What are the developmental patterns in division examples which teachers should help pupils discover and understand?

9. What method should be used in verifying the accuracy of computation in division?

10. What diagnostic procedures may teachers use to determine the understandings, progress, and needs of pupils in division of integers?

The Meaning of Division

The division of integers is the thought and computation process used to find the ratio between two numbers. One of the numbers, the dividend, notates *how many* in all of the equal groups. Another number, the divisor, notates *how many* in one of the equal groups. The ratio between one of the equal groups and the number of the equal groups that are the component parts of the dividend is notated as the quotient. To illustrate, in the example $5\overline{)30}^{\,?}$ as notated on paper, there is one group of 5 (the divisor). The dividend is a number equal to 6 equal groups of 5 each. The ratio of 5 to 30 = the ratio of 1 to 6. The number, 6, is the quotient. The dividend, 30, is 6 times as large as the divisor, 5.

There is a relationship between division and addition. The dividend is a number that notates the *sum* of equal addends. The divisor is a number that notates *how many* in each equal addend. The quotient is a number that tells *how many* of the equal addends must be added to equal the dividend.

There is also a close relationship between division and multiplication. The dividend corresponds to the product. Both are notated numbers used to represent the total amount of some quantity. The divisor corresponds to the multiplicand. Both notate a number that identifies one of the equal groups that are one of the component parts of a larger number. The quotient is like the multiplier. Both notate a number that tells how many of the equal groups compose the larger group.

Division has been considered a difficult process even from earliest times. Only those nations with a high degree of civilization used division. Nevertheless as far back as A.D. 800 Al-Khowarzimi, an Arabic writer, used an interesting method of division described by Cajori.[1] The Greeks and Romans performed division by making successive subtractions. See the diagram below which illustrates how it is possible to subtract to answer the question, "A group of 30 objects equals how many groups of 5 objects each?"

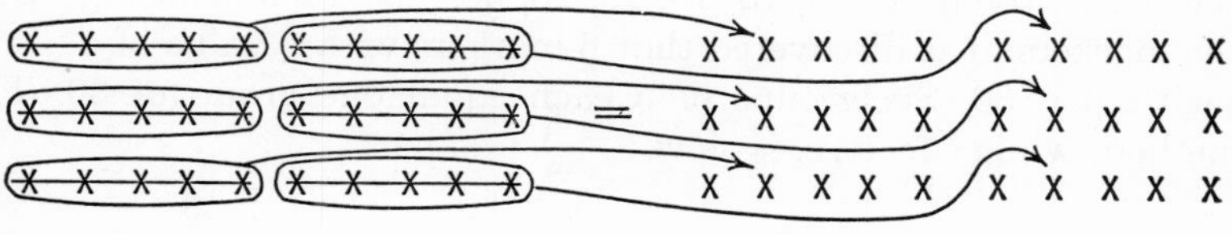

When using concrete objects, the use of subtraction to answer the above question is satisfactory. However, the use of successive subtractions cannot illustrate what is done on paper. Examine the division example $\begin{array}{r}?\\5\overline{)30}\end{array}$. The divisor is 5 and the dividend is 30. The numbers 5 and 30 notate numbers that identify like decimal units but each number is independent of the other.

In using successive subtraction to find the answer to the question, "A group of 30 objects equals how many groups of 5 ob-

[1]Florian Cajori, *A History of Mathematics,* New York: The Macmillan Company, 1938, p. 105.

jects each?" the 5 in each successive subtraction notates 5 of the 30 objects being subtracted and each time a 5 is subtracted some of the original group is physically removed. This process can be notated as shown at the right. The original amount, 30, ceases to exist after the first subtraction. Observe that it becomes 25, then 20, then 15, then 10, then 5, and finally no ones are left.

$$\begin{array}{r} 30 \\ -5 \\ \hline 25 \\ -5 \\ \hline 20 \\ -5 \\ \hline 15 \\ -5 \\ \hline 10 \\ -5 \\ \hline 5 \\ -5 \\ \hline 0 \end{array}$$

Division is both a mathematical and a mental process. Observe again the example $\begin{array}{r} ? \\ 5\overline{)30} \end{array}$. The question can be interpreted as, "How many groups of 5 each equal a group of 30?" Several methods can be used to find the answer. In none of them is anything physical done to either divisor or dividend. In the following paragraphs some of the methods are discussed.

The Counting Method

Counting is one of the processes which might be used to find the answer to the example at the right. By allowing one counter to represent each group of 5 objects represented by the divisor, the count would be, "5, 10, 15, 20, 25, 30." By then counting the markers, it is discovered that 6 markers with a value of 5 each equal 30. Six groups of 5 each equal one group of 30. This method, while effective, is slow.

$$\begin{array}{r} ? \\ 5\overline{)30} \end{array}$$

The Addition Method

Addition is another method that can be used to find the answer to the example $\begin{array}{r} ? \\ 5\overline{)30} \end{array}$. In using this method, the dividend, 30, is considered as a sum and the divisor, 5, is considered as one of the equal addends of that sum. Study the example at the right. The method is seen to be one of first adding the divisor (addend) to itself and then continuing to add it to the sum of previous addition until a sum equal to the dividend is obtained. Six addends of 5 each are seen to equal 30. The addition method, too, while effective, is slow.

$$\begin{array}{r} 5 \\ +5 \\ \hline 10 \\ +5 \\ \hline 15 \\ +5 \\ \hline 20 \\ +5 \\ \hline 25 \\ +5 \\ \hline 30 \end{array}$$

The Multiplication Method—Dividend a Product, Divisor a Multiplicand

The division example, $\begin{array}{r}?\\5\overline{)30}\end{array}$, may be considered as asking the question, "How many groups of 5 each equal 30?" Both the dividend, 30, and the divisor, 5, may be considered as representing groups of the same kinds of objects, i.e., both may represent cents, both may represent cookies, etc. The fastest method of finding the answer to the question asked by the example is to use multiplication. The example becomes ($? \times 5 = 30$). The answer, derived from a knowledge of multiplication facts is, "$6 \times 5 = 30$." The answer is 6.

In computing the answer to examples such as $\begin{array}{r}?\\3\overline{)18}\end{array}$, $\begin{array}{r}?\\7\overline{)28}\end{array}$, $\begin{array}{r}?\\9\overline{)45}\end{array}$, $\begin{array}{r}?\\2\overline{)60}\end{array}$, $\begin{array}{r}?\\4\overline{)800}\end{array}$, first decide upon the question asked by each example. To illustrate, in the example $\begin{array}{r}?\\3\overline{)18}\end{array}$, the question might be considered as being, "How many 3's = 18?" or, "*What number* times 3 = 18?" or, "18 = *what number* times 3?" The multiplication example to use in finding the answer to the question asked by the example might be: $6 \times 3 = 18$ or $18 = 6 \times 3$.

For the sake of simplicity in expressing the question asked by division examples, the children may be encouraged to think of the question in a way that makes sense to them. In the example $\begin{array}{r}?\\7\overline{)28}\end{array}$, the question might be expressed, "How many 7's = 28?" In the example $\begin{array}{r}?\\9\overline{)45}\end{array}$ the question might be expressed, "How many 9's = 45?" In the example $\begin{array}{r}?\\2\overline{)60}\end{array}$, the question might be expressed, "How many 2's = 60 (6 tens)? In the example $\begin{array}{r}?\\4\overline{)800}\end{array}$, the question might be expressed, "How many 4's = 800 (8 hundreds)? The multiplication example to use in finding the answer to each of the above questions is: $4 \times 7 = 28$; $5 \times 9 = 45$; 30 (3 tens) $\times 2 = 60$; 200 (2 hundreds) $\times 4 = 800$.

The Multiplication Method— Dividend a Product, Divisor a Multiplier

There is another kind of question answered by division. Consider the question, "How many stamps will be in a group if 10 stamps are arranged in 5 equal groups?" Neither subtraction, counting, nor addition can be used to answer it because the 5 represents groups and the 10 represents stamps. The question can be answered by distributing the stamps, one at a time into 5 groups and then by counting the number of stamps in each group. Study the accompanying illustration.

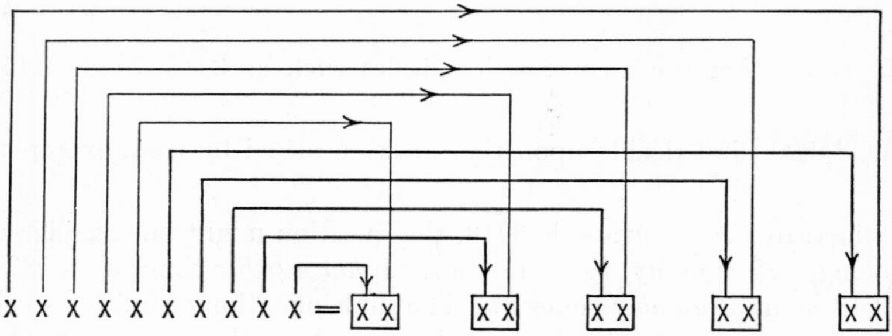

From the illustration, it can be seen that when 10 objects are distributed one at a time into 5 equal groups, there will be 2 objects in each group. Multiplication as a thought process is the fastest method of finding the answer to the question, "How many objects will be in a group if 10 objects are put into 5 equal groups?" The multiplication example would be ($5 \times ? = 10$). The answer, discovered by using knowledge learned in studying the multiplication facts, is $5 \times \mathit{2} = 10$.

The correct way to notate the example for the above question is $\begin{array}{r}5\\ ?\overline{)10}\end{array}$. This notation is contrary to general practice. It is customary to use the same notation; i.e., $\begin{array}{r}?\\ 5\overline{)10}\end{array}$, for both of the following questions: "A group of 10 objects equals how many groups of 5 objects?" and "How many objects will be in a group if 10 objects are put into 5 equal groups?" For either of the two questions, the numbers 5 and

10 may be considered abstractly and notated in the example $\begin{array}{r} ? \\ 5\overline{)10} \end{array}$. Then the example can be considered as asking the question, "How many numbers like the divisor equal the dividend? Mathematically the question is, "What number times the divisor equals the dividend?" or "The dividend equals what number times the divisor?"

Social and Mathematical Questions Answered by Division

In a social situation it is sometimes necessary to find the answer to the question, "How many equal groups can be made from a quantity of known value?" A representative problem follows:

1. We have 24 pieces of candy and plan to put 6 pieces in a bag. How many bags of candy can we fill?

After dramatizing the social situation, the learner can see that 4 groups of 6 pieces of candy each = 24 pieces of candy. In doing the dramatization he could place a group of 6 pieces of candy in 1 bag, 6 in another, 6 in another, and 6 in another and then count the bags. He would find that 4 bags could be filled.

The fastest thought and computation process used to find how many bags of candy can be filled is to divide, as shown in the example at the right. Observe that the question asked in the problem is, "How many bags of candy can we fill?" The answer is found by thinking, "What number times 6 pieces of candy equals 24 pieces of candy?" or "24 = what number times 6?"

$$\begin{array}{r} ?\ \text{quotient} \\ 6\ \text{divisor}\overline{)24}\ \text{dividend} \end{array} \quad \text{or} \quad \begin{array}{r} 4 \\ 6\overline{)24} \end{array}$$

Sometimes it is necessary to find how many in an equal group when a known number has been changed or thought to be changed into a given number of equal-sized groups. A representative problem follows:

2. We have 20 pieces of candy and plan to divide them equally among 4 boys. How many pieces of candy will each boy receive?

When dramatizing the social situation, the 20 pieces may be distributed, 1 piece at a time, among the 4 boys. Each boy may then count his pieces of candy. He has 5 pieces.

Division is a faster way to find how many pieces of candy each boy will receive. Properly notated the example would appear as shown at the right. The dividend, 20, shows how many pieces of candy in all. The quotient, 4, tells how many groups. The question asked in the problem is, "How many pieces of candy will each boy receive?" The answer is found by thinking, "Four times what number = 20?" The answer is, "Four times *5* = 20." As stated earlier in this chapter the example would be notated $\overset{?}{4\overline{)20}}$. The answer to the example is *5*.

$$\text{? divisor}\overline{)20}\ \text{dividend (4 quotient)} \quad \text{or} \quad \overset{4}{?\overline{)20}}$$

Sometimes it is necessary to find the ratio between numbers used to notate the two numbers of known value as given in a problem. A representative problem follows:

3. John's uncle gave him 10¢ for each 5¢ he earned on a Saturday. At this rate, how much should his uncle give him for each cent he earns?

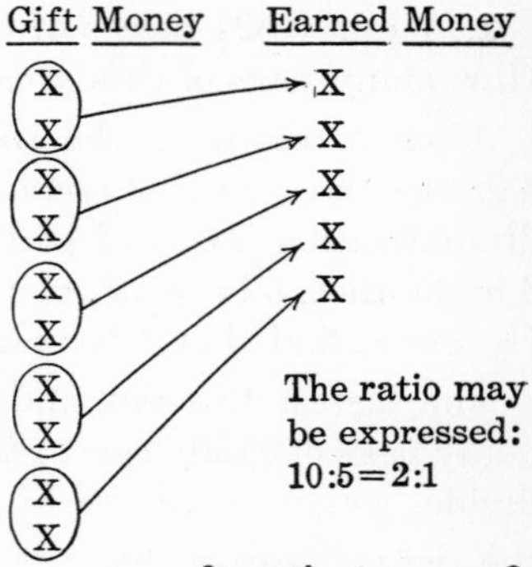

To answer the question, John could arrange the money earned and the money received as a gift in two groups as shown at the right. The illustration shows that 2¢ are received as a gift for each 1¢ earned.

The fastest thought and computation process used to find how much he will receive from his uncle for each cent earned is to divide. Observe that the question asked is, "At this rate, how much should his uncle give him for each cent he earns?" The answer, determined by dividing, is that his uncle will give him 2 times the amount he earns. Two times 1 cent equals 2 cents, so the answer is "two cents."

$$\text{5 divisor}\overline{)10}\ \text{dividend (? quotient)} \quad \text{or} \quad \overset{?}{5\overline{)10}}$$

After analyzing easy problems solved by division, the learner can discover and understand that division examples such as those at the right can represent a variety of social situations. However, in the representative example as notated on paper, the dividend, 20, is understood to be the number equal to the total of all the equal addends that are represented by the divisor, 5, i.e., the dividend 20 equals a certain

$$\overset{?}{5\overline{)20}} \quad \text{or} \quad \overset{?}{5\overline{)20}}$$

number of equal addends of 5 each. The quotient, 4, is understood to be the number that shows how many of the addends of 5 each are equal to 20. Correct ways of thinking and expressing the example are, "How many 5's = 20?" "What number times 5 = 20?" "Twenty = What number times 5?"

The dividend shows the total amount (sum or product). The divisor shows the amount of each equal addend. The quotient shows how many equal-size groups or addends. The computation signs, $\overline{)\quad}$ and $\div$, ask the question, "What number times the divisor equals the dividend?" or "The dividend equals what number times the divisor?"

Division Facts—Dividends and Divisors One-Place Numbers

There are 23 division facts with dividends that are one-place numbers.

$1\overline{)1}$	$1\overline{)2}$	$1\overline{)3}$	$1\overline{)4}$	$1\overline{)5}$	$1\overline{)6}$	$1\overline{)7}$	$1\overline{)8}$
$1\overline{)9}$	$2\overline{)2}$	$2\overline{)4}$	$2\overline{)6}$	$2\overline{)8}$	$3\overline{)3}$	$3\overline{)6}$	$3\overline{)9}$
$4\overline{)4}$	$4\overline{)8}$	$5\overline{)5}$	$6\overline{)6}$	$7\overline{)7}$	$8\overline{)8}$	$9\overline{)9}$	

Division Facts—Dividends More Than Ten

There are 58 division facts with dividends of 10 or more

$2\overline{)10}$	$2\overline{)12}$	$2\overline{)14}$	$2\overline{)16}$	$2\overline{)18}$	$3\overline{)12}$	$3\overline{)15}$	$3\overline{)18}$	
$3\overline{)21}$	$3\overline{)24}$	$3\overline{)27}$	$4\overline{)12}$	$4\overline{)16}$	$4\overline{)20}$	$4\overline{)24}$	$4\overline{)28}$	
$4\overline{)32}$	$4\overline{)36}$	$5\overline{)10}$	$5\overline{)15}$	$5\overline{)20}$	$5\overline{)25}$	$5\overline{)30}$	$5\overline{)35}$	
$5\overline{)40}$	$5\overline{)45}$	$6\overline{)12}$	$6\overline{)18}$	$6\overline{)24}$	$6\overline{)30}$	$6\overline{)36}$	$6\overline{)42}$	
$6\overline{)48}$	$6\overline{)54}$	$7\overline{)14}$	$7\overline{)28}$	$7\overline{)35}$	$7\overline{)42}$	$7\overline{)49}$	$7\overline{)56}$	$7\overline{)21}$
$7\overline{)63}$	$8\overline{)16}$	$8\overline{)24}$	$8\overline{)32}$	$8\overline{)40}$	$8\overline{)48}$	$8\overline{)56}$	$8\overline{)64}$	
$8\overline{)72}$	$9\overline{)18}$	$9\overline{)27}$	$9\overline{)36}$	$9\overline{)45}$	$9\overline{)54}$	$9\overline{)63}$	$9\overline{)72}$	$9\overline{)81}$

Teaching Helps—The Division Facts

The children will profit from a discussion of social situations in which they have experienced dividing. To illustrate, in party situations they may have had to seat pupils in groups of four around a table or they may have had to share a candy treat so that each received the same amount of candy. In certain games, the children may have been divided into couples. By thinking about the situations experienced, they can easily recall that a group of 6 = 3 groups of 2 each, that a group of 8 = 4 groups of 2 each. Ask the children to make a list of objects which are often arranged by twos, threes, fours, or even fives. After thinking about the various arrangements in equal groups they may be expected to write statements such as: 8 lights = 2 groups of 4 lights each, 9 wheels = 3 groups of 3 wheels each, etc.

A good procedure to use in teaching the abstract division facts is to have children experiment with groups to discover various ways into which they can be divided into equal groups. As a class exercise, six children may be asked to come to the front of the room and the number 6 written on the chalkboard to represent the idea of six children. Then the teacher may ask, "How many 2's = 6?" and a 2 written in front of the 6 to represent the idea of how many are to be placed in each group. The division sign may be written to separate the 6 from the 2. The answer, 3, is written above the 6.

Additional experience with six would include reconstituting the group of six in response to the question, "How many 3's = 6?" Upon completion of a study of six, the children may follow the above outlined procedure in studying eight, nine, and ten by responding to questions such as: "How many 2's = 8?" "How many 4's = 8?" "How many 3's = 9?" etc.

The task of arranging and rearranging children to demonstrate answers to questions such as, "How many 5's = 45?" is impracticable. However, it is relatively simple to take 45 small cards and separate them into groups of 5. The pupils may make practice cards to use in drill situations.

The Use of Zero in Division

Observe that there are no zero facts. Considering zero as either a divisor or dividend violates the principle of division. A dividend such as 5 cannot be changed or thought to be changed to units of zero (0) each so there are no basic facts such as $0\overline{)5}$. A dividend such as zero cannot exist because a dividend notates a sum. In the example, $5\overline{)0}$, there simply are no units in the dividend to be divided.

Although there are no zero facts as such, zero does have an important role to play in division. When notated in any decimal place in the divisor, it indicates no units of that decimal value to divide. In examples such as that at the right, there are no tens in the dividend to divide. A 0 is put in the quotient to hold the tens place. A zero in any place in the quotient is used as a place holder to show that there are no units or not enough units of that decimal value in the dividend to be divided by the divisor.

$$\begin{array}{r} 201 \\ 3\overline{)603} \end{array}$$

Division—Uneven—Dividend a One- or Two-Place Number and Divisor a One-Place Number

$$\begin{array}{cc} (a) & (b) \\ \begin{array}{r} ? \\ 2\overline{)9} \end{array} & \begin{array}{r} ? \\ 3\overline{)14} \end{array} \end{array}$$

1. In example (*a*), $2\overset{?}{\overline{)9}}$, the question asked is, "How many 2's = 9?" The division is uneven because when a group of 9 is divided into groups of 2 each, one of the units in the dividend, 9, is left. Observe that: XXXXXXXXX = XX + XX + XX + XX + X. The original group, 9, = 4 groups of 2 each with a remainder of 1. The remainder is $\frac{1}{2}$ of another group (1 of 2 equal parts of another group). Abstractly the steps in finding the answer or quotient for example (*a*) are:

a. Think of the next number smaller than 9 that can be evenly divided by 2. (This number is 8.)

b. Divide the number 8 by 2. (How many 2's equal 8?)

c. Express the difference between 9 and 8 either as a remainder, 1, or a fraction, $\frac{1}{2}$.

The quotient in example (*a*) is 4 *R*1 (4 groups of 2 each with a remainder of 1) or $4\frac{1}{2}$ (4 groups of 2 each and $\frac{1}{2}$ of another group).

2. In example (*b*), $3\overset{?}{\overline{)14}}$, the question asked is, "How many 3's equal 14?" The division is uneven because neither the number 14,

nor the next smaller number, 13, can be evenly divided by 3. But the next smaller number, 12, is evenly divisible by 3. Divide 12 by 3 to find the quotient, 4. The difference between 14 and 12, which is 2, may be expressed as a remainder or as $\frac{2}{3}$ of another group. The quotient is, "4 groups of 3 each and a remainder of 2 equal 14," or "4 groups of 3 each and $\frac{2}{3}$ of another group equal 14." ($14 \div 3 = 4\ R2$ or $14 \div 3 = 4\frac{2}{3}$.)

Generalized Rule

To find the quotient in examples that cannot be divided evenly, think of the next smaller number that can be divided evenly and use it as the dividend. The difference between this smaller number and the dividend will be the remainder.

Dividing Tens and Then Ones by a One-Place Divisor

$$4\overline{)84} = ? \qquad \begin{array}{r} 21 \\ \times 4 \\ \hline ? \end{array}$$

The computation processes in the examples at the right are closely related. The question asked by the division example can be thought of as, "What number × 4 = 84?" The answer is computed by dividing the partial dividends, 8 tens, and then 4 ones. The question asked by the multiplication example is, "What number = 4 × 21?" The answer is computed by multiplying the ones to find the first partial product and then multiplying the tens to find the second partial product, and adding the partial products.

The use of partial products and partial dividends is shown on the grids below:

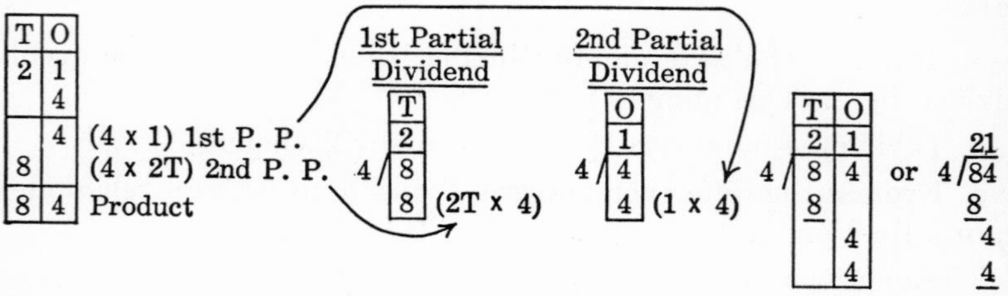

The questions and corresponding answer in the above multiplication example are: (1) What number = 4 × 1? (answer—4); (2) What number = 4 × 2 tens? (answer—8 tens); and (3) What number = 4 × 21? (answer—84).

The questions and corresponding answers in the above division example are: (1) What number × 4 ones = 8 tens? (answer—2 tens); (2) What number × 4 ones = 4 ones? (answer—1 one); and (3) What number × 4 ones = 84? (answer—21).

Other representative division examples with partial dividends of tens and ones are given below.

(*a*)

	T	*O*
	3	0
2)	6	0
	6	
		0

(*b*)

	T	*O*	
	2	0	*R*1
3)	6	1	
	6		
		1	

(*c*)

	T	*O*	
	3	4	*R*1
2)	6	9	
	6		
		9	
		8	
		1	

(*d*)

	T	*O*
	4	5
2)	9	0
	8	
	1	0
	1	0

(*e*)

	T	*O*	
	2	4	*R*2
3)	7	4	
	6		
	1	4	
	1	2	
		2	

1. In example (*a*) the question asked is, "How many 2's = 60?" or "What number × 2 = 60?" There are enough tens to divide and the first partial dividend is 6 tens. Six tens divided into 2 equal groups = 3 tens in a group. *TTTTTT* = *TTT TTT*. From the above example it can be seen that 6 tens = 3 tens × 2. The first partial quotient is 3 tens. In the second partial dividend, 0, there are no ones to divide. A 0 is put in the quotient to hold the ones place. The second partial quotient is 0. The total quotient is 3 tens and 0 ones or 30. The answer to the question asked by the example is 30 (30 × 2 = 60).

2. In example (*b*) the question is, "How many 3's = 61?" or "What number × 3 = 61?" There are enough tens to divide and the first partial dividend is 6 tens. Six tens = 2 tens × 3. The first partial quotient is 2 tens. The second partial dividend is 1. There are not enough ones to divide and a 0 is put in the quotient to hold the ones place. There is a remainder of 1. The answer to the question in example (*b*) is, "Twenty groups of 3 each + a remainder of 1 = 61." The answer may be written 20 *R*1 or $20\frac{1}{3}$.

3. In example (*c*) the question asked is, "How many 2's = 69?" or "What number × 2 = 69?" There are enough tens to divide and

the first partial dividend is 6 tens. Six tens = 2 tens × 3. The first partial quotient is 3 tens. The 9 ones are brought down. They are the second partial dividend; 9 ones = 4 × 2 ones + a remainder of 1 one. The second partial quotient is 4. The total quotient is 34 *R*1 or $34\frac{1}{2}$.

In example (*d*) shown at the right, the question asked is, "How many 2's = 90?" or "What number × 2 = 90?" The first partial dividend is 9 tens; 9 tens ÷ 2 = 4 tens + 1 ten remaining. The first quotient figure is 4 tens. Ten ones are substituted for the 1 ten remaining and the second partial dividend is 10 ones; 10 ones ÷ 2 = 5. The second partial quotient is 5. The total quotient and answer to the question in the example is 45.

```
  45
2)90
  8
  10
  10
```

In example (*e*) shown at the right, the question asked is, "How many 3's = 74?" or "What number × 3 = 74?" The first partial dividend is 7 tens; 7 tens ÷ 3 = 2 tens + 1 ten remaining. The first quotient figure is 2 tens. Ten ones are substituted for 1 ten and they are added to the 4 ones brought down. The second partial dividend is 14 ones; 14 ones ÷ 3 = 4 ones + 2 ones remainder. The second partial quotient is 4. The total quotient and answer to the question in the example is 24 *R*2 or $24\frac{2}{3}$.

```
  24 R2
3)74
  6
  14
  12
   2
```

Generalized Rule

In a division example having a two-place dividend with a figure in the tens' place equal to or larger than the one-place divisor, the first partial dividend is tens. Divide the tens to find the first partial quotient. Multiply and then subtract to find a remainder (if any). If there is a remainder, substitute 10 ones for each ten and add them to the ones brought down. The second partial dividend is ones. Divide, multiply, and subtract as with tens. The second partial quotient is ones. The total quotient is the sum of the partial quotients.

Short Division or Long Division?

The question is often asked, "Should long division or short division be taught first?" The answer should be obvious. Short division, in which the learner must rely greatly upon memory, should be deferred until the learner has developed an understanding of the steps required in dividing two-place numbers.

Substituting Tens for Hundreds in First Partial Dividends

In the example, $\overset{?}{5\overline{)150}}$, the question asked is, "How many 5's = 150?" or "What number × 5 = 150?" The 1 in the hundreds place is smaller than the 5 in the divisor so there are not enough hundreds to divide. The figures in the partial dividend must be equal to or larger than the figures in the divisor, so 10 tens are substituted for 1 hundred and added to 5 tens. The first partial dividend is 15 tens and the second is 0, as shown in the examples below.

```
    ?       1st Partial    2d Partial
5)150        Dividend       Dividend

               H T             O              H T O
               ---             -              -----
                 3             0      or        3 0       or      30
             5)1 5           5)0             5)1 5 0            5)150
               1 5                             1 5                15
               ---                             ---                --
                                                   0               0
```

In computing the first partial quotient, divide: 15 tens ÷ 5 = 3 tens. In the second partial dividend, 0, there are no ones to divide. A 0 is put in the quotient to hold the ones place. The second partial quotient is 0. The total quotient is 3 tens and 0 ones or 30. The answer to the question asked by the example is 30 (30 × 5 = 150).

Other examples in which the figure in the hundreds place is smaller than the divisor are shown below.

```
    (a)           (b)           (c)             (d)          (e)
   H T O         H T O         H T O           H T O        H T O
   -----         -----         -----           -----        -----
     2 0 R5        7 1           7 1 R3          4 3          5 7 R1
 7)1 4 5       6)4 2 6       4)2 8 7         8)3 4 4      2)1 1 5
   1 4           4 2           2 8             3 2          1 0
   ---           ---           ---             ---          ---
       5             6             7             2 4          1 5
                     6             4             2 4          1 4
                     -             -             ---          ---
                                   3                            1
```

1. In example (*a*) the question asked is, "How many 7's = 145?" or "What number × 7 = 145?" The 1 in the hundreds place is smaller than the 7 in the divisor so there are not enough hundreds to divide. Ten tens are substituted for 1 hundred and they are added to the 4 tens to make the first partial dividend 14 tens; 14 tens ÷ 7 = 2 tens. The first partial quotient is 2 tens. In the second partial dividend, 5, there are not enough ones to divide. A 0 is put in the quotient to hold the ones place. The total quotient is 2 tens, 0 ones, + a remainder of 5. The answer to the question, "What number × 7 = 145?" is, "20 × 7 + a remainder of 5 = 145."

2. In example (*b*), the question asked is "How many 6's = 426?" or "What number × 6 = 426?" The first partial dividend is 42 tens because the 4 in the hundreds place is too small to divide by 6 in the divisor and 40 tens have been substituted for the 4 hundreds and then added to the 2 in the tens place; 42 tens ÷ 6 = 7 tens, which is the first quotient figure. The 6 ones brought down become the second partial dividend. The 6 in the second partial dividend is as large as the divisor 6; 6 ÷ 6 = 1. The second quotient figure is 1. The total quotient is 71.

3. In example (*c*) the computation is identical to that in example (*b*) except that some of the second partial dividend, 7, is left as a remainder. The answer to the question, "What number × 4 = 287?" is "71 × 4 + a remainder of 3 = 287."

4. In example (*d*), $8\overset{?}{\overline{)344}}$, the question is, "How many 8's = 344?" or "What number × 8 = 344?" There are not enough hundreds to divide. The procedure to follow is to take the 3 hundreds and for them substitute 30 tens, which are added to the 4 tens; 34 tens ÷ 8 = 4 tens. Find the product of 4 tens × 8, which is 32 tens. Find the difference between 34 tens and 32 tens. The difference is 2 tens. There are not enough tens to divide. Then substitute for the 2 tens 20 ones, which when added to the 4 ones equal 24 ones. Divide the ones; 24 ones ÷ 8 = 3. Write 3 in the ones place in the quotient. The total quotient is 43.

5. In example (*e*), $2\overset{?}{\overline{)115}}$, the computation is done in the same way as in example (*d*), but some of the dividend is left after the division has been completed. The quotient in example (*e*) could be expressed 57 *R*1 or $57\frac{1}{2}$. What is the meaning of the quotient?

In the following examples there are enough hundreds to divide.

(*a*)	(*b*)	(*c*)	(*d*)	(*e*)	(*f*)
300	201	209	430	321	319
2)600	4)804	3)627	2)860	3)963	2)638
6	8	6	8	9	6
00	04	27	6	6	3
	4	27	6	6	2
			0	3	18
				3	18

(*g*)	(*h*)	(*i*)
250	131	238
3)750	7)917	4)952
6	7	8
15	21	15
15	21	12
0	7	32
	7	32

Observe that hundreds are divided in the same way as tens and ones. In example (*a*) the question is, "How many groups of 2 each equal 600?" or "What number × 2 = 600?" The answer can be determined by computing with the hundreds. Six hundreds divided into two equal groups = 3 hundreds in a group. *H H H H H H* = *HHH HHH*. From the illustration it can be seen that 6 hundreds = 3 hundreds × 2. The first partial quotient is 3 hundreds. Why is the 3 written in the hundreds place? There are no tens and no ones to divide so the second partial quotient is 0 and the third partial quotient is also 0. The total quotient is 3 hundreds 0 tens and 0 ones. The answer to the question in the example is, "Three hundred 2's = 600" (300 × 2 = 600).

Observe that in example (*b*), $\overset{?}{4\overline{)804}}$, there are enough hundreds, no tens, and enough ones to divide. The question is, "How many 4's = 804?" or "What number × 4 = 804?" To find the answer first divide, multiply, and subtract the hundreds. Write 0 in the second partial dividend and in the second partial quotient because there are no tens to divide. Then divide, multiply, and subtract the ones. The quotient is 201 (201 × 4 = 804).

In example (*c*), $\overset{?}{3\overline{)627}}$, there are enough hundreds to divide so divide, multiply, and subtract the hundreds. Bring down the 2 tens. There are not enough tens to divide, so write a 0 in the quotient and bring down the 7 ones. Then take the 2 tens and for them substitute 20 ones which are added to the ones; 27 ones ÷ 3 = 9. Multiply 9 × 3. The product is 27. There is no difference between 27 and 27. The quotient in example (*c*) is 209.

In example (*d*), $\overset{?}{2\overline{)860}}$, there are enough hundreds and enough tens but no ones to divide. How many groups of 2 each equal 8 hundred? How many groups of 2 each equal 6 tens? Why would a zero be written in the ones place in the quotient? 860 = ? × 2?

In example (*e*), $\overset{?}{3\overline{)963}}$, there are enough hundreds, tens, and ones to divide. 9 hundreds = ? hundreds × 2? 6 tens = ? tens × 2? 3 = ? ones × 2? 963 = ? × 2?

In example (*f*), $\overset{?}{2\overline{)638}}$, there are enough hundreds, tens, and ones to divide but the division of 3 tens by 2 is uneven division. Otherwise the steps in finding the answer in example (*f*) are identical with the steps in finding the answer to example (*e*).

In example (*g*), (*h*), and (*i*) shown at the right the division of hundreds is uneven. In example (*g*), 10 tens were substituted for the 1 hundred remaining after the first partial quotient was computed. What was the second partial dividend? The second partial quotient? The third partial quotient? The total quotient?

What are the partial dividends in example (*h*)? What is the quotient in example (*h*)?

In example (*i*) the second and the third partial dividends are two-place numbers. Why? What is the total quotient in example (*i*)?

$$\begin{array}{r} (g) \\ 250 \\ 3\overline{)750} \\ 6 \\ \hline 15 \\ 15 \\ \hline 0 \end{array} \qquad \begin{array}{r} (h) \\ 131 \\ 7\overline{)917} \\ 7 \\ \hline 21 \\ 21 \\ \hline 7 \\ 7 \\ \hline \end{array} \qquad \begin{array}{r} (i) \\ 238 \\ 4\overline{)952} \\ 8 \\ \hline 15 \\ 12 \\ \hline 32 \\ 32 \\ \hline \end{array}$$

Dividing Larger Numbers by a One-Place Divisor

The understandings developed in dividing one-place, two-place, and three-place numbers can be applied to the division of larger numbers. In the example, $\begin{array}{r} ? \\ 8\overline{)9268} \end{array}$, the question asked is, "How many 8's = 9268?" or "What number × 8 = 9268?" The answer is computed by separating the dividend into partial dividends (P.D.).

1st P.D. 2d P.D. 3d P.D. 4th P.D.

$$\begin{array}{r} ? \\ 8\overline{)9268} \end{array} \text{ or } \begin{array}{r} \underline{Th} \\ 1 \\ 8\overline{)9} \\ 8 \\ \hline 1 \end{array} + \begin{array}{r} \underline{H} \\ 1 \\ 8\overline{)12} \\ 8 \\ \hline 4 \end{array} + \begin{array}{r} \underline{T} \\ 5 \\ 8\overline{)46} \\ 40 \\ \hline 6 \end{array} + \begin{array}{r} \underline{O} \\ 8 \\ 8\overline{)68} \\ 64 \\ \hline 4 \end{array} = \begin{array}{l} \quad\ \underline{Th\ H\ T\ O} \\ \quad\ 1\ \ 1\ \ 5\ \ 8\ \ R4 \\ 8\overline{)9\ \ 2\ \ 6\ \ 8} \\ \quad\ 8 \\ \quad\ \overline{1\ \ 2} \\ \quad\ \ \ \ \ 8 \\ \quad\ \ \ \ \overline{4\ \ 6} \\ \quad\ \ \ \ 4\ \ 0 \\ \quad\ \ \ \ \ \ \ \overline{6\ \ 8} \\ \quad\ \ \ \ \ \ \ 6\ \ 4 \\ \quad\ \ \ \ \ \ \ \ \ \overline{\ \ \ 4} \end{array} \qquad \begin{array}{l} \quad 1158\ R4 \\ 8\overline{)9268} \\ \quad 8 \\ \quad \overline{12} \\ \quad\ \ 8 \\ \quad\ \overline{46} \\ \quad\ 40 \\ \quad\ \ \overline{68} \\ \quad\ \ 64 \\ \quad\ \ \ \overline{\ 4} \end{array}$$

The answer to the question asked by each partial dividend is computed separately to find each partial quotient. The quotient is the sum of the partial quotients. The answer to the question, "What number × 8 = 9268?" is "1158 × 8 + a remainder of 4 = 9268."

Generalized Rules

Long Division Method

Think of the dividend as decimal units that can be divided into groups as indicated by the divisor, and answer the question, "How many units like the divisor equal the dividend?" When answering the question, begin by determining the first partial dividend that will have figures equal to or larger than the divisor. Divide to find the first partial quotient. Multiply, subtract, and bring down to find the second partial dividend. Repeat the steps of divide, multiply, subtract, and bring down until each figure in the dividend has been divided. The total quotient equals the sum of the partial quotients.

Short Division Method

This method is similar to the long division method but all computation is done mentally.

Dividing Two-Place Dividends by a Two-Place Divisor

(*a*)	(*b*)	(*c*)	(*d*)	(*e*)
2	4	3	6	2 R3
$30\overline{)60}$	$21\overline{)84}$	$25\overline{)75}$	$15\overline{)90}$	$40\overline{)83}$
60	84	75	90	80
—	—	—	—	—
				3

Many of the understandings developed in dividing by a one-place divisor are applicable to dividing by a two-place divisor. The figures in the dividend that are equal to or larger than the two-place divisor are the first partial dividend. The figure in the tens place of the divisor is the *trial divisor*. Dividing by a trial divisor is the same as dividing by a one-place divisor.

In example (*a*), $\overset{?}{30\overline{)60}}$, the question asked is, "How many 30's = 60?" or "What number × 30 = 60?" The 6 in the tens place of the dividend is smaller than the divisor, 30; 60 ones are substituted for 6 tens. Then the dividend 60 ones is large enough to be divided by 30 ones. The trial divisor is 3; 6 tens ÷ 3 tens = 2. As shown in the illustration, *T T T T T T* = *TTT TTT*, 6 tens = 2 groups of 3 tens each. The answer to the question, "What number × 30 = 60?" is "2 × 30 = 60." The quotient is 2. The steps in finding the answer are: Divide, Multiply, and Subtract.

In example (*b*), $\overset{?}{21\overline{)84}}$, the question is, "How many groups of 21 each equal 84?" or, "What number × 21 = 84?" In this example there are not enough tens to divide by 21. Take the 8 tens and for them substitute 80 ones and add them to the 4 ones. (80 + 4 = 84). Then 84 ones can be divided by 21 ones. For the purpose of computation use 2 as the trial divisor. To find the trial quotient, divide the tens; 8 tens ÷ 2 tens = 4 (*T T T T T T T T* = *TT TT TT TT*). To find if the trial quotient is the true quotient, multiply mentally 4 × 21. A good short cut in multiplying mentally is that of first multiplying the tens: 4 × 2 tens = 80. Then multiply the ones: 4 × 1 = 4. Then add 80 + 4. The sum of these partial products is 84. This product, 84, equals the dividend. The trial quotient is the true quotient. The quotient in example (*b*) is 4.

$$\begin{array}{r} 4 \\ 21\overline{)84} \\ 84 \\ \text{—} \end{array}$$

In example (*c*), $\overset{?}{25\overline{)75}}$, the question is, "How many groups of 25 each equal 75?" or, "What number × 25 = 75?" To find the trial quotient divide 7 tens by 3 tens. Multiply mentally to see if the trial quotient is the true quotient; 3 × 25 = 75. The product, 75, equals the dividend, 75. The trial quotient, 3, is the true quotient.

$$\begin{array}{r} 3 \\ 25\overline{)75} \\ 75 \\ \hline \end{array}$$

In example (*d*), $\overset{?}{15\overline{)90}}$, the trial quotient is determined by dividing 9 tens by 1 ten. The trial quotient is 9. By multiplying mentally we find that 9 × 1 ten = 90 and 9 × 5 = 45; 90 + 45 = 135, which is more than the dividend, 90. The trial quotient is too large. Try the next figure smaller than 9. Multiply mentally again; 8 × 15 = 120. Since 120 is more than 90, the trial quotient is still too large. Try 7; 7 × 15 = 105. Since 105 is more than 90, the trial quotient is still too large. Try 6; 6 × 15 = 90. The product, 90, equals the dividend 90. Six is the true quotient.

$$\begin{array}{r} 6 \\ 15\overline{)90} \\ 90 \\ \hline \end{array}$$

In example (*e*), $\overset{?}{40\overline{)83}}$, the trial quotient and the true quotient are 2 (2 × 40 = 80). Since the difference between the dividend, 83, and the product 80 cannot be divided into equal groups of 40 each, it is written as a remainder. The quotient is 2 *R*3 or $2\frac{3}{40}$.

$$\begin{array}{r} 2\ R3 \\ 40\overline{)83} \\ 80 \\ \hline 3 \end{array}$$

Observe that in each of the examples (*a*) to (*e*) the steps are: divide, multiply, subtract. The trial quotient is computed by dividing the tens in the dividend by the tens in the divisor. The true quotient is determined by finding the product of the trial quotient times the divisor. Unless this product is then equal to or smaller than the dividend, try the next smaller number as a trial quotient and multiply again. The suggested method of finding the trial quotient is effective because it can be used in all types of division examples.

Division of Three-Place Dividends by Two-Place Divisors

(*a*)	(*b*)	(*c*)	(*d*)
$\begin{array}{r} 2 \\ 84\overline{)168} \\ 168 \\ \hline \end{array}$	$\begin{array}{r} 8 \\ 79\overline{)632} \\ 632 \\ \hline \end{array}$	$\begin{array}{r} 6 \\ 18\overline{)108} \\ 108 \\ \hline \end{array}$	$\begin{array}{r} 3\ R2 \\ 35\overline{)107} \\ 105 \\ \hline 2 \end{array}$

In example (*a*) the question is, "How many groups of 84 each equal a group of 168?" or "What number × 84 = 168?" There are not enough hundreds to divide by 84. Take 1 hundred and for it substitute 10 tens, which are added to the 6 tens (10 + 6 = 16). There are not enough tens to divide by 84. Take the 16 tens and for them substitute 160 ones, which are added to the 8 ones (160 + 8 = 168). Then there are enough ones to divide by 84. To find the trial quotient use 8 as the trial divisor. Then divide the tens (16 tens ÷ 8 tens = 2). The trial quotient is 2. By multiplying mentally, 2 × 84, the product is computed as 168. This equals the dividend so the true quotient is 2. Why is it written in the ones place of the quotient?

$$\begin{array}{r} 8 \\ 79\overline{)632} \\ 632 \\ \hline \end{array}$$

In example (*b*), $\overset{?}{79\overline{)632}}$, the question is, "How many groups of 79 equal 632?" or "What number × 79 = 632?" The trial divisor is 7 and the trial quotient is determined by dividing 63 in the dividend by the 7 in the divisor. The trial quotient is 9; 9 × 79 = (9 × 70) or 630 + (9 × 9) or 81. But 630 + 81 = 711 which is more than 632. The next trial quotient is 8; 8 × 79 = 560 + 72 = 632. The true quotient is 8. The answer to the question, "How many groups of 79 equal 632?" is "Eight groups of 79 equal 632."

$$\begin{array}{r} 6 \\ 18\overline{)108} \\ 108 \\ \hline \end{array}$$

In example (*c*), $\overset{?}{18\overline{)108}}$, the question is, "How many groups of 18 equal 108?" or "What number × 18 = 108?" To find the trial quotient figure, divide the 10 in the dividend by the 1 in the divisor (10 ÷ 1 = 10). The trial quotient appears to be 10. However, since no figure greater than 9 can be written in any decimal place, the trial quotient must be 9. By multiplying mentally, it can be seen that 9, then 8, and then 7 are all too large to be the true quotient. The true quotient is 6 (6 × 18 = 60 + 48 = 108). Six groups of 18 each equal 108 (6 × 18 = 108).

$$\begin{array}{r} 3\ R2 \\ 35\overline{)107} \\ 105 \\ \hline 2 \end{array}$$

In example (*d*), $\overset{?}{35\overline{)107}}$, some of the dividend is left after the true quotient, 3, is determined. The quotient is 3 *R*2 or $3\frac{2}{35}$.

Division of Partial Dividends When Dividing Three-Place Dividends by Two-Place Divisors

There is a close relationship between the computational steps used in finding the answer to the question asked by a division example and in finding the answer to the question asked by the corresponding multiplication example. The multiplication example below asks the

H	*T*	*O*				
	3	2			32	
	2	3		or	$\times$23	
	9	6	3 ones $\times$ 32		96	first partial product
6	4		2 tens $\times$ 32		64	second partial product
7	3	6			736	

question, "What number equals 23 × 32?" The answer is computed by multiplying by ones to find the first partial product, multiplying by tens to find the second partial product, and adding the partial products to find the total product. The answer to the question in the example is, "732 equals 23 × 32." Each partial product is as large as or larger than the multiplicand. Why?

As stated earlier in this chapter (see pp. 99 and 100), the question asked by a division example may be stated in several ways. In the division example, $\begin{array}{r} ? \\ 32\overline{)736} \end{array}$, which is the division example that corresponds to the multiplication example, 23 × 32 = 736, the question may be thought of as being, "What number times 32 = 736?" or "736 = what number × 32?" In the multiplication example, the product was computed by first finding partial products. In the division example, the quotient can be computed by separating the dividend 736 into partial dividends. The first partial dividend must be as large as or larger than the divisor.

The example, $\begin{array}{r} ? \\ 32\overline{)736} \end{array}$, is computed by separating it into partial dividends as shown on the grids below.

```
1st P.D.                   2d P.D.
  H T                        T O                    H T O
  ---                        ---                    -----
    2                          3                      2 3           23
 ------                     ------                 --------        ----
32) 7 3                    32) 9 6                32) 7 3 6   or  32)736
    6 4  2 tens × 32           9 6  3 ones × 32       6 4           64
    ---                        ---                    ---           --
      9                                                 9 6         96
                                                        9 6         96
                                                        ---         --
```

The first partial dividend asks the question, "What number × 32 = 73 tens?" By using 3 as a trial divisor and dividing, 7 ÷ 3, the trial quotient is computed as 2. The trial quotient is the true quotient. The product of 2 tens × 32 = 64 tens. It is the same as the second partial product in the corresponding multiplication example, 23 × 32 (see p. 117). The answer to the question is, "2 tens × 32 = 9 tens less than 73 tens).

The second partial dividend is the sum of 9 tens (which are left when 64 is subtracted from 73) and 6 ones. The second partial dividend asks the question, "What number × 32 = 96?" By using the trial divisor 3 and dividing 9 ÷ 3, the trial quotient is computed as 3. The trial quotient is the true quotient. The product of 3 ones × 32 = 96 ones, which is the same as the first partial product in the multiplication example 23 × 32.

The total quotient is 23. The answer to the question, "What number × 32 = 736?" is "23 × 32 = 736." If the question is stated another way, "736 = what number × 32?" the answer is, "736 = 23 × 32."

In each of the following examples 10 tens are substituted for each hundred and the first partial dividend is tens.

```
(a)             1st P.D.     2d P.D.
                  H T           O          H T O
                  ---           -          -----
      ?             2           0            2 0          20
   ------        ------       -----        --------      ------
   40)800        40) 8 0      40) 0   or   40) 8 0 0     40)800
                     8 0          -            8 0         80
                     ---                       ---         --
                                                   0        0
```

(*b*)

	1st P.D.	*2d P.D.*		
	H T	*O*	*H T O*	
?	3	0	3 0	30
14)420	14) 4 2	14) 0	14) 4 2 0	14)420
	4 2	–	4 2	42
			0	0

(*c*)

	1st P.D.	*2d P.D.*		
	H T	*T O*	*H T O*	
?	1	2	1 2 *R*45	12 *R*45
67)849	67) 8 4	67)17 9	67) 8 4 9	67)849
	6 7	13 4	6 7	67
	1 7	4 5	1 7 9	179
			1 3 4	134
			4 5	45

In example (*a*) the question is, "What number × 40 = 800?" The first partial dividend is 80 tens (8 hundreds = 80 tens). By using 4 as a trial divisor and dividing, 8 ÷ 4, the trial quotient is computed as 2; 2 tens × 40 = 80 tens. The trial quotient is the true quotient. In the second partial dividend there are no ones to divide. A zero is put in the quotient to hold the ones place. The answer to the question, "What number × 40 = 800?" is "20 × 40 = 800." The quotient is 20.

Example (*b*), shown at the right, is computed in the same way as example (*a*) except that the trial quotient for the first partial dividend is 4. The true quotient for the first partial dividend is 3. The total quotient is 30.

30
14)420
42
0

Example (*c*), shown at the right, asks the question, "What number × 67 = 849?" The first partial dividend is 84 tens. It asks the question, "What number × 67 = 84 tens?" Using 6 as a trial divisor and dividing, 8 ÷ 6 = 1, the trial quotient is computed as 1; 1 ten × 67 = 67 tens. The difference between 84 tens and 67 tens is 17 tens.

The number 17 tens is too small to be divided by 67 so 9 ones are brought down and added to 17 tens. The second partial dividend is 179. This asks the question, "What number × 67 = 179?" Using 6 as a

12 *R*45
67)849
67
179
134
45

trial divisor and dividing $17 \div 6 = 2$, the trial quotient is computed as 2. The trial quotient, $2 \times 67 = 134$. The difference between 179 and 134 is 45. The answer to the question in the second partial dividend is, "$2 \times 67 +$ a remainder of $45 = 179$."

The total quotient is the sum of the partial quotients. It is 12 R45.

EXERCISE

Find the quotient for each example. Explain the thought process used in dividing the tens and in dividing the ones.

$$\begin{array}{r} ? \\ 2\overline{)800} \end{array} \quad \begin{array}{r} ? \\ 22\overline{)660} \end{array} \quad \begin{array}{r} ? \\ 12\overline{)365} \end{array} \quad \begin{array}{r} ? \\ 15\overline{)310} \end{array} \quad \begin{array}{r} ? \\ 40\overline{)480} \end{array} \quad \begin{array}{r} ? \\ 42\overline{)509} \end{array} \quad \begin{array}{r} ? \\ 13\overline{)884} \end{array}$$

Division of Larger Numbers

Division of larger numbers is accomplished by separating the dividend into partial dividends and computing the partial quotient for each partial dividend. The total quotient equals the sum of the partial quotients.

(*a*) *1st P.D.* (*tens*) *2d P.D.* (*ones*)

$$\begin{array}{r} ? \\ 40\overline{)1200} \end{array} = \begin{array}{r} 3 \\ 40\overline{)120} \\ 120 \\ \hline \end{array} + \begin{array}{r} 0 \\ 40\overline{)0} \end{array} = \begin{array}{r} 30 \\ 40\overline{)1200} \\ 120 \\ \hline 0 \end{array}$$

(*b*) *1st P.D.* (*tens*) *2d P.D.* (*ones*)

$$\begin{array}{r} ? \\ 30\overline{)1860} \end{array} = \begin{array}{r} 6 \\ 30\overline{)186} \\ 180 \\ \hline \end{array} + \begin{array}{r} 2 \\ 30\overline{)60} \\ 60 \\ \hline \end{array} = \begin{array}{r} 62 \\ 30\overline{)1860} \\ 180 \\ \hline 60 \\ 60 \\ \hline \end{array}$$

(*c*)

```
            1st P.D.   2d P.D.
             (tens)     (ones)
      ?         9          7          97 R7
14)1365    14)136  +  14)105  =  14)1365
               126         98        126
               ---         --        ---
                            7         105
                                       98
                                      ---
                                        7
```

(*d*)

```
            1st P.D.   2d P.D.    3d P.D.
             (hun.)     (tens)     (ones)
      ?        2          0          9           209
14)2926    14)29  +  14)12  +  14)126  =  14)2926
              28                   126         28
              --                   ---         --
               1                               126
                                               126
                                               ---
```

(*e*) (*f*) (*g*)

```
   410          284 R21         1014 R1
21)8610      29)8257         56)56785
   84           58              56
   --           --              --
    21          245              78
    21          232              56
    --          ---              --
     0           137             225
                 116             224
                 ---             ---
                  21               1
```

In example (*a*) the question is, "What number × 40 = 1200?" The 1 in the thousands place is too small to divide by 40. Ten hundreds are substituted for 1 thousand and are added to the 2 hundreds. Then there are 12 hundreds. The figure 12 (hundreds) is too small to divide by 40 so 120 tens are substituted for 12 hundreds. The question asked by the first partial dividend is, "What number × 40 = 120 tens?" By using a trial divisor of 4 and dividing, 12 ÷ 4 = 3, the trial quotient is computed as 3. The answer to the question is, "3 tens × 40 = 120 tens."

In the second partial dividend, 0, there are no ones to divide. A 0 is put in the quotient to hold the ones place. The total quotient is 30.

Example (*b*) at the right is similar to example (*a*) except that there are enough ones in the second partial dividend to divide by 30. How many tens were in the first partial dividend after tens were substituted for 1 thousand and for 8 hundreds? The second partial dividend is 60 ones. Why? The total quotient is 62.

```
      62
30)1860
   180
    60
    60
```

In example (*c*) at the right, the first partial dividend is 136 tens and the second partial dividend is 105. Both are three-place numbers. The computation for each partial dividend is done separately with 1 used as a trial divisor. Is the trial quotient the true quotient in either of the partial dividends? The total quotient is 97 *R*7 or $97\frac{7}{14}$.

```
      97 R7
14)1365
   126
    105
     98
      7
```

In example (*d*) at the right, the first partial dividend is 29 hundreds and the first partial quotient is 2 hundreds. The number 12, in the second partial dividend is too small to be divided by 14. A 0 is put in the second partial quotient to hold the tens' place. The third partial dividend is 126 ones, which can be divided by 14. The third partial quotient is 9. The total quotient is 209.

```
     209
14)2926
   28
    126
    126
```

In example (*e*) at the right, the first partial dividend is 86 hundreds, the second partial dividend is 21 tens, and the third partial dividend is 0. By computing the partial quotients and adding them, the total quotient is computed as 410.

```
     410
21)8610
   84
    21
    21
     0
```

In example (*f*) at the right, the first partial dividend is 82 hundreds, the second partial dividend is 245 tens, and the third partial dividend is 137 ones. The trial divisor is 2. What is the trial quotient when answering the question, "What number × 29 = 82 hundreds?" What is the true quotient? What questions are asked by the other partial dividends? The quotient is 824 *R*21.

```
     284 R21
29)8257
   58
   245
   232
    137
    116
     21
```

In example (g) at the right, the first partial dividend is 56 thousands, the second is 7 hundreds, the third is 78 tens, and the fourth is 225 ones. Observe that first the thousands, then the hundreds, then the tens, and then the ones are divided. The total quotient is 1014 $R1$ or $1014\frac{1}{56}$.

$$\begin{array}{r} 1014\ R1 \\ 56\overline{)56785} \\ \underline{56} \\ 78 \\ \underline{56} \\ 225 \\ \underline{224} \\ 1 \end{array}$$

Generalized Rule

When dividing two-place or larger dividends by two-place divisors, first determine the partial dividend large enough to be divided by the number in the divisor. Then divide, multiply, and subtract. The difference, together with the largest undivided decimal unit brought down from the dividend is the second partial dividend. The second partial dividend is divided in the same way as the first partial dividend. Additional partial dividends are divided in the same way as the first partial dividend and second partial dividend until all decimal units in the dividend have been divided.

EXERCISE

Explain the thought process used in finding the answer to each example below:

(*a*)	(*b*)	(*c*)	(*d*)	(*e*)
$33\overline{)6699}$	$15\overline{)3068}$	$47\overline{)6110}$	$23\overline{)3212}$	$12\overline{)11052}$

Dividing by a Three-Place Divisor

(*a*)

$$\begin{array}{r} 7 \\ 106\overline{)742} \\ \underline{742} \end{array}$$

(*b*)

$$\begin{array}{r} 4\ R11 \\ 546\overline{)2195} \\ \underline{2184} \\ 11 \end{array}$$

(*c*)

$$\begin{array}{rcrcrcr}
 & & \textit{1st P.D.} & & \textit{2d P.D.} & & \\
? & & 3 & & 0 & & 30 \\
320\overline{)9600} & = & 320\overline{)960} & + & 320\overline{)0} & = & 320\overline{)9600} \\
 & & 960 & & & & 960 \\
 & & & & & & 0
\end{array}$$

(*d*)

$$\begin{array}{rcrcrcr}
 & & \textit{1st P.D.} & & \textit{2d P.D.} & & \\
? & & 5 & & 0 & & 50\ R15 \\
419\overline{)20965} & = & 419\overline{)2096} & + & 419\overline{)15} & = & 419\overline{)20965} \\
 & & 2095 & & & & 2095 \\
 & & 1 & & & & 15
\end{array}$$

(*e*)

$$\begin{array}{rcrcrcr}
 & & \textit{1st P.D.} & & \textit{2d P.D.} & & \\
? & & 3 & & 4 & & 34\ R6 \\
203\overline{)6908} & = & 203\overline{)690} & + & 203\overline{)818} & = & 203\overline{)6908} \\
 & & 609 & & 812 & & 609 \\
 & & 81 & & 6 & & 818 \\
 & & & & & & 812 \\
 & & & & & & 6
\end{array}$$

(*f*)

$$\begin{array}{rcrcrcrcr}
 & & \textit{1st P.D.} & & \textit{2d P.D.} & & \textit{3d P.D.} & & \\
? & & 2 & & 3 & & 5 & & 235 \\
879\overline{)206565} & = & 879\overline{)2065} & + & 879\overline{)3076} & + & 879\overline{)4395} & = & 879\overline{)206565} \\
 & & 1758 & & 2637 & & 4395 & & \\
 & & 307 & & 439 & & & &
\end{array}$$

In example (*a*), $106\overline{)742}$ with a "?" over it, the question asked is, "What number × 106 equals 742?" The trial divisor is 1 hundred. The first trial quotient is determined by dividing; 7 hundreds ÷ 1 hundred = 7, which is the trial quotient. By multiplying mentally, 7 × 106, like this: 7 × 1 hundred = 7 hundreds and then 7 × 6 ones = 42 ones, it is easy to see that the trial quotient is the true quotient. The answer to the question asked by the example is, "7 × 106 = 742." The quotient is 7.

In example (*b*), $546\overline{)\overset{?}{2195}}$, the question asked is, "What number $\times$ 546 = 2195?" The trial divisor is 5. The figure 2 in the thousands place of the dividend is smaller than the trial divisor 5; 20 hundreds are substituted for the 2 thousands and are added to the 1 in the hundreds place. The trial quotient equals 4 (21 hundreds $\div$ 5 hundreds = 4). By multiplying mentally, 4 $\times$ 546, it is easy to see that the trial quotient is the true quotient. The answer to the question, "What number $\times$ 546 = 2195?" is 4.

In example (*c*), $320\overline{)\overset{?}{9600}}$, the question is, "What number $\times$ 320 = 9600? The question can be most easily answered if 9600 is separated into partial dividends. The first partial dividend is 960 tens. The first trial divisor is 3 hundreds. Since the first partial dividend is tens, the first trial quotient will be tens and the total quotient will be a two-place number. The first trial quotient is determined by dividing 9 thousands by 3 hundreds. The first trial quotient is 3 tens. By multiplying mentally it is seen that the trial quotient is the true quotient. There are no decimal units to divide in the second partial dividend. A 0 is put in the ones place of the quotient to hold the ones place. The quotient is 30.

In example (*d*), $419\overline{)\overset{?}{20965}}$, the question is, "What number $\times$ 419 = 20965? The dividend can be separated into partial dividends. The first trial dividend is 2096 tens so the quotient will be a two-place number. Dividing 20 thousands by a trial divisor of 4 hundreds gives a trial quotient of 5 tens. By multiplying mentally it can be seen that the trial quotient is the true quotient. The next steps are to multiply, subtract, and add the remainder to the next figure in the dividend to form the second partial dividend. The second partial dividend, 15, is smaller than the divisor 419; therefore, a 0 is put in the ones place of the quotient to hold the ones place. The quotient is 50 *R*15.

In example (*e*), $203\overline{)\overset{?}{6908}}$, the first partial dividend is 690 tens. Since there are enough tens to divide, the first quotient figure will be written in the tens' place and the quotient will be a two-place number. In example (*e*) the second partial dividend, 818, is larger than the divisor 203. The second trial quotient figure is 4. After multiplying mentally it is seen to be the second true quotient figure. The quotient in example (*e*) is 34 *R*6.

Example (*f*), $879\overline{)206565}$, and the corresponding multiplication examples are computed on the decimal grid below.

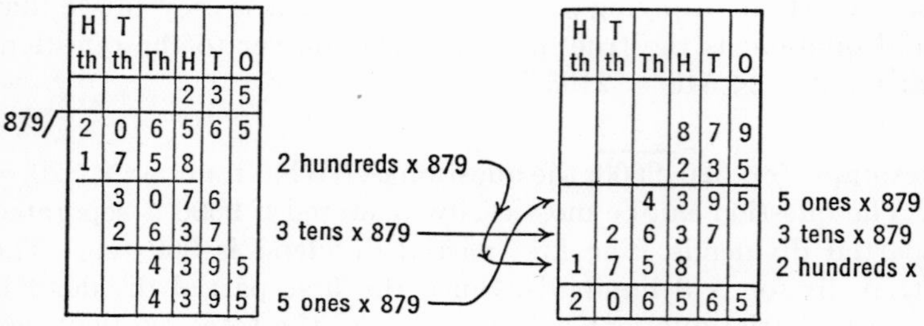

As shown on p. 125, the first partial dividend is 2065 hundreds. Therefore the first partial quotient will be in the hundreds' place. The second partial dividend is 3076 tens and the third partial dividend is 4395. The mental process of divide, multiply, subtract, and then bring down is the same when finding the answer to the question asked by each partial dividend.

The first question asked by the multiplication example is, "What number equals 5 × 879?" The answer is, "4395 = 5 × 879." The last question asked by the division example is, "What number × 879 = 4395?" The answer is, "5 × 879 = 4395."

The second question asked by the multiplication example is, "What number equals 3 tens × 879?" The answer is, "2637 tens = 3 tens × 879." The second question asked by the division example is, "What number × 879 = 3076 tens?" The answer is, "3 tens × 879 + a remainder of 439 = 3076 tens."

The last question asked by the multiplication example is, "What number equals 2 hundreds × 879?" The answer is, "1758 hundreds = 2 hundreds × 879." The first question asked by the division example is, "What number × 879 = 2065 hundreds?" The answer is, "2 hundreds × 879 + a remainder of 307 = 2065 hundreds.

The questions asked by the partial dividends in division examples can be answered by using the multiplication facts.

Generalized Rule

When dividing three-place or larger dividends by three-place divisors, first determine the partial dividend large enough to be divided by the divisor. Use the first figure in the divisor as a trial divisor and divide the first figure (or the first two figures) in the first partial dividend to find the trial quotient. Then multiply and subtract. The difference, together with the next largest undivided decimal unit that is brought down from the dividend is the second partial dividend. Repeat the steps of divide, multiply, subtract, and bring down and continue until each partial dividend has been divided. The total quotient is the sum of the partial quotients.

EXERCISE

Find the answer to each example. Explain the thought process required to find each answer.

104)624 729)5115 320)12800 407)13838 275)268125

Verifying Answers in Division

The quotient in division is a number that indicates the number of groups like the divisor that equal the number notated by the dividend. Division examples can be checked by adding the divisor as many times as specified by the quotient. This method is effective for checking examples with small quotients but is impractical for other examples. To verify the accuracy of division examples with larger quotients, pupils may repeat carefully each step taken to find the quotient. Pupils should be given the opportunity to ask a classmate to verify the accuracy of their computation.

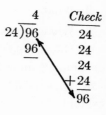

4	*Check*
24)96	24
96	24
	24
	+24
	96

As the children become proficient with division and understand how to answer the questions asked by division examples, they may be permitted to check their work by multiplying the divisor by the quotient and adding the remainder, if any, to the product. The example at the right asks the question, "What number × 24 = 185?" It is logical to use multiplication as a check. However, the quotient should be used as the multiplier and

7 *R*17	*Check*
24)185	24
168	×7
17	168
	+17
	185

the divisor as the multiplicand so as to keep the check consistent with the question asked by the example.

As children become still more mature in their understanding of division, they may be permitted to use the more abstract method of using either the quotient or divisor as the multiplier. They have learned in multiplication that reversing the multiplier and multiplicand does not change the product, and they may be permitted to use this knowledge in checking division examples. However, the meaning of the example is changed when the multiplier and multiplicand are reversed.

Diagnosing Pupil Growth

As suggested in earlier chapters, children should be given an opportunity to examine and to discuss the ideas developed in their study. Representative questions that may be discussed include the following:

1. How can you tell when you are to divide to find the answer to the question in a problem?

2. What does each number in a division example tell?

3. What does the sign $\overline{)\quad}$ or ÷ ask you to do?

4. How could you use counting to answer the question in the division example 18 ÷ 6 = *?* ?

5. How could you use addition to answer the question in the example 24 ÷ 8 = *?* ?

6. How could you use multiplication to answer the question in the example 45 ÷ 5 = *?* ?

7. What do you do when there are too few decimal units to divide in the second partial dividend?

8. What does a zero in any decimal place in the quotient tell?

9. When dividing by a two-place divisor, what figure is the trial divisor?

10. What figure in a three-place divisor is the trial divisor?

11. What is the procedure when the first trial quotient is not the first true quotient?

12. How would you multiply mentally: 6 × 59? 9 × 109?

13. What computation steps are used in answering the question asked by each example consisting of the divisor and the partial dividends?

14. How do you check the answer in division?

Test items such as the following may be included on pencil and paper tests.

Part I—Meanings

1. You divide to find (how many in all the equal groups? how many in each equal group? how many more?).

2. If you forget the answer to the example 72 ÷ 9 = ?, you can find it by using the multiplication fact (9 × 8 = 72, 8 × 9 = 72, 10 × 9 = 90).

3. The sign that asks you to divide is (×, +, $\overline{)\quad}$, −).

4. The divisor in a division example notates (the total number or sum, the number of equal groups, the number in each equal group).

5. The number that tells how many in all the equal groups is the (divisor, quotient, dividend).

6. In dividing a four-place number by a one-place number, first divide the (ones, tens, hundreds, thousands).

7. In dividing a three-place number with too few hundreds but enough hundreds and tens together to divide by the divisor (substitute 10 tens for each hundred and add them to the tens, substitute 10 tens for each hundred and add them to the ones, substitute 10 tens for each one).

Part II—Vocabulary

Fill the blanks using one of these words or signs: divisor, dividend, quotient, divide, remainder, trial divisor, partial dividend, ÷, one, two.

1. When you know how many in all the equal groups and how many in one of the equal groups, you ______ to find how many equal groups.

2. The sign read, "divide," is ______ .

3. In a division example with a two-place divisor and three-place dividend, the quotient will be either a ______ -place or a ______ -place number.

4. The figure used in computing the first partial quotient is the trial ______ .

5. The ______ is the part of the dividend left after it has been divided into equal groups.

6. The number that tells how many in all the equal groups is the ______ .

7. The first ______ is a number consisting of the first figures in a four-place divisor equal to or larger than the number notating the divisor.

Part III—Computation

Write the answer to each example below and be ready to explain your thinking.

A.	$\overset{?}{3\overline{)9}}$	$\overset{?}{2\overline{)8}}$	$\overset{?}{4\overline{)7}}$	$\overset{?}{2\overline{)9}}$	$\overset{?}{9\overline{)36}}$	$\overset{?}{7\overline{)42}}$	$\overset{?}{8\overline{)43}}$	$\overset{?}{6\overline{)39}}$
B.	$\overset{?}{2\overline{)80}}$	$\overset{?}{3\overline{)60}}$	$\overset{?}{5\overline{)52}}$	$\overset{?}{4\overline{)83}}$	$\overset{?}{3\overline{)63}}$	$\overset{?}{4\overline{)72}}$	$\overset{?}{2\overline{)67}}$	$\overset{?}{3\overline{)79}}$
C.	$\overset{?}{4\overline{)240}}$	$\overset{?}{8\overline{)592}}$	$\overset{?}{3\overline{)186}}$	$\overset{?}{5\overline{)409}}$	$\overset{?}{3\overline{)600}}$	$\overset{?}{4\overline{)804}}$	$\overset{?}{5\overline{)520}}$	$\overset{?}{7\overline{)770}}$

D.	$\overset{?}{4\overline{)727}}$	$\overset{?}{5\overline{)745}}$	$\overset{?}{6\overline{)3500}}$	$\overset{?}{4\overline{)3750}}$	$\overset{?}{6\overline{)8924}}$	$\overset{?}{9\overline{)78956}}$
E.	$\overset{?}{24\overline{)72}}$	$\overset{?}{14\overline{)29}}$	$\overset{?}{23\overline{)184}}$	$\overset{?}{14\overline{)100}}$	$\overset{?}{20\overline{)800}}$	$\overset{?}{13\overline{)687}}$
F.	$\overset{?}{30\overline{)1260}}$	$\overset{?}{37\overline{)2812}}$	$\overset{?}{23\overline{)4715}}$	$\overset{?}{56\overline{)13609}}$	$\overset{?}{334\overline{)668}}$	$\overset{?}{857\overline{)962758}}$

Summary

Division is a fundamental operation in arithmetic used to find the ratio between two numbers. One of the numbers, the dividend, notates *how many* in all the equal groups. The other number, the divisor, notates *how many* in one of the equal groups. The quotient is a number that tells how many groups notated by the divisor equal the dividend.

The dividend in a division example is like the product, the divisor is like the multiplicand, and the quotient is like the multiplier in the corresponding multiplication example. The quotient in any division example can be computed by using the corresponding multiplication example.

A division example asks a question which, when answered, is the quotient. In the example, $\begin{array}{r} ? \\ 5\overline{)40} \end{array}$, the question is, "How many groups of 5 equal a group of 40?" or "How many 5's = 40?" or "What number × 5 = 40?" or "40 = what number × 5?" The answer to each question is, "8." The quotient is 8. The ratio of 5 to 40 is the same as the ratio of 1 to 8.

In the example $\begin{array}{r} ? \\ 5\overline{)425} \end{array}$, the question may be considered, "What number × 5 ones = 425 ones?" To simplify computation, the dividend may be separated into partial dividends. The first partial dividend must be a number equal to or larger than the divisor so that it can be divided into groups as indicated by the divisor. In the example, $\begin{array}{r} ? \\ 5\overline{)425} \end{array}$, the 4 in the hundreds' place is too small to divide into groups of 5 each. The first partial dividend is 42 tens which asks the question, "What number × 5 ones = 42 tens?" The answer is, "8 tens × 5 ones + a remainder of 2 tens = 42 tens." The second partial dividend is 25 ones, which, when divided by 5 ones = 5. The total quotient, 85, is the sum of the partial quotients 8 tens and 5 ones.

When the divisor is a two-place or larger number, a trial divisor, which is the figure in the divisor that has the largest decimal value, is used in computing the trial quotient. The first figure in the partial dividend if equal to or larger than the trial divisor is divided by the trial divisor to find the first partial quotient. If the first figure in the partial dividend is smaller than the divisor, then 10 of the next smaller decimal units are substituted for each larger unit and are added to the decimal units in that place to make a number large enough to divide. Then one of the basic multiplication facts can be used to find the trial quotient. To discover if the trial quotient is the true quotient, the divisor is multiplied mentally by the trial quotient. If the product of this mental multiplication is larger than the partial dividend, the next smaller number is used as a trial quotient. The process of dividing by the trial divisor and multiplying mentally is repeated until the true quotient figure has been determined.

Division examples follow a specific developmental pattern determined by the complexity of the examples. The learner should be expected to become competent in the use of one-place divisors before being asked to compute with two-place or larger divisors.

SUGGESTED QUESTIONS FOR TEACHER SELF-EVALUATION

1. What is the relationship between counting and division? Between addition and division? Between multiplication and division?

2. What understandings developed in the study of multiplication can be applied to division?

3. What is your interpretation of the mathematical meaning of division?

4. What mathematical and social questions are answered by using division?

5. What meanings should a teacher help pupils understand for: divisor, dividend, quotient, partial dividend, trial divisor, trial quotient, true quotient?

6. Why is it possible to use the multiplication facts in computing the trial quotient?

7. What methods might a teacher use to help children discover and understand the basic division combinations with dividends of less than 10? With dividends of more than 10?

8. What methods would you use to help children discover and understand the use of zero in: (*a*) the divisor, (*b*) the dividend, (*c*) the quotient?

9. What are the developmental levels of division examples?

10. What are the psychological steps and mathematical meanings involved in computing answers to these examples:

$3\overline{)9}$ $2\overline{)7}$ $6\overline{)24}$ $5\overline{)17}$ $30\overline{)90}$ $20\overline{)76}$ $20\overline{)120}$ $45\overline{)95}$

$36\overline{)72}$ $22\overline{)484}$ $32\overline{)450}$ $36\overline{)1702}$ $66\overline{)3059}$

SUGGESTED ACTIVITIES

1. Prepare a *division combination facts chart* that shows the division facts in mathematical sequence.

2. Examine the new textbooks in arithmetic to appraise the meanings and methods that are presented for division.

3. Prepare a summary of mathematical meanings related to division that teachers should understand.

4. Prepare representative diagnostic tests to help determine (*a*) mathematical understandings, (*b*) computational ability, (*c*) vocabulary development.

5. Preview a number of filmstrips or films and evaluate them in terms of how they might be used to help children learn division.

6. Make a collection of number games you might use in helping children memorize division facts.

7. Construct some teaching materials to use in helping you teach division to children.

PRACTICE EXERCISES

Division of whole numbers. (*Note:* All division facts with divisors of 2 to 9 are reviewed in these examples.)

1. $4\overline{)188}$ $2\overline{)596}$ $7\overline{)224}$ $3\overline{)1161}$ $8\overline{)11{,}024}$

2. $4\overline{)3944}$ $2\overline{)1530}$ $6\overline{)15{,}216}$ $7\overline{)6636}$ $7\overline{)112}$ $8\overline{)763{,}696}$

3. $7\overline{)399}$ $3\overline{)1788}$ $3\overline{)1236}$ $9\overline{)47{,}511}$ $5\overline{)129{,}335}$

4. $2\overline{)862}$ $4\overline{)21{,}284}$ $5\overline{)46{,}570}$ $9\overline{)552{,}465}$ $6\overline{)88{,}788}$

5. $32\overline{)96}$ $13\overline{)92}$ $26\overline{)59}$ $39\overline{)312}$ $16\overline{)112}$ $56\overline{)427}$

6. $37\overline{)749}$ $39\overline{)858}$ $65\overline{)738}$ $19\overline{)608}$ $15\overline{)595}$ $74\overline{)5964}$

7. $28\overline{)2726}$ $63\overline{)3119}$ $27\overline{)8100}$ $19\overline{)9135}$ $247\overline{)743}$ $683\overline{)4782}$

8. $219\overline{)8765}$ $645\overline{)19{,}425}$ $209\overline{)5852}$ $375\overline{)18{,}385}$ $124\overline{)29{,}140}$

$732\overline{)319{,}340}$

9. Division in the quinary number system. Find the quotient for each example.

(*a*)	(*b*)	(*c*)	(*d*)	(*e*)
$3\overline{)25}$	$4\overline{)30}$	$4\overline{)203}$	$12\overline{)44}$	$32\overline{)422}$

10. Division in the duodecimal number system. Find the quotient for each example.

(a)	(b)	(c)	(d)	(e)
$4\overline{)64}$	$9\overline{)736}$	$5E\overline{)5E7}$	$TE\overline{)35E}$	$2T\overline{)8E0}$

Problems

1. The school bus has a capacity of 48 pupils. How many trips must be made to take 175 pupils to the picnic grounds?

2. Camping expenses of $37.15 were shared equally by 12 boys. What was each boy's share?

3. Mr. Nelson needs 5 pounds of grass seed for each 1000 square feet of lawn. How many pounds does he need for a lawn 75 feet wide and 125 feet deep?

4. A librarian paid a bill of $310.20 for a shipment of 165 library books. What was the average cost of each book?

5. A man earned $91.65 in a week. If his pay is $2.35 an hour, how many hours had he worked?

6. At an average speed of 225 miles per hour, how long will it take a plane to make a flight of 1150 miles?

7. Mr. Halle paid a gas bill of $29.70 for gas that cost 33¢ a gallon. How many 18-gallon tankfuls of gas did he use?

SELECTED REFERENCES

1. Brueckner, Leo J., and Grossnickle, Foster E., *How to Make Arithmetic Meaningful.* Philadelphia: John C. Winston Company, 1947.

2. Buckingham, B. R., *Elementary Arithmetic, Its Meaning and Practice.* Boston: Ginn & Company, 1947.

3. Christofferson, H. C., "Meaning in Division." *The Arithmetic Teacher*, February, 1957.

4. Clark, John R., and Eads, Laura K., *Guiding Arithmetic Learnings.* Yonkers, N. Y.: World Book Company, 1954.

5. Gunderson, Agnes G., "Teaching Multiplication and Division Facts." *Grade Teacher*, April, 1956.

6. John, Lenore, "The Effect of Using the Long Division Form in Teaching Division of One-Digit Numbers." *Elementary School Journal*, May, 1930.

7. Morton, Robert Lee, *Teaching Children Arithmetic*. Morristown, N. J.: Silver Burdett Company, 1953.

8. Spencer, Peter Lincoln, and Brydegaard, Marguerite, *Building Mathematical Concepts in the Elementary School*. New York: Henry Holt and Company, Inc., 1952.

9. Spitzer, Herbert F., *The Teaching of Arithmetic*, 2d ed. Boston: Houghton Mifflin Company, 1954.

10. Van Engen, Henry, and Gibb, E. Glenadine, *General Mental Functions Associated with Division*. Cedar Falls, Iowa: Iowa State Teachers College, 1956.

7

Meaning and Use of Common Fractions

Introduction

Fraction symbols are commonly used to record or communicate ideas of quantities which result from the separation of the quantity 1 into equal component parts. In a fraction, one number notates the number of equal component parts. The other number notates the number of equal parts under consideration.

A representative fraction, $\frac{3}{4}$, has two terms, a numerator 3 and a denominator 4. The denominator 4 represents the total number of equal parts. The numerator 3 represents the number of equal parts under consideration. The denominator identifies the name of the fraction.

There are other uses of the fraction symbol that will be discussed on later pages in this chapter. The variety of meanings that can be communicated with a fraction symbol often leads to confusion and teachers are faced with a stimulating challenge when helping pupils develop correct ideas of the mathematical meanings of fractions.

Exploratory Questions

Teachers may find it helpful to appraise their understanding of the mathematical meanings of and computational operations with fractions. When reading the chapter decide upon the answers to help pupils to discover and understand each of the following questions.

1. What is the mathematical meaning or meanings which may be identified by a fraction symbol?

2. In what ways may a fraction be interpreted as a number?

3. What are the different mathematical meanings that a fractional symbol (a fraction) notates or identifies?

4. What meanings should teachers help pupils to learn for: (*a*) a proper fraction? (*b*) an improper fraction? (*c*) a mixed number? (*d*) a complex fraction?

5. What are the operational meanings pupils should understand:
   (*a*) When substituting a fraction for another fraction with higher terms?
   (*b*) When substituting a fraction for another fraction with lower terms?
   (*c*) When substituting a fraction for an integer?

6. Recall your study of the computational processes with fractions. What meanings can you help pupils to learn about:
   (*a*) Addition and subtraction of fractions?
   (*b*) Multiplication of fractions?
   (*c*) Division of fractions?

7. What meanings related to integers also apply to common fractions?

8. Why is the use of the like-fraction unit method in division of fractions more meaningful than the inversion method?

9. How may fractional units be illustrated on a number line?

10. How are fractions used in personal and business situations?

11. What are the important mathematical generalizations about common fractions that teachers should help pupils to develop from their study of and work with fractions?

Definition of Fractions

Fractions are mathematical symbols that may notate or may identify several specific or quantitative meanings. The meaning expressed by a common fraction depends on the situation in which the fraction is used.

A fraction may be thought of as a number when it notates or expresses:

1. A fractional unit that is less than one ($\frac{1}{4}$ ft, $\frac{2}{3}$ yd).
2. Fractional units that are more than one ($\frac{5}{4}$ ft, $\frac{8}{3}$ mile).
3. One or more units of a given number of units ($\frac{3}{5}$ of a bag of 5 marbles).
4. Incompleted division ($5\overline{)7} = 1\frac{2}{7}$).

A fraction may be used to express or to notate relationship between two numbers.

$$\frac{\$12}{\$24} \qquad \frac{36 \text{ ft}}{9 \text{ ft}} \qquad \frac{42}{84} \qquad \frac{5}{3} \qquad \frac{1}{2} \qquad \frac{2}{1}$$

An abstract fraction, $\frac{5}{6}$, identifies the relationship between the numerator 5 and the denominator 6.

Fractions as Related to Integers

The concept of a fraction to notate a number may be discovered by using a number line.

Integers

1 notates a unit of length from 0 to 1.

2 notates two units of length of the size 1 or 2 ones.

3 notates three units of length each equal in length to the length of 1.

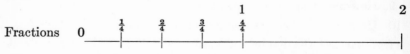

Fractions

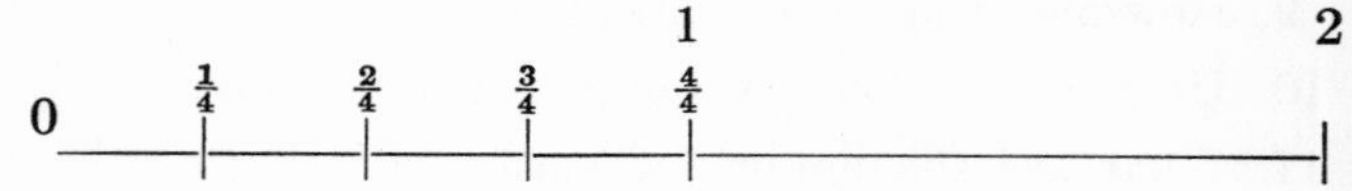

$\frac{1}{4}$ notates a unit of length that is equal to $\frac{1}{4}$ of the unit 1.

$\frac{2}{4}$ notates two units of length, each is equal to $\frac{1}{4}$ of the unit 1.

$\frac{4}{4}$ notates four units of length that are equivalent in length to the unit 1.

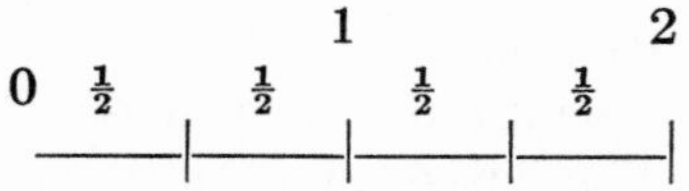

$\frac{1}{2}$ notates a unit of length that is equal to $\frac{1}{2}$ of the unit 1.

$\frac{3}{2}$ notates three units of length, each is equal to $\frac{1}{2}$ of the unit 1 and together are equivalent to $1\frac{1}{2}$ or $\frac{3}{2}$ of the unit 1.

The number lines illustrate the meaning of the term "broken numbers" or common fractions.

Kind or Form of a Fraction

Proper Fraction

A fraction with a numerator that is smaller than the denominator is called a proper fraction ($\frac{1}{2}$, $\frac{2}{3}$, $\frac{3}{4}$, $\frac{5}{6}$). It shows that the fraction unit or units are less than 1.

$\frac{1}{2}$ shows that an object or a number has been divided or thought to be divided into two even divisions and that one of the two equal-sized fractional units is being considered.

$\frac{3}{4}$ shows that an object or a number has been divided or thought to be divided into four equal divisions and that three of the four equal-sized fractional units are being considered.

Improper Fraction

A fraction with a numerator equal to or larger than the denominator is called an improper fraction ($\frac{2}{2}$, $\frac{7}{4}$, $\frac{8}{3}$). It shows that the number of fractional units notated by the numerator are equal to one or more than one.

$\frac{2}{2}$ is equivalent to 1.

$\frac{7}{4}$ is equivalent to $\frac{4}{4} + \frac{3}{4}$ or 1 and $\frac{3}{4}$ or $1\frac{3}{4}$.

$\frac{8}{3}$ is equivalent to $\frac{3}{3} + \frac{3}{3} + \frac{2}{3}$ or $1 + 1 + \frac{2}{3}$ or $2\frac{2}{3}$.

Any integer when written with the denominator 1 becomes an improper fraction.

4 is equivalent to $\frac{4}{1}$. 8 is equivalent to $\frac{8}{1}$.

An improper fraction notates fractional units equivalent to one undivided unit or to more than one undivided unit.

$\frac{5}{2}$ equals $\frac{2}{2} + \frac{2}{2} + \frac{1}{2}$ or $1 + 1 + \frac{1}{2}$ or $2\frac{1}{2}$

Complex Fraction

A fraction that is written to show that the denominator is a fraction and the numerator is a fraction is called a complex fraction $\frac{\frac{3}{4}}{\frac{1}{2}}$.

A fraction that is written to show that the denominator is an integer and the numerator is a fraction is called a complex fraction $\frac{\frac{5}{2}}{4}$.

A fraction that is written to show that the denominator is a fraction and the numerator is an integer is called a complex fraction $\frac{4}{\frac{1}{2}}$.

A Fraction May Notate One or More Fractional Units Less Than One

$\frac{3}{4}$ ft $\frac{2}{3}$ yd $\frac{3}{8}$ lb $\frac{5}{6}$

The fraction $\frac{3}{4}$ ft shows that 1 foot was divided into 4 even divisions, which changed the 1 foot into four equal-length fractional units and that three of the fractional units are being considered.

1 ft to $\frac{1}{4}$ $\frac{1}{4}$ $\frac{1}{4}$ $\frac{1}{4}$

$\frac{3}{4}$

The fraction $\frac{2}{3}$ yard shows that 1 yard was divided into 3 even divisions which changed the 1 yard into 3 even-length fractional units, and that two of the fractional units are being considered.

1 yd to $\frac{1}{3}$ $\frac{1}{3}$ $\frac{1}{3}$

$\frac{2}{3}$ yd

The fraction $\frac{3}{8}$ pound shows that 1 pound has been divided into eight even divisions or may be thought of as having been divided into eight even divisions, and three of the fractional units—each 2 ounces in weight—are being considered.

The fraction $\frac{5}{6}$ is abstract. It shows that the unit one has been divided or may be divided into six even divisions and that five of the new fractional units are being considered.

Mathematical meanings to be learned are:

1. The denominator of a fraction may show the number of even divisions any object or number has been divided into or thought to have been changed into.

2. The numerator of a fraction may show the number of fractional units that are being considered.

3. An abstract fraction may show the number of even divisions and the number of fractional units of one undivided unit or number.

A Fraction May Show Incomplete Division

(*a*) (*b*)

$$5\overline{)7} \quad \text{or} \quad \begin{array}{r} 1\frac{2}{5} \\ 5\overline{)7} \\ \underline{5} \\ 2 \end{array} \qquad\qquad \begin{array}{r} 14\frac{2}{34} \\ 34\overline{)478} \\ \underline{34} \\ 138 \\ \underline{136} \\ 2 \end{array}$$

The fraction $\frac{2}{5}$ in the quotient shows incompleted division. The remainder, 2, is equal to two units of another group of five units as notated by the divisor.

The fraction $\frac{2}{34}$ in the quotient of example (*b*) notates incompleted division. The remainder 2 is $\frac{2}{34}$ of another 34 (divisor). If the division were completed, then the quotient would be a whole number and a decimal fraction.

A Fraction May Notate or Show Relationship Between Two Numbers

When a fraction expresses relationship it shows the relation or ratio between the numerator and denominator. The fraction may be a proper fraction or an improper fraction.

$\frac{3}{4}$ is interpreted as 3 out of 4.
$\frac{7}{12}$ is interpreted as 7 out of 12.
$\frac{9}{3}$ is interpreted as 9 to 3.

Summary

A fraction is a number.

A fraction as a number may notate a fractional unit or units.

A fraction as a number may notate one or more units of a given number of equal units.

A fraction may show relationship between the two numbers.

Equivalent Fractions or Changing the Terms of a Fraction

A. Changing a Fraction to Higher Terms

$\frac{1}{2}$ is equivalent to $\frac{2}{4}$.

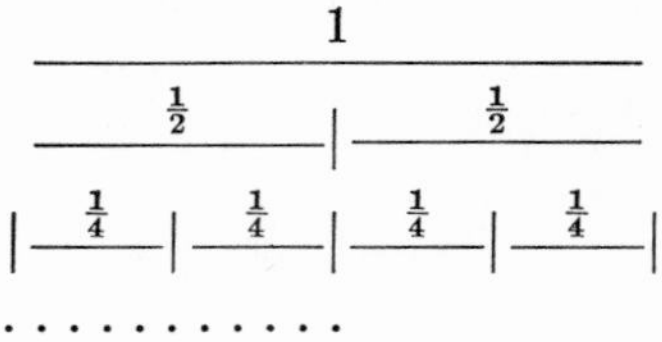

$\frac{1}{2}$ shows that an undivided unit—a line segment—was divided into two even divisions and that one of the even fractional units is being considered 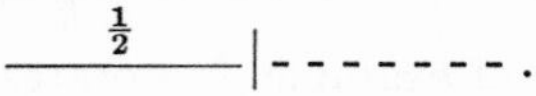

$\frac{2}{4}$ shows that the undivided unit—a line of the same length—was divided into four even divisions and that two of the even fractional units are being considered. Each fractional unit is one-half as large as the fractional unit notated by $\frac{1}{2}$.

$\frac{3}{4}$ of a rectangle is equivalent to $\frac{6}{8}$ of another rectangle of equal size.

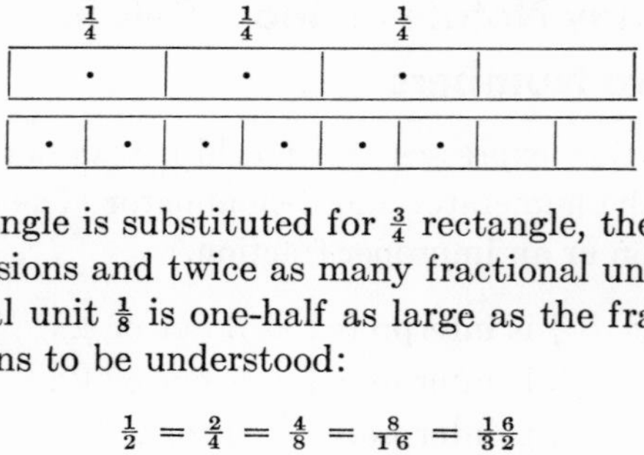

When $\frac{6}{8}$ rectangle is substituted for $\frac{3}{4}$ rectangle, there are twice as many even divisions and twice as many fractional units.

The fractional unit $\frac{1}{8}$ is one-half as large as the fractional unit $\frac{1}{4}$.

Generalizations to be understood:

$$\frac{1}{2} = \frac{2}{4} = \frac{4}{8} = \frac{8}{16} = \frac{16}{32}$$

$$\frac{3}{4} = \frac{6}{8} = \frac{12}{16} = \frac{24}{32}$$

$$\frac{2}{3} = \frac{4}{6} = \frac{6}{9} = \frac{12}{18} = \frac{24}{36}$$

$$\frac{5}{8} = \frac{10}{16} = \frac{15}{24} = \frac{30}{48}$$

(*a*) When notating the equivalent for any fraction, the equivalent fraction will show twice, three, four, and so forth, as many even divisions, and the fractional units will be one-half or one-third, or one-fourth, etc. as small.

$\frac{1}{2} = \frac{2}{4}$ $\qquad$ $\frac{2}{3} = \frac{6}{9}$ $\qquad$ $\frac{3}{8} = \frac{12}{32}$

(*b*) The generalized rule applied to notating the equivalent for any fraction is "Multiply the denominator and the numerator by the same number."

$$\frac{1}{2} = \frac{2 \times 1}{2 \times 2} \text{ or } \frac{2}{4} \qquad \frac{2}{3} = \frac{3 \times 2}{3 \times 3} \text{ or } \frac{6}{9} \qquad \frac{3}{8} = \frac{4 \times 3}{4 \times 8} \text{ or } \frac{12}{32}$$

(*c*) The mathematical principle derived is, "Multiplying the denominator and numerator of any given fraction by the same number does not change the value of the given fraction."

Write the equivalents for these fractions:

$$\frac{1}{2},\ \frac{1}{4},\ \frac{3}{4},\ \frac{1}{3},\ \frac{2}{3},\ \frac{1}{8},\ \frac{3}{8},\ \frac{1}{6},\ \frac{5}{6},\ \frac{3}{10},\ \frac{7}{9}$$

B. Changing a Fraction to Lower Terms

$\frac{2}{4}$ reduced to $\frac{1}{2}$

$\frac{6}{8}$ reduced to $\frac{3}{4}$

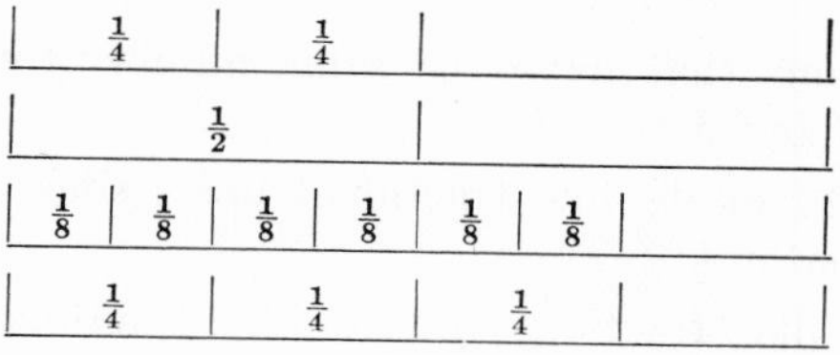

The fraction $\frac{2}{4}$ shows that an undivided unit—a line segment—was divided into four even divisions and that two of the even fractional units are being considered or notated 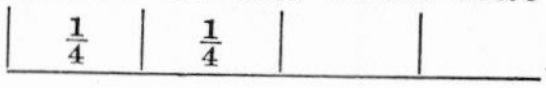.

When the equivalent $\frac{1}{2}$ is substituted for $\frac{2}{4}$, it shows that a line of the same length was divided into two even divisions and that one of the even fractional units is being considered or is notated.

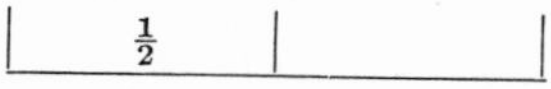

The fraction $\frac{1}{2}$ shows that one-half of the line is equal in length to $\frac{2}{4}$ of the same or similar line.

When $\frac{6}{8}$ is reduced to $\frac{3}{4}$, there are one-half as many fractional units and each is twice as large.

$$\frac{8}{16} = \frac{4}{8} = \frac{2}{4} = \frac{1}{2}$$

$$\frac{18}{24} = \frac{9}{12} = \frac{3}{4}$$

$$\frac{24}{36} = \frac{12}{18} = \frac{6}{9} = \frac{4}{6} = \frac{2}{3}$$

$$\frac{15}{24} = \frac{5}{8}$$

Generalizations to be understood regarding reduction (changing a fraction to lower terms):

1. When reducing a fraction to lower terms, the denominator will show fewer even divisions and the numerator will show fewer but larger fractional units.

2. The generalized rule applied to the notating of a fraction reduced to lower terms is "Divide the denominator and the numerator by the same number."

3. The mathematical principle derived is, "Dividing the denominator and numerator of any given fraction by the same number does not change the value of the given fraction."

Like Fractions

Fractions that have the same number for the denominator are called "like fractions."

$\frac{1}{4}$, $\frac{3}{4}$, $\frac{5}{4}$ notate like fractional units since they have the similar denominator 4.

Since like fractions notate like fractional units, the concepts learned in adding integers apply to adding like fractions.

$$\frac{1}{4} + \frac{3}{4} + \frac{5}{4} = \frac{9}{4} \text{ or } 2\frac{1}{4}$$

Similarly, the concepts learned about subtracting, multiplying, and dividing integers apply to subtracting, multiplying, and dividing like fractions.

$$\frac{5}{8} - \frac{3}{8} = \frac{5-3}{8} \text{ or } \frac{2}{8} \text{ or } \frac{1}{4}$$

$$3 \times \frac{2}{3} = \frac{3 \times 2}{3} \text{ or } \frac{6}{3} \text{ or } 2$$

$$\frac{3}{4} \div \frac{1}{4} = 3 \div 1 \text{ or } 3$$

Generalizations to be understood:

1. Like fractions are fractions that have like denominators.

2. Addition, subtraction, multiplication, and division of like fractions employ the principles that apply to addition, subtraction, multiplication, and division of integers.

Unlike Fractions

Fractions that have unlike numbers for the denominator are called unlike fractions.

Such fractions as $\frac{2}{3}$, $\frac{3}{4}$, $\frac{5}{6}$ are unlike fractions because they do not have the same number for the denominator. Therefore, these fractions must be written as like fractions before they can be added, subtracted, multiplied, or divided.

Like fractions may be substituted for unlike fractions by finding a number that will be a like or common denominator for each fraction.

$\frac{1}{2}$ and $\frac{2}{3}$ and $\frac{3}{4}$ are unlike fractions. The common denominator needed to express these fractions as like fractions is 12.

$\frac{1}{2}$ is equivalent to $\frac{6}{12}$, $\frac{2}{3}$ is equivalent to $\frac{8}{12}$, $\frac{3}{4}$ is equivalent to $\frac{9}{12}$.

Then the like fractions $\frac{6}{12}$, $\frac{8}{12}$, $\frac{9}{12}$ are substituted for the unlike fractions—$\frac{1}{2}$, $\frac{2}{3}$, $\frac{3}{4}$.

Find the common denominator that makes it possible to substitute like fractions for the unlike fractions:

(*a*) $\frac{2}{3}$, $\frac{5}{6}$, $\frac{7}{12}$
(*b*) $\frac{1}{2}$, $\frac{2}{3}$, $\frac{3}{8}$, $\frac{5}{16}$
(*c*) $\frac{2}{3}$, $\frac{3}{4}$, $\frac{5}{6}$, $\frac{3}{8}$

Generalizations to be understood:

1. Unlike fractions may be notated as like fractions by finding a number that will be a denominator common to the fractions.

2. When unlike fractions have been notated as like fractions, they notate like fractional units.

3. When unlike fractions have been changed to like fractions, then they may be added, subtracted, multiplied, or divided as integers.

DIAGNOSTIC OR REVIEW QUESTIONS

1. Why may a fraction be interpreted as a number?
2. What are the different meanings a fraction may identify?
3. What does the denominator of a fraction show?
4. What does the numerator of a fraction identify?
5. How is the measurement size of a fraction unit to be found?
6. How may a fraction show relationship between two numbers?

7. What is the difference in meaning between like fractions and unlike fractions?

8. What is the meaning of a proper fraction? Of an improper fraction? Of a complex fraction? Of a mixed number?

9. What is the meaning of a fraction equivalent for a fraction?

10. What meanings are related to the process of substituting a fraction for a fraction with higher terms? Of reducing fractions to lower terms?

11. Why do the principles related to the four fundamental operations with whole numbers apply to like fractions?

12. What meanings are involved in changing unlike fractions to like fractions?

13. What is the meaning and function of a common denominator when changing unlike fractions to like fractions?

14. What is the meaning of equivalent fractions?

EXERCISES

1. Draw a number line and show the meaning of $\frac{1}{2}$, $\frac{3}{4}$, $\frac{5}{8}$.

2. Put an *X* in $\frac{3}{4}$ of the circles.

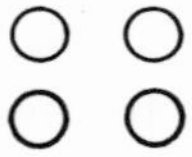

3. Draw a rectangle and shade $\frac{5}{8}$ of it.

4. Draw and mark lines to show that $\frac{6}{8}$ is equivalent to $\frac{3}{4}$.

5. Change to improper fractions $2\frac{1}{2}$, $8\frac{3}{4}$, $12\frac{5}{6}$, $24\frac{2}{3}$.

Addition of Fractions with a Sum Under One

(*a*)	(*b*)	(*c*)	(*d*)	(*e*)	(*f*)
$\frac{1}{4}$	$\frac{1}{3}$	$\frac{3}{5}$	$\frac{1}{6}$	$\frac{2}{8}$	$\frac{5}{12}$
$+\frac{1}{4}$	$+\frac{1}{3}$	$+\frac{1}{5}$	$\frac{2}{6}$	$\frac{3}{8}$	$\frac{1}{12}$
			$+\frac{2}{6}$	$+\frac{2}{8}$	$+\frac{3}{12}$
$\frac{2}{4}$ or $\frac{1}{2}$	$\frac{2}{3}$	$\frac{4}{5}$	$\frac{5}{6}$	$\frac{7}{8}$	$\frac{9}{12}$ or $\frac{3}{4}$

The fractions in (*a*) are like since they have a common denominator, 4. The numerators 1 and 1 are combined or added to give 2 for the numerator in the sum.

The fractions in (*b*) are like since the common denominator is 3. The sum of the numerators is 2 and the answer to the example is $\frac{2}{3}$.

A similar thought process is used to find the sum for examples (*c*), (*d*), (*e*), and (*f*).

The numerators or numbers identifying fractional units, in each example were thought to be combined into one group and the sum or total of the numerators was written over the like denominator.

In example (*a*) the sum $\frac{2}{4}$ may be written in lower terms, $\frac{1}{2}$, and in example (*f*) the sum $\frac{9}{12}$ may be notated as $\frac{3}{4}$, to show lowest terms.

Generalized Rule

When adding fractions with like or common denominators find the sum of the numerators and write it over the common denominator. (If the sum may be changed to lower terms, then notate the sum in the lowest terms.)

EXERCISE

Find the sum to these examples (remember to reduce to lowest terms).

(*a*)	(*b*)	(*c*)	(*d*)	(*e*)	(*f*)	(*g*)	(*h*)	(*i*)
$\frac{1}{3}$	$\frac{1}{4}$	$\frac{2}{5}$	$\frac{2}{6}$	$\frac{2}{6}$	$\frac{3}{8}$	$\frac{2}{8}$	$\frac{5}{12}$	$\frac{3}{16}$
$+\frac{1}{3}$	$\frac{1}{4}$	$+\frac{3}{5}$	$+\frac{2}{6}$	$\frac{1}{6}$	$+\frac{5}{8}$	$\frac{1}{8}$	$+\frac{3}{12}$	$\frac{5}{16}$
	$+\frac{1}{4}$			$+\frac{1}{6}$		$+\frac{3}{8}$		$+\frac{4}{16}$

Addition of Like Fractions with Sum One or Larger

(*a*)	(*b*)	(*c*)
$\frac{1}{2}$	$\frac{3}{4}$	$\frac{3}{6}$
$\frac{1}{2}$	$\frac{2}{4}$	$\frac{4}{6}$
		$\frac{2}{6}$
$\frac{2}{2}$ or 1	$\frac{5}{4}$ or $\frac{4}{4} + \frac{1}{4}$ or $1\frac{1}{4}$	$\frac{9}{6}$ or $\frac{6}{6} + \frac{3}{6}$ or $1\frac{3}{6}$ or $1\frac{1}{2}$

The example (*a*) may be illustrated by drawing rectangles (length, 4 inches)

$$\boxed{\tfrac{1}{2}} + \boxed{\tfrac{1}{2}} = \boxed{\tfrac{1}{2} \mid \tfrac{1}{2}} = \boxed{\quad 1 \quad}$$

2 in. 2 in. 2 in. 2 in. 4 in.

The example (b), $\frac{3}{4} + \frac{2}{4}$, may be illustrated by drawing rectangles.

$$(\boxed{\frac{1}{4}} + \boxed{\frac{1}{4}} + \boxed{\frac{1}{4}}) + (\boxed{\frac{1}{4} \quad \frac{1}{4}}) =$$

2 in. 2 in. 2 in. 2 in. 2 in.

$$\boxed{\frac{1}{4} \mid \frac{1}{4} \mid \frac{1}{4} \mid \frac{1}{4} \mid \frac{1}{4}} = \boxed{\qquad 1 \qquad} + \boxed{\frac{1}{4}}$$

2 in. 2 in. 2 in. 2 in. 2 in. 8 in. 2 in.

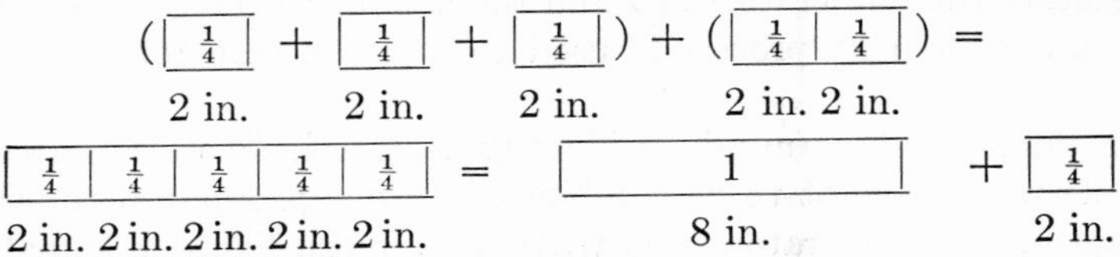

Construct rectangles to illustrate the thought process in finding the answer to example (c), $\frac{3}{6} + \frac{4}{6} + \frac{2}{6}$.

Generalized Rule

When adding like fractions when the sum is one or larger, add the numerator and notate the sum of the numerators over the common denominator. Then reduce the sum to an integer or to an integer and a fraction. (Notate the sum in the equivalent lowest terms.)

EXERCISE

Add these fractions. Change to lowest terms.

(a)	(b)	(c)	(d)	(e)	(f)
$\frac{3}{4}$	$\frac{3}{5}$	$\frac{2}{3}$	$\frac{3}{4}$	$\frac{5}{8}$	$\frac{5}{12}$
$\frac{3}{4}$	$\frac{2}{5}$	$\frac{1}{3}$	$\frac{1}{4}$	$\frac{3}{8}$	$\frac{3}{12}$
$+\frac{2}{4}$	$+\frac{4}{5}$	$+\frac{2}{3}$	$\frac{2}{4}$	$\frac{1}{8}$	$\frac{1}{12}$
			$+\frac{3}{4}$	$+\frac{3}{8}$	$\frac{7}{12}$
					$+\frac{4}{12}$

(g) 6 one-thirds + 5 one-thirds + 7 one-thirds = ?

(h) 5 one-fourths + 3 one-fourths + 6 one-fourths = ?

Addition of Unlike Fractions

Fractions with denominators that are not similar are called unlike fractions. The denominators show that the fractional units are unlike parts of 1 or a group of 1's.

$$
\begin{array}{c}
\frac{1}{2} \\
+\frac{1}{4} \\
\hline
\end{array}
\quad
\boxed{\qquad 1 \qquad}
\boxed{\frac{1}{2} \quad \vdots}
\boxed{\frac{1}{4} \quad \vdots}
$$

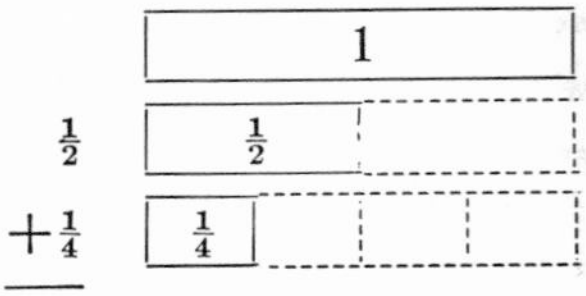

In addition of fractions as in addition of integers, only numbers showing units of similar value can be added. Therefore, to add unlike fractions, the first step to be taken is to find a denominator that is common or can be used for each fraction.

$\frac{3}{4} + \frac{1}{8} = ?$ or $\frac{6}{8} + \frac{1}{8} = ?$ $\frac{6}{8} + \frac{1}{8} = \frac{7}{8}$

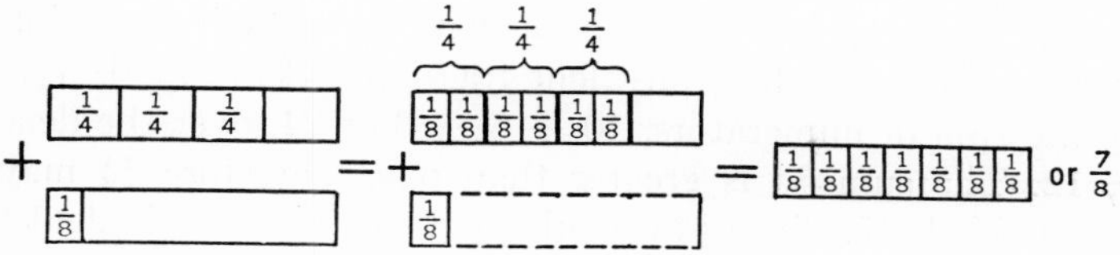

The thought process in finding the sum for the example $\frac{2}{3} + \frac{3}{4} = ?$ can be illustrated by rectangles (the length of rectangle is 12 in.).

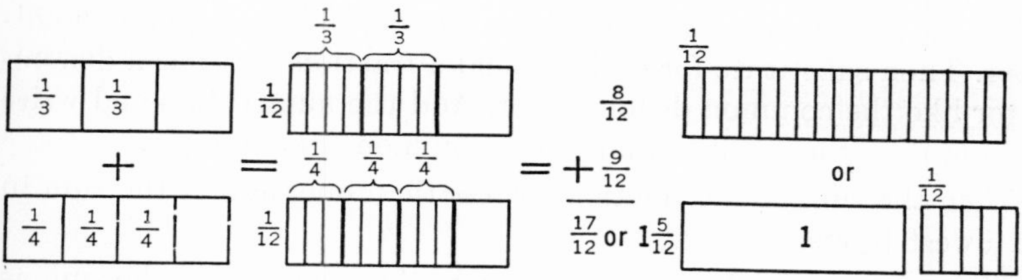

In the fractions $\frac{2}{3}$ and $\frac{3}{4}$ neither thirds nor fourths is a common denominator. Since a fraction may be substituted for a fraction with higher terms, the first step is to find a number that can be divided evenly by 3 and 4. The number is 12. Therefore the common denominator is 12. The fraction $\frac{2}{3}$ may be notated as $\frac{8}{12}$ and the fraction $\frac{3}{4}$ may be notated as $\frac{9}{12}$. The numerators may be added since the denominators are like. (The common denominator, twelfths, shows that the fractional units are alike or similar in size.)

Addition of Unlike Fractions—Sum Under One or Over One

(a)

$$\begin{array}{r} \frac{2}{5} \\ +\frac{1}{2} \\ \hline \end{array} \quad \text{or} \quad \begin{array}{r} \frac{4}{10} \\ +\frac{5}{10} \\ \hline ? \end{array} \quad \begin{array}{r} \frac{4}{10} \\ \frac{5}{10} \\ \hline \frac{9}{10} \end{array}$$

(b)

$$\begin{array}{r} \frac{5}{6} \\ \frac{2}{3} \\ +\frac{1}{2} \\ \hline \end{array} \quad \begin{array}{c} \\ \text{or} \\ \text{or} \\ \\ \end{array} \quad \begin{array}{r} \frac{10}{12} \\ \frac{8}{12} \\ +\frac{6}{12} \\ \hline ? \end{array} \quad \begin{array}{r} \frac{10}{12} \\ \frac{8}{12} \\ \frac{6}{12} \\ \hline \frac{24}{12} \text{ or } \frac{12}{12} + \frac{12}{12} \text{ or } 2 \end{array}$$

When finding the sum of the fractions in example (*a*), $\frac{2}{5} + \frac{1}{2}$, the first step is to notate the fractions with a common denominator; then find the sum of the equivalent fraction, $\frac{4}{10} + \frac{5}{10}$ and write the sum of the numerator 9 over the denominator 10. The sum is $\frac{9}{10}$. The sum is notated in lowest terms.

When finding the sum of the fractions in example (*b*), $\frac{5}{6} + \frac{2}{3} + \frac{1}{2}$, the first step is to notate the fractions with a common denominator; then find the sum of the equivalent fractions, $\frac{10}{12} + \frac{8}{12} + \frac{6}{12}$, and notate the sum of numerators, 10 + 8 + 6 or 24, over the denominator, 12. The sum $\frac{24}{12}$ is greater than one. Therefore $\frac{24}{12}$ may be thought as $\frac{12}{12} + \frac{12}{12}$. Since $\frac{12}{12}$ is equivalent to 1, $\frac{24}{12}$ is equivalent to 2. (The sum $\frac{24}{12}$ has been reduced to lowest terms.)

Generalized Rule

To find the sum of unlike fractions, first find the common denominator. Then substitute for each addend a fraction that has a denominator like the common denominator. Add the numerators and write the sum over the number that is the common denominator.

When the sum of the fractions is less than one, notate the sum in the lowest terms.

When the sum of the fractions is more than one notate the sum as a mixed number. (Change the fraction in the mixed number to lowest terms.)

EXERCISE

Add these examples. Notate the sum in lowest terms:

(*a*) $\frac{3}{4} + \frac{5}{6} + \frac{2}{3} = ?$ (*d*) $\frac{2}{3} + \frac{5}{6} + \frac{7}{8} + \frac{5}{12} = ?$

(*b*) $\frac{1}{2} + \frac{3}{4} + \frac{7}{8} = ?$ (*e*) $\frac{3}{5} + \frac{3}{4} + \frac{7}{10} = ?$

(*c*) $\frac{4}{6} + \frac{5}{8} + \frac{3}{4} = ?$ (*f*) $\frac{3}{7} + \frac{3}{5} + \frac{5}{7} = ?$

Addition of Mixed Numbers

Mixed numbers identify an integer and a fraction. The meanings and computation processes related to addition of integers and fractions apply to the addition of mixed numbers.

(*a*)	(*b*)		(*c*)	
$24\frac{1}{3}$	$36\frac{1}{2}$	or $36\frac{2}{4}$	$46\frac{3}{4}$	or $46\frac{9}{12}$
$+32\frac{1}{3}$	$+48\frac{1}{4}$	$48\frac{1}{4}$	$+34\frac{5}{6}$	$+34\frac{10}{12}$
$56\frac{2}{3}$	?	$84\frac{3}{4}$	?	$80\frac{19}{12}$ or 80+ $1\frac{7}{12}$ or $81\frac{7}{12}$

Generalized Rule

When adding mixed numbers, the fractions are added first and notated in the lowest terms. Then the integers are added.

When the fractions in mixed numbers are unlike, the first step is to find the common denominator and then write the equivalent for the fractions. Add the numerators of the like fractions and notate the sum in the lowest terms. Add the integers and to the sum add any integers where the sum of the fraction has been notated as an integer and a fraction.

EXERCISE

Find the sum of these examples. Explain the meaning involved in each step of computation.

(*a*)	(*b*)	(*c*)	(*d*)	(*e*)
$3\frac{1}{4}$	$12\frac{3}{4}$	$36\frac{5}{8}$	$87\frac{2}{3}$	$240\frac{2}{3}$
$+2\frac{1}{4}$	$+24\frac{3}{4}$	$+28\frac{3}{4}$	$+40\frac{2}{3}$	$475\frac{3}{4}$
				$+287\frac{5}{6}$

(*f*) $46\frac{2}{5} + 24\frac{3}{4} + 8\frac{7}{10} = ?$

(*g*) $106\frac{2}{3} + 76\frac{3}{4} + 270\frac{5}{8} = ?$

(*h*) $37\frac{1}{2} + 14\frac{3}{4} + 9\frac{2}{3} + 24\frac{3}{8} = ?$

(*i*) 46 one-eighths + 56 one-fourths + 36 one-sixths = ?

(*j*) 30 one-thirds + 40 one-ninths + 304 one-eighteenths = ?

Subtraction of Fractions

Subtraction of fractions involves meanings and computation processes similar to the subtraction of integers. Subtraction is the process used to find the difference between two notated fractions, between an integer and a fraction, or between two mixed numbers.

In a concrete situation, subtraction may be interpreted as the measurement process used to find what fraction is left after a fractional part has been removed from a quantity. What is left when $\frac{2}{3}$ of a yard of ribbon has been removed from 1 yard of ribbon? This is the "take-away" or "remove a part" application of subtraction.

When the minuend and the subtrahend are notated or known then subtraction is the process used to answer, "What is the difference between two fractions?" or "How much larger is one fraction than another fraction?"

The meanings and principles related to finding the difference between two integers can be applied to finding the difference between two fractions.

	T	O					
	7	8	ft	52 yd	$\frac{7}{8}$ lb	$42\frac{1}{4}$ miles	$41\frac{5}{4}$
−	5	4	ft	−27 yd	$-\frac{6}{8}$ lb	$-28\frac{1}{2}$ miles or	$-28\frac{2}{4}$
	2	4	ft	25 yd	$\frac{1}{8}$ lb	?	$13\frac{3}{4}$

Subtraction of Like Fractions

Fractions with the same number for the denominator identify like fractional units. They are called "like fractions." The minus sign in the subtraction example asks, "What is the difference between the numerators of the fractions?"

(*a*)

$$\begin{array}{r} \frac{7}{8}\text{ lb} \\ -\frac{4}{8}\text{ lb} \\ \hline ?\text{ lb} \end{array} \quad \text{or} \quad \begin{array}{r} \frac{7}{8}\text{ lb} \\ -\frac{4}{8}\text{ lb} \\ \hline \frac{3}{8}\text{ lb} \end{array} \quad \text{or} \quad \begin{array}{r} 7\text{ one-eighths of lb} \\ -4\text{ one-eighths of lb} \\ \hline 3\text{ one-eighths of lb} \end{array}$$

(*b*)

$$\begin{array}{r} \frac{3}{4}\text{ ft} \\ -\frac{2}{4}\text{ ft} \\ \hline ? \end{array} \quad \text{or} \quad \begin{array}{r} \frac{3}{4}\text{ ft} \\ -\frac{2}{4}\text{ ft} \\ \hline \frac{1}{4}\text{ ft} \end{array} \quad \text{or} \quad \begin{array}{r} 3\text{ one-fourths of 1 ft} \\ -2\text{ one-fourths of 1 ft} \\ \hline 1\text{ one-fourth of 1 ft} \end{array}$$

In example (*a*) the question asked is, "What is the difference between the fraction $\frac{7}{8}$ pound and $\frac{4}{8}$ pound?" The fractions have the same denominator, thus the question may be answered by finding the difference between the numerators ($\frac{7}{8}$ lb $-$ $\frac{4}{8}$ lb $=$ $\frac{3}{8}$ lb).

In example (*b*) the question asked is, "What is the difference between $\frac{3}{4}$ feet and $\frac{2}{4}$ feet?" The difference is $\frac{1}{4}$ foot.

Generalized Rule

To find the difference between two like fractions, find the difference between the numerators.

EXERCISES

Subtract these fractions.

(a)	(b)	(c)	(d)	(e)
$\frac{5}{6}$ yd	$\frac{7}{8}$ lb	$\frac{7}{12}$ ft	$\frac{2}{3}$ yd	$\frac{9}{10}$ mile
$-\frac{4}{6}$ yd	$-\frac{4}{8}$ lb	$-\frac{2}{12}$ ft	$-\frac{1}{3}$ yd	$-\frac{7}{10}$ mile
? yd	? lb	? ft	? yd	? mile

(f)	(g)	(h)	(i)	(j)
$\frac{5}{6}$ doz	$\frac{7}{8}$ lb	$\frac{7}{12}$ ft	$\frac{3}{4}$ in	$\frac{9}{10}$ mile
$-\frac{1}{6}$ doz	$-\frac{3}{8}$ lb	$-\frac{5}{12}$ ft	$-\frac{1}{4}$ in	$-\frac{5}{10}$ mile
? doz	? lb	? ft	? in	? mile

Subtraction of Unlike Fractions

Unlike fractions are fractions with a different denominator ($\frac{3}{4}$, $\frac{1}{2}$, $\frac{5}{6}$).

The meanings and principles that apply to addition of unlike fractions may be applied to finding the difference between two unlike fractions.

The first step to be taken or thought of is to find a denominator that is common to the minuend and the subtrahend.

$$\frac{3}{4} - \frac{1}{2} \text{ or } \frac{3}{4} - \frac{2}{4} = ? \qquad \frac{7}{8} - \frac{3}{4} \text{ or } \frac{7}{8} - \frac{6}{8} = ?$$

When fractions with a common denominator have been substituted, the question to answer is, "What is the difference between the minuend and subtrahend?" or "What is the difference between the numerators?"

$\frac{2}{3}$ yd	$\frac{4}{6}$ yd	$\frac{4}{6}$ yd	$\frac{5}{8}$ lb	$\frac{5}{8}$ lb	$\frac{5}{8}$ lb
$-\frac{1}{6}$ yd or	$-\frac{1}{6}$ yd or	$-\frac{1}{6}$ yd	$-\frac{1}{2}$ lb or	$-\frac{4}{8}$ lb or	$-\frac{4}{8}$ lb
?	?	$\frac{3}{6}$ yd or $\frac{1}{2}$ yd	?	?	$\frac{1}{8}$ lb

The difference between $\frac{4}{6}$ yd and $\frac{1}{6}$ yd is $\frac{3}{6}$ yd or $\frac{1}{2}$ yd.

The difference between $\frac{5}{8}$ lb and $\frac{1}{2}$ lb is $\frac{1}{8}$ lb.

Generalized Rule

To find the difference between two unlike fractions, first write the equivalents of the two fractions so that the fractions have the same number as the denominator. Then subtract the numerators.

EXERCISE

Find the answer to these examples. Notate the answer in lowest terms.

(a)	(b)	(c)	(d)	(e)
$\frac{3}{4}$	$\frac{5}{6}$	$\frac{7}{8}$	$\frac{11}{12}$	$\frac{9}{10}$
$-\frac{1}{2}$	$-\frac{1}{3}$	$-\frac{1}{2}$	$-\frac{3}{4}$	$-\frac{1}{2}$
?	?	?	?	?

Subtraction of Mixed Numbers

The meanings and principles that apply to the subtraction of integers and the subtraction of fractions can be applied to finding the difference between two mixed numbers.

(a)	(b)				
$4\frac{3}{4}$	$24\frac{1}{2}$	or	$23\frac{3}{2}$	or	$23\frac{6}{4}$
$-2\frac{1}{4}$	$-11\frac{3}{4}$		$-11\frac{3}{4}$		$-11\frac{3}{4}$
$2\frac{2}{4}$ or $2\frac{1}{2}$	?		?		$12\frac{3}{4}$

In example (*a*) the fractions that are a part of the mixed numbers are like fractions. The first step to take is to find the difference between $\frac{3}{4}$ and $\frac{1}{4}$. The second step is to find the difference between 4 and 2.

In example (*b*) the fractions that are a part of the two mixed numbers are unlike (they have a different number for the denominator). The first step in thinking is to find a number that will be a denominator common to the two fractions and then write the fraction equivalents so that the fractions will have a common denominator. The second step in thinking is to find the difference between $\frac{6}{4}$ and $\frac{3}{4}$. The third step in thinking is to find the difference between 23 and 11. Notate the difference or answer as an integer and a fraction. (Reduce the fraction to lowest terms when required.)

EXERCISE

Find the answer to each example. Explain the thinking required to find each answer.

(a)	(b)	(c)	(d)	(e)
$12\frac{3}{4}$	$36\frac{1}{2}$	$70\frac{2}{5}$	$301\frac{1}{4}$	$870\frac{2}{3}$
$-8\frac{1}{2}$	$-14\frac{3}{4}$	$-48\frac{7}{10}$	$-187\frac{7}{8}$	$-299\frac{5}{6}$
?	?	?	?	?

Summary of Meanings That Apply to Subtraction of Fractions

The meanings and computation processes used in subtracting integers are used in subtracting fractions. The minuend in a subtraction example tells how many in one group. The subtrahend tells how many in the other group. The missing fraction, the difference, is computed by finding the numerical difference between the minuend and the subtrahend.

In computing with integers, ones can be subtracted from ones, tens from tens, etc. In computing with fractions, halves can be subtracted from halves, thirds from thirds, fourths from fourths, etc. In brief, only like units can be subtracted. Consequently, when denominators are unlike, it is necessary to think of the denominator common to both fractions and to rewrite the fractions in an equivalent number of units common to both.

When the minuend and the subtrahend notate like fraction units, the question asked by the minus sign is, "What is the difference between the two fractions?"

In subtracting mixed numbers, like units are compared in sequence with the smallest units being subtracted first, i.e., first fractions, then ones, tens, hundreds are subtracted. If there are less units in any place in the minuend than in the corresponding place in the subtrahend, one of the next larger units is taken and for it is substituted an equivalent number of smaller units, which are added to the units in the place at the right.

Multiplication of Fractions

The Multiplier an Integer

Multiplication of fractions is a thought process and a computation process used to answer the question, "How many in all when a given number of fractions or mixed numbers are thought to be grouped together?" The meanings and principles that apply to the multiplication of integers can be applied to finding the product when the multiplicand is a fraction or mixed number.

(*a*)	*Addition*	*Multiplication*
$\frac{3}{4}$	$\frac{3}{4}$	$\frac{3}{4}$
$\times 4$	$\frac{3}{4}$	$\times 4$
———	$\frac{3}{4}$	———
?	$+\ \frac{3}{4}$	$\frac{12}{4}$ or 3
	———	
	$\frac{12}{4}$ or 3	

(*b*)	*Addition*	*Multiplication*
$6\frac{2}{3}$	$6\frac{2}{3}$	$6\frac{2}{3}$
$\times 5$	$6\frac{2}{3}$	$\times 5$
———	$6\frac{2}{3}$	———
?	$6\frac{2}{3}$	$3\frac{1}{3}$
	$6\frac{2}{3}$	30
	———	———
	$3\frac{1}{3}$	$33\frac{1}{3}$
	30	
	———	
	$33\frac{1}{3}$	

The example, $4 \times \frac{3}{4} = ?$ asks the question, "What is the product or sum of 4 $\frac{3}{4}$'s when they are thought together?" or "How many in all?"

The example, $5 \times 6\frac{2}{3} = ?$ asks the question, "What is the product or sum of 5 numbers, each a mixed number $6\frac{2}{3}$, when they are thought together?" or "How many in all?"

Relation of Meanings for Multiplication of Integers to Multiplication of Fractions

Teachers should introduce the multiplication of fractions, when the multiplier is an integer, by asking pupils to recall these meanings they have learned about multiplication of integers:

(*a*) The multiplier shows the number of integers to be combined or thought to be combined in one group and the product is notated with a number that has the numerical value of all the integers. $4 \times 28 = ?$

(*b*) The multiplicand shows the numerical size of each of the given numbers to be combined into one group. $8 \times 56 = ?$

(*c*) Only like value integers can be multiplied or can be combined. $5 \times 36 = ?$ (The example shows five 36's.)

(*d*) The product is the number that notates the total numerical value of all the numbers when combined. $7 \times 42 = 294$

$2 \times \frac{1}{3} = ?$ The example asks the question, "How many thirds in all?"

$$\begin{array}{r} \frac{1}{3} \\ +\frac{1}{3} \\ \hline \frac{2}{3} \end{array} \qquad \begin{array}{r} \text{1 one-third} \\ \text{+1 one-third} \\ \hline \text{2 one-thirds} \end{array} \qquad \begin{array}{r} \frac{1}{3} \\ \times 2 \\ \hline \frac{2}{3} \end{array}$$

$8 \times \frac{3}{4} = ?$ The example asks the question, "How many fourths in all?"

$$\frac{3}{4} + \frac{3}{4} + \frac{3}{4} + \frac{3}{4} + \frac{3}{4} + \frac{3}{4} + \frac{3}{4} + \frac{3}{4} = \frac{24}{4} \text{ or}$$

$$\begin{array}{cccccc} \frac{4}{4} + & \frac{4}{4} + & \frac{4}{4} + & \frac{4}{4} + & \frac{4}{4} + & \frac{4}{4} \text{ or } 6 \\ 1 & 1 & 1 & 1 & 1 & 1 \end{array}$$

$$\begin{array}{r} \frac{3}{4} \\ \times 8 \\ \hline \frac{24}{4} \text{ or } 6 \end{array} \qquad 8 \times \frac{3}{4} = \frac{8 \times 3}{4} \text{ or } \frac{24}{4} \text{ or } 6$$

Generalized Rule

To find the product of a given number of fractions, multiply the numerator of the fraction by the number that is the multiplier and write the product over the number that is the denominator of the fraction. When the product is an improper fraction, notate the product as a mixed number.

EXERCISE

Compute the product of these examples. Explain the computation.

(*a*)	(*b*)	(*c*)	(*d*)	(*e*)	(*f*)	(*g*)
$\frac{1}{2}$	$\frac{2}{3}$	$\frac{3}{4}$	$\frac{7}{8}$	$\frac{5}{6}$	$\frac{2}{3}$	$\frac{3}{16}$
×3	×9	×24	×18	×10	×14	×4
?	?	?	?	?	?	?

Multiplication of Fractions—Multiplier Is an Integer and Multiplicand Is a Mixed Number

(*a*)

$$\begin{array}{r} 4\frac{2}{3} \\ \times 5 \\ \hline ? \end{array} \qquad \begin{array}{r} 4\frac{2}{3} \\ 4\frac{2}{3} \\ 4\frac{2}{3} \\ 4\frac{2}{3} \\ 4\frac{2}{3} \\ \hline 3\frac{1}{3} \\ 20 \\ \hline 23\frac{1}{3} \end{array} \qquad 5 \times 4\frac{2}{3} = 5 \times \frac{14}{3} = \frac{5 \times 14}{3} = \frac{70}{3} \text{ or } 23\frac{1}{3}$$

(*b*)

$$\begin{array}{r} 24\frac{3}{8} \\ \times 12 \\ \hline ? \end{array} \qquad \begin{array}{r} 24\frac{3}{8} \\ \times 12 \\ \hline 4\frac{1}{2} \\ 48 \\ 240 \\ \hline 292\frac{1}{2} \end{array} \qquad \begin{array}{l} 12 \times \frac{3}{8} = \frac{36}{8} = 4\frac{4}{8} = 4\frac{1}{2} \\ \;\;2 \times 24 = 48 \\ 1\text{T} \times 24 = 240 \end{array}$$

The horizontal method of computation is:

$$12 \times 24\frac{3}{8} = 12 \times \frac{195}{8} = \frac{12 \times 195}{8} = \frac{2340}{8} = 292\frac{4}{8} \text{ or } 292\frac{1}{2}$$

Example (*a*), $5 \times 4\frac{2}{3} = ?$ asks the question, "What number notates all the five $4\frac{2}{3}$'s when thought together?"

The first thought process is to find the product of five $\frac{2}{3}$'s. The partial product is $\frac{10}{3}$ or $3\frac{1}{3}$. The next thought process is to find the product of 5 fours. This partial product is 20. The final thought process is to add the partial products and notate the total product.

Example (*b*), $12 \times 24\frac{3}{8} = ?$ asks the question, "What number notates all the twelve $24\frac{3}{8}$'s when thought together?"

The first thought process is to find the product of $12 \times \frac{3}{8}$, which is $\frac{36}{8}$ or $4\frac{4}{8}$ or $4\frac{1}{2}$. The second thought process is to find the product of 2×24, which is 48. The third thought process is to find the product of 1 ten $\times$ 24, which is 24T or 240. The fourth thought process is to add the partial products and notate the total product.

Generalized Rule

To find the product of a multiplication example when the multiplier is an integer and the multiplicand is a mixed number, first find the product of the given number of the fractions, then find the product of the given number of integers. Add the partial products and notate a number that has the numerical value of all the mixed numbers together.

EXERCISE

Find the product in the examples. Explain the computation.

(*a*)	(*b*)	(*c*)	(*d*)	(*e*)	(*f*)
$9\frac{3}{4}$	$10\frac{5}{8}$	$30\frac{2}{3}$	$25\frac{1}{2}$	$407\frac{3}{8}$	$500\frac{1}{2}$
$\times 8$	$\times 6$	$\times 12$	$\times 31$	$\times 20$	$\times 25$
?	?	?	?	?	?

Multiplication of Fractions—Multiplier Is a Fraction

The multiplication of an integer, a fraction, or a mixed number by a fraction presents another meaning in multiplication. The question to be answered when the multiplier is a fraction is, "How many in a fractional part of a given integer?" or "What is a fractional part of a given fraction?" or "How many in a fractional part of a given mixed number?"

The thought process is to find a fractional part of a given integer, or a given fraction, or a given mixed number. The product will show what is the fractional part.

(*a*) $\frac{1}{2} \times 1 = ?$

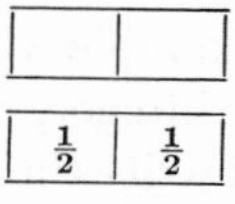

$\frac{1}{2} \times 1 = \frac{1}{2}$

The unit 1 is thought to be divided into two even divisions, which gives two fractional units or parts. One-half of the two fractional units is $\frac{1}{2}$ or 1 one-half.

(*b*) $\frac{3}{4} \times 4 = ?$

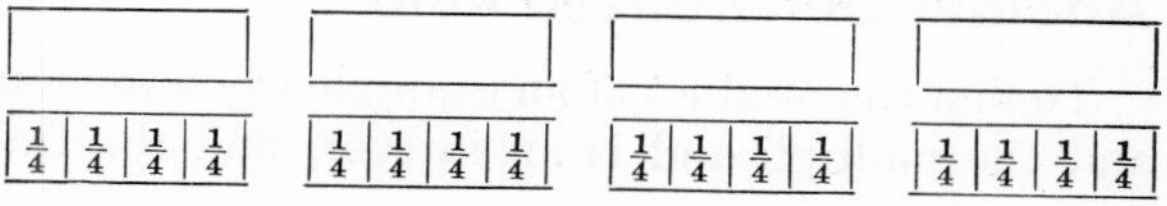

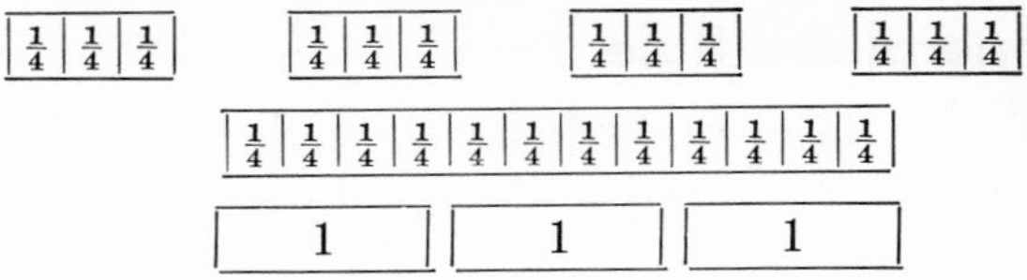

The multiplicand notates 4 ones. The multiplier $\frac{3}{4}$ asks what is $\frac{3}{4}$ of each of the 4 ones, and what is the total of all fractional parts. Each of the ones is thought to be divided into four even divisions. Then 3 one-fourths of the 4 one-fourths of each of the 4 ones are considered. Then all the 3 one-fourths of each of the 4 ones are thought to be combined, giving 12 one-fourths. The improper fraction $\frac{12}{4}$ is changed to lowest terms and notated with its equivalent, which is 3.

The short thought process is to think that $\frac{3}{4}$ of one is $\frac{3}{4}$ and since there are 4 ones in the multiplicand, $4 \times \frac{3}{4}$ will give the total number of $\frac{3}{4}$'s or $\frac{12}{4}$. The improper fraction is thought to be notated with its equivalent 3 ones.

(c) $\frac{3}{4} \times 9 = ?$ ☐ ☐ ☐ ☐ ☐ ☐ ☐ ☐ ☐ — The multiplicand

┌─ $2\frac{1}{4}$ ─┐
☐ ☐ ☐ — $\frac{1}{4}$ of 9 is $2\frac{1}{4}$

┌──── $6\frac{3}{4}$ ────┐
☐ ☐ ☐ ☐ ☐ ☐ ☐ ☐ ☐ — $\frac{3}{4}$ of 9 is $3 \times 2\frac{1}{4}$ or $6\frac{3}{4}$

Example (c) is illustrated to show another thought process used to find what is $\frac{3}{4} \times 9$. First find what is $\frac{1}{4}$ of 9? The partial product is $2\frac{1}{4}$. Then $3 \times 2\frac{1}{4} = 6\frac{3}{4}$. Therefore $\frac{3}{4} \times 9$ is $6\frac{3}{4}$.

Generalized Rule

To find the product of an example when the multiplier is a fraction and the multiplicand is an integer, multiply the integer by the numerator of the fraction and write the product over the denominator of the fraction that is the multiplier and then change the product, if needed, to lowest terms.

Another Generalized Rule

To find the product of an example when the multiplier is a fraction and the multiplicand is an integer, find the fractional part of one

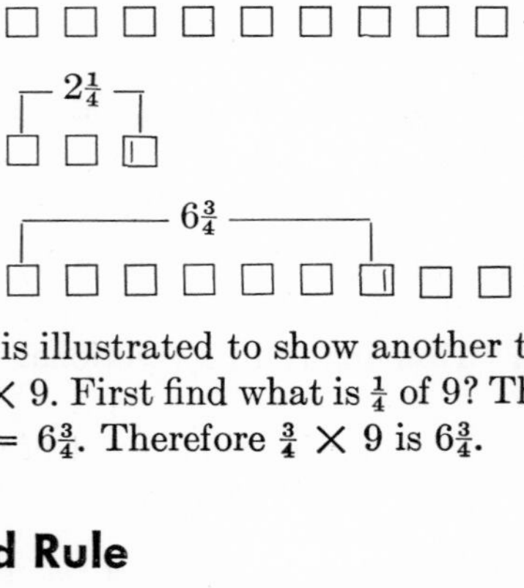

and then multiply it by the number of ones notated in the multiplicand and write the product over the denominator of the multiplier.

$\frac{2}{3} \times 8$ = first $\frac{2}{3}$ of $1 = \frac{2}{3}$, second, $8 \times \frac{2}{3} = \frac{16}{3}$ or $5\frac{1}{3}$

EXERCISE

Compute the answer for each example. Explain the process.

(*a*) $\frac{3}{4} \times 6 = ?$ (*b*) $\frac{2}{5} \times 25 = ?$ (*c*) $\frac{2}{3} \times 38 = ?$

(*d*) $\frac{5}{8} \times 45 = ?$ (*e*) $\frac{7}{12} \times 86 = ?$

Multiplication of Fractions—Multiplier Is a Fraction and Multiplicand Is a Fraction

(*a*) $\frac{1}{2} \times \frac{3}{4} = ?$ The example asks the question, "What is $\frac{1}{2}$ of $\frac{3}{4}$?" The thought process used to find the answer can be illustrated.

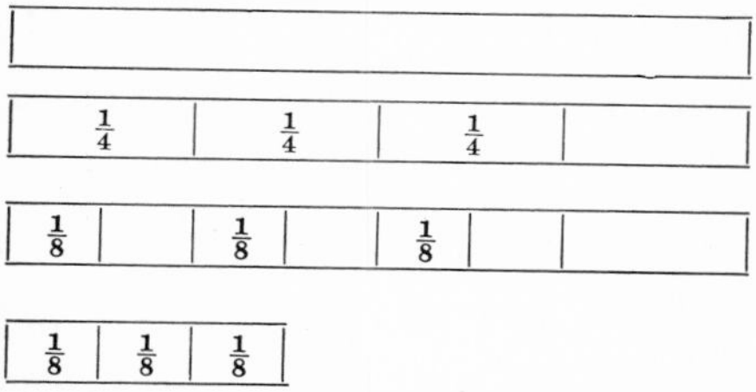

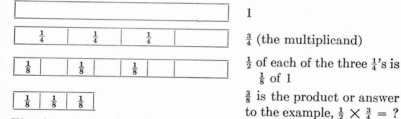

1

$\frac{3}{4}$ (the multiplicand)

$\frac{1}{2}$ of each of the three $\frac{1}{4}$'s is $\frac{1}{8}$ of 1

$\frac{3}{8}$ is the product or answer to the example, $\frac{1}{2} \times \frac{3}{4} = ?$

The thought process to find $\frac{1}{2}$ of $\frac{3}{4}$, is to first find $\frac{1}{2}$ of each of the $\frac{1}{4}$'s and then to write a fraction that notates all the $\frac{1}{8}$'s together.

(*b*) $\frac{3}{4} \times \frac{3}{4} = ?$ The example asks the question, "What is $\frac{3}{4}$ of $\frac{3}{4}$?" The thought process used to find the answer can be illustrated.

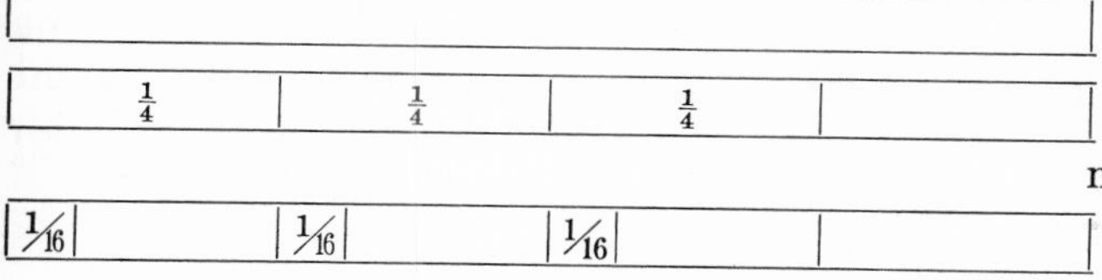

1

$\frac{3}{4}$ (the multiplicand)

$\frac{1}{4}$ of each of the three $\frac{1}{4}$'s is $\frac{1}{16}$ of 1

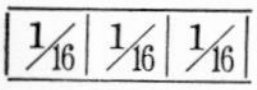

$\frac{1}{4}$ of all three $\frac{1}{4}$'s is $\frac{3}{16}$

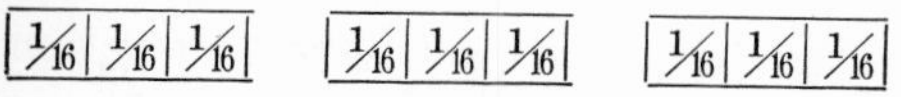

Since $\frac{3}{4} = 3 \times \frac{1}{4}$, then $\frac{3}{4}$ of all three $\frac{1}{4}$'s =

$3 \times \frac{3}{16} = \frac{9}{16}$

A Generalized Rule

To find the fractional part of a fraction, multiply the numerator of the multiplicand by the numerator of the multiplier and write the number over the product of the denominator in the multiplicand and the denominator in the multiplier. Notate the product or answer, when required, in lowest terms.

Another Generalized Rule

To find the fractional part of a given fraction, first multiply one of the fractional units as notated in the multiplicand by the multiplier. Then multiply this fraction by the number that is the numerator in the multiplicand.

$\frac{3}{4} \times \frac{3}{4} = ?$ $\quad \frac{3}{4}$ of $\frac{1}{4} = \frac{3}{16}$, then $3 \times \frac{3}{16} = \frac{9}{16}$

EXERCISE

Compute each example. Explain the mathematical thought process.

(*a*) $\frac{1}{2} \times \frac{3}{4} = ?$ (*b*) $\frac{3}{4} \times \frac{1}{2} = ?$ (*c*) $\frac{2}{3} \times \frac{5}{6} = ?$

(*d*) $\frac{3}{4} \times \frac{3}{8} = ?$ (*e*) $\frac{2}{3} \times \frac{3}{4} = ?$ (*f*) $\frac{3}{4} \times \frac{3}{4} = ?$

(*g*) $\frac{5}{8} \times \frac{3}{4} = ?$ (*h*) $\frac{3}{8} \times \frac{5}{8} = ?$

Multiplication of Fractions—Multiplicand Is a Mixed Number—Multiplier Is a Fraction

What is $\frac{2}{3}$ of $3\frac{1}{2}$ pounds of candy?

1 lb	1 lb	1 lb	$\frac{1}{2}$ lb
$\frac{1}{3}$ lb | $\frac{1}{3}$ lb	$\frac{1}{3}$ lb | $\frac{1}{3}$ lb	$\frac{1}{3}$ lb | $\frac{1}{3}$ lb	$\frac{1}{6}$ | $\frac{1}{6}$

$$\frac{6}{3} + \frac{2}{6} = \frac{12}{6} + \frac{2}{6} = \frac{14}{6} = 2\frac{2}{6} = 2\frac{1}{3}$$

Method I

$$3 \text{ lb} \times \frac{2}{3} = 2 \text{ lb} \quad + \quad \frac{1}{2} \text{ lb} \times \frac{2}{3} = \frac{2}{6} = 2\frac{1}{3} \text{ lb} \qquad \boxed{3\frac{1}{2} \times \frac{2}{3} = 2\frac{1}{3}}$$

Method II $\frac{2}{3} \times 3\frac{1}{2}$ lb candy $= \frac{2}{3} \times \frac{7}{2}$ lb candy $= \dfrac{2 \times 7}{3 \times 2} = 2\frac{2}{6}$

The authors recommend Method I or the Vertical Method when multiplying a mixed number by a fraction. This method is more similar to the method used in multiplication of integers and this form is consistent with the forms desired when multiplying a mixed number by a mixed number.

Generalized Rule

To find the fractional part of a mixed number first multiply the fraction in the multiplicand by the multiplier; second, multiply the integer in the multiplicand by the multiplier. Then add the partial products and write the number or product that shows the desired fractional part of the multiplicand.

EXERCISE

Find the answer to each example. Explain the thought process.

(a)	(b)	(c)	(d)	(e)	(f)
$2\frac{1}{2}$	$4\frac{1}{4}$	$6\frac{2}{3}$	$5\frac{3}{4}$	$24\frac{5}{6}$	$20\frac{5}{8}$
$\times\frac{1}{2}$	$\times\frac{1}{2}$	$\times\frac{2}{3}$	$\times\frac{3}{4}$	$\times\frac{1}{2}$	$\times\frac{3}{8}$
?	?	?	?	?	?

Multiplication of Mixed Numbers

To find the product of two mixed numbers, the computation involves these meanings which have been developed previously:

1. Finding a fractional part of a fraction.
2. Finding a fractional part of an integer.
3. Finding the product of an integer multiplied by a fraction.
4. Finding the product of an integer multiplied by an integer.

What is the product of $24\frac{3}{4} \times 32\frac{1}{2}$?

	$\frac{3}{8} =$	$\frac{3}{4} \times \frac{1}{2} = \frac{3}{8}$
$32\frac{1}{2}$	24	$\frac{3}{4} \times 32 = 24$
$24\frac{3}{4}$	12	$24 \times \frac{1}{2} = 12$
	128	$4 \times 32 = 128$
?	640	$2T \times 32 = 640$
	$804\frac{3}{8}$	

Summary of Meanings That Apply to Multiplication of Fractions

Multiplication of fractions is a thought process and computation process used to find the product (sum) of two or more fractions that notate equal size groups of fraction units. The product can be computed by adding the fraction that tells how many fraction units in a group (the multiplicand) as many times as indicated by the multiplier. The multiplicand can be thought of as an equal addend and the multiplier can be thought of as notating the number of equal addends.

An example such as $4 \times \frac{3}{4} = ?$ asks the question, "What number equals 4 groups of $\frac{3}{4}$ each?" In finding the answer, the numerator, 3, which tells how many $\frac{1}{4}$'s in a group is multiplied by 4. The product is 12 ($\frac{1}{4}$'s) and the number equal to 4 groups of $\frac{3}{4}$ each is $\frac{12}{4}$ or 3.

An example such as $4 \times 5\frac{3}{4}$ is computed by first finding the answer to two questions: (1) "What number equals 4 groups of $\frac{3}{4}$ each?" (2) "What number equals 4 groups of 5 each?" Before finding the answer to the question, "What number equals 4 groups of $5\frac{3}{4}$ each?" the answers to questions (1) and (2) are added to find the total product. The smaller units are multiplied first, and the succeedingly larger units in sequence.

The principle of computing with like units can be extended to the multiplication of a mixed number. In the example, $4 \times 5\frac{3}{4}$, the mixed number $5\frac{3}{4}$ can be rewritten as $\frac{23}{4}$. Then the example becomes $4 \times \frac{23}{4}$.

When the multiplier is a fraction, the example asks a question which can be answered by thinking of the multiplicand as being separated into parts as indicated by the multiplier and of finding "how many" in each part. To illustrate, $\frac{1}{3}$ of 9 asks the question, "How many in 1 of the 3 equal parts of 9?" The example $\frac{3}{4} \times 8$ asks the question, "How many in 3 of the 4 equal parts of 8?" The example $\frac{2}{3} \times \frac{3}{4}$ asks the question, "How many in 2 of the 3 equal parts of $\frac{3}{4}$?"

When multiplying mixed numbers, first the smaller and the succeedingly larger units are computed to find partial products. Partial products are added to find the total product.

Generalized Rule

To find the product of two mixed numbers:

First, multiply the fraction in the multiplicand by the fraction in the multiplier.

Second, multiply the integer in the multiplicand by the fraction in the multiplier.

Third, multiply the fraction in the multiplicand by the integer in the multiplier.

Fourth, multiply the integer in the multiplicand by the integer in the multiplier.

Fifth, add the partial products to find the total product.

EXERCISE

Read each example to interpret the question. Then compute the answer. Explain the thought process required to find the partial products and the total product.

(*a*)	(*b*)	(*c*)	(*d*)	(*e*)
$3\frac{1}{2}$	$8\frac{3}{4}$	$24\frac{2}{3}$	$54\frac{1}{2}$	$60\frac{2}{3}$
$\times 4\frac{1}{2}$	$\times 7\frac{1}{2}$	$\times 12\frac{1}{3}$	$\times 20\frac{3}{8}$	$\times 20\frac{3}{4}$
?	?	?	?	?

Division of Fractions

Introduction

Many of the meanings and principles that apply to the division of integers may be used in the division of fractions. These meanings and principles when reviewed may assist pupils in learning that there is not a sharp separation between division with integers and division with fractions or mixed numbers.

1. Division is a mathematical process of changing the dividend into groups that have a numerical value equivalent to the divisor.

2. Division is also a mathematical process of changing the dividend into a specified number of even groups to find the numerical value of each group.

3. Division is also a mathematical process used to find the ratio relation between the dividend and the divisor.

4. The quotient shows the number of even groups that are thought to be found when the dividend is interpreted to be rearranged into groups with a numerical value equivalent to the divisor.

(*a*)
```
          8 groups of 6 ft
6 ft)48 ft
     48 ft
     -----
```

(*b*)
```
             6 lb
7 group)42 lb
        42 lb
        -----
```

(*c*)
```
     14
12)168
   12
   --
    48
    48
    --
```

The major difference between division with fractions and division with integers is the numerical value of the numbers. In division of integers the numbers are integers. In division of fractions the numbers identify units with a numerical value of less than one.

```
   8
9)72
  72
  --
```

$\frac{3}{4} \div \frac{2}{4} = 3$ one-fourths $\div$ 2 one fourths $= 1\frac{1}{2}$

Division of Fractions—Dividend an Integer—Divisor a Fraction

In a concrete situation, division may be interpreted as physically changing the dividend into groups having a numerical value equivalent to the divisor. A representative problem resolved by such a physical change is described below.

James was building a scooter. He needed to cut a piece of wood 4 feet long into pieces which would be $\frac{1}{2}$ foot long. He decided to use division to find the number of $\frac{1}{2}$ foot pieces he would make.

$4 \text{ ft} \div \frac{1}{2} \text{ ft} = \frac{4}{1} \text{ ft} \div \frac{1}{2} \text{ ft} = \frac{8}{2} \text{ ft} \div \frac{1}{2} \text{ ft} = 8 \div 1$ or $\frac{8}{1} = 8$ pieces $\frac{1}{2}$ ft long.

The thought process James used in computation was this. He knew the dividend was 4 feet and the divisor was $\frac{1}{2}$ foot. He wrote the question he wanted to answer as a mathematical question, $4 \text{ ft} \div \frac{1}{2} \text{ ft} = ?$ He had learned that in division only like numbers can be compared or divided so he thought of 4 feet as a fraction $\frac{4}{1}$. He recognized that the dividend and divisor were not yet alike so he substituted $\frac{8}{2}$ for $\frac{4}{1}$ so that the denominator would be similar to the denominator in the divisor. He now knew that the fractions were alike so he thought of the numerator in the dividend as being grouped into lengths equal to 1 (one-half) $8 \div 1 = 8$.

He found that 8 halves can be thought of as 8 groups of $\frac{1}{2}$ foot each. The process of division helped James to know that he would have 8 pieces of wood after he cut a piece of wood 4 feet long into pieces $\frac{1}{2}$ foot long each.

(*a*) $12 \div \frac{3}{8} = ?$ $12 \div \frac{3}{8} = \frac{12}{1} \div \frac{3}{8} = \frac{96}{8} \div \frac{3}{8} = \frac{96}{3} = 32$ groups of $\frac{3}{8}$

The quotient in example (*a*) is computed by the *like fraction* or *division* method. It is consistent with the thought process in changing or thinking of the dividend changed into groups with numerical value equivalent to the divisor; 12 is equivalent to 32 groups with numerical size, $\frac{3}{8}$. Since the denominator of the dividend was unlike the denominator in the divisor, a denominator, $\frac{1}{8}$, was found to be common to each fraction. Then the numerators were divided (96 one-eighths ÷ 3 one-eighths = 32 groups of three-eighths).

(*b*) $12 \div \frac{3}{8} = ?$ $$12 \div \frac{3}{8} = \overset{4}{\cancel{12}} \times \frac{8}{\underset{1}{\cancel{3}}} = 32$$

The quotient in example (*b*) is computed by using the *inversion method.* This method involves an understanding of the reciprocal of a number.

$3 \times \frac{1}{3} = 1$ $4 \times \frac{1}{4} = 1$ The reciprocal of 3 is $\frac{1}{3}$ The reciprocal of 4 is $\frac{1}{4}$

Any number multiplied by its reciprocal equals 1. $a \times \frac{1}{a} = 1$

$3 \times 4 = 12$ $\frac{1}{3} \times 12 = 4$ $\frac{1}{4} \times 12 = 3$. When one factor of a product is known, the other factor may be found by multiplying the product by the reciprocal of the known factor. $5 \times 3 = 15$ $\frac{1}{3} \times 15 = 5$ $6 \times \frac{3}{4} = \frac{18}{4} = 4\frac{2}{4} = 4\frac{1}{2}$ $\frac{4}{3} \times 4\frac{1}{2} = \frac{4}{3} \times \frac{9}{2} = \frac{36}{6} = 6$

In the *inversion method,* the dividend can be thought of as the product of the divisor and another number. The application of the idea of reciprocal permits the dividend to be multiplied by the reciprocal of the divisor to find the other number.

$$12 \div \frac{2}{3} = \overset{6}{\cancel{12}} \times \frac{3}{\underset{1}{\cancel{2}}} = 18$$ (18 is the other number. $\frac{2}{3} \times 18 = 12$)

Cancellation can be used in the *inversion method* of division. The thought process in cancellation $\overset{6}{\cancel{12}} \times \frac{3}{\underset{1}{\cancel{2}}} = 18$, is:

If the number of equal divisions, 2, is reduced by one-half, then the denominator becomes 1 ($\frac{1}{2}$ of two divisions is one division). If the size of the multiplier, 12, is also reduced by one-half, the multiplier becomes 6 ($\frac{1}{2}$ of 12 = 6; $12 \times \frac{3}{2} = 6 \times 3 = 18$).

The *inversion method* permits the application of a mathematical principle; however, it involves a change in meaning of the process from *division* to multiplication.

The authors recommend teaching the *like-fraction method* for the reason that it is consistent with the ideas and questions involved in division of either integers or fractions.

Generalized Rule

To find the quotient in an example when the dividend is an integer and the divisor is a fraction, first notate the dividend as a fraction with a denominator of 1. Notate the fraction that is the dividend so that the denominator will be like the denominator in the divisor. Then divide the numerator of the dividend by the numerator of the divisor to find the quotient.

EXERCISE

Compute the quotient for each example, first by the *like-fraction method* and second by the *inversion method.* Explain the thought process applied to each method.

(*a*) $4 \div \frac{1}{2} = ?$

(*b*) $9 \div \frac{2}{3} = ?$

(*c*) $14 \div \frac{5}{8} = ?$

(*d*) $18 \div \frac{5}{6} = ?$

(*e*) $20 \div \frac{3}{4} = ?$

(*f*) $30 \div \frac{7}{8} = ?$

Division of Fractions—Dividend Is a Fraction—Divisor Is a Fraction

The meanings and operational principles used in dividing an integer by a fraction may be applied to finding the quotient when dividing a fraction by a fraction.

It is important to remember that a fraction is a number.

Either the like-division method or the inversion method may be used to find the quotient.

(*a*) $\frac{3}{4} \div \frac{1}{4} = ?$ $\frac{3}{4} \div \frac{1}{4} = \frac{3}{1}$ or $3 \div 1 = 3$ There are 3 groups of $\frac{1}{4}$'s in $\frac{3}{4}$.

(*b*) $\frac{3}{4} \div \frac{1}{4} = ?$ $\frac{3}{\cancel{4}_1} \times \frac{\cancel{4}^1}{1} = 3$ (If $\frac{1}{4}$ is one of the factors of $\frac{3}{4}$, then the other factor may be found by multiplying $\frac{3}{4}$ by the reciprocal of $\frac{1}{4}$ which is $\frac{4}{1}$. $\frac{\cancel{4}^1}{1} \times \frac{3}{\cancel{4}_1} = 3$)

(*c*) $\frac{7}{8} \div \frac{2}{3} = ?$ $\frac{7}{8} \div \frac{2}{3} = \frac{21}{24} \div \frac{16}{24} = 21 \div 16$ or $\frac{21}{16} = 1\frac{5}{16}$ groups of $\frac{2}{3}$'s. To check the quotient, multiply the divisor by the quotient ($1\frac{5}{16} \times \frac{2}{3} = \frac{21}{16} \times \frac{2}{3} = \frac{42}{48}$ or $\frac{7}{8}$).

(*d*) $\frac{7}{8} \div \frac{2}{3} = ?$ $\frac{7}{8} \div \frac{2}{3} = \frac{7}{8} \times \frac{3}{2} = \frac{21}{16} = 1\frac{5}{16}$ groups of $\frac{2}{3}$'s. To check the quotient, multiply the divisor by $1\frac{5}{16}$ ($1\frac{5}{16} \times \frac{2}{3} = \frac{21}{16} \times \frac{2}{3} = \frac{42}{48} = \frac{7}{8}$).

Study the thought process and computation used in computing the quotient for examples (*a*) and (*c*).

Study the thought process and the computation used in computing the quotient for examples (*b*) and (*d*).

Why is the like-division method more consistent with the meaning of division?

In the inversion method, why is the divisor inverted and the process changed to multiplication?

What is the meaning of the quotient for each example?

How may the accuracy of the quotient be checked?

Generalized Rule

Like-Division Method

To find the quotient when the dividend is a fraction and the divisor is a fraction, first change the dividend and the divisor to like fractions. Then divide the numerator of the dividend by the numerator of the divisor ($\frac{7}{8} \div \frac{3}{4} = \frac{7}{8} \div \frac{6}{8} = 1\frac{1}{6}$).

Inversion Method

To find the quotient when the dividend is a fraction and the divisor is a fraction, multiply the dividend by the reciprocal of the divisor

$$\left(\frac{7}{8} \div \frac{3}{4} = \frac{7}{\underset{2}{\cancel{8}}} \times \frac{\overset{1}{\cancel{4}}}{3} = \frac{7}{6} \text{ or } 1\frac{1}{6}\right).$$

EXERCISE

Find the quotient for each example. Explain the thought process involved in the computation. Explain the meaning of the quotient.

(*a*) $\frac{3}{4} \div \frac{1}{2} = ?$ (*d*) $\frac{15}{16} \div \frac{7}{8} = ?$

(*b*) $\frac{3}{4} \div \frac{2}{3} = ?$ (*e*) $\frac{21}{24} \div \frac{3}{4} = ?$

(*c*) $\frac{7}{8} \div \frac{5}{6} = ?$ (*f*) $\frac{32}{36} \div \frac{7}{9} = ?$

Division of Fractions—Mixed Numbers

The meanings that apply to division of integers or fractions apply to the division of mixed numbers. Either the *like-fraction* method or the *inversion method* may be used. The *like-fraction* method is more consistent with the question asked and answered by division.

Like-Fraction Method

(*a*) $8\frac{2}{3} \div 2\frac{1}{2} = ?$ $8\frac{2}{3} \div 2\frac{1}{2} = \frac{26}{3} \div \frac{5}{2} = \frac{52}{6} \div \frac{15}{6} = \frac{52}{15} = 3\frac{7}{15}$

Inversion Method

(*b*) $8\frac{2}{3} \div 2\frac{1}{2} = ?$ $8\frac{2}{3} \div 2\frac{1}{2} = \frac{26}{3} \times \frac{2}{5} = \frac{52}{15}$ or $3\frac{7}{15}$

To check the accuracy of the quotient: $3\frac{7}{15} \times 2\frac{1}{2} = \frac{52}{15} \times \frac{5}{2} = \frac{260}{30}$
$= 8\frac{2}{3}$

(*c*) $24\frac{5}{6} \div 7\frac{3}{4} = ?$ $24\frac{5}{6} \div 7\frac{3}{4} = \frac{149}{6} \div \frac{31}{4} = \frac{298}{12} \div \frac{93}{12} = \frac{298}{93}$ or $3\frac{19}{93}$

(*d*) $24\frac{5}{6} \div 7\frac{3}{4} = ?$ $24\frac{5}{6} \div 7\frac{3}{4} = \frac{149}{6} \div \frac{31}{4} = \frac{149}{\underset{3}{\cancel{6}}} \times \frac{\overset{2}{\cancel{4}}}{31} = \frac{298}{93} = 3\frac{19}{93}$

What is the generalized rule to find the quotient when the dividend and the divisor are mixed numbers when the *like-fraction* method is used? When the *inversion method* is used?

What is the meaning of the quotient when the dividend and the divisor are *mixed numbers*?

EXERCISE

Find the quotient for each example. Explain the thought process involved. Also explain the meaning of the quotient.

(*a*) $6\frac{3}{4} \div 2\frac{1}{2} = ?$	(*d*) $46\frac{1}{2} \div 8\frac{2}{3} = ?$
(*b*) $24\frac{1}{2} \div 3\frac{3}{8} = ?$	(*e*) $240\frac{3}{4} \div 30\frac{1}{2} = ?$
(*c*) $18\frac{2}{3} \div 4\frac{1}{6} = ?$	(*f*) $300\frac{7}{8} \div 15\frac{3}{4} = ?$

Division of Fractions—Dividend Less Than the Divisor

Division is a thought process and a computation method to find:

(*a*) the number of groups in the dividend that is equal in numerical value to the divisor.

(*b*) the ratio relationship between the dividend and the divisor.

$\frac{1}{2} \div \frac{3}{4} = ?$ The divisor is a fraction larger than the dividend. Therefore, the dividend cannot be changed or thought to be changed into groups with a numerical value of $\frac{3}{4}$. The quotient will show a fractional part of a group with a numerical value equal to the divisor.

$\frac{1}{2} \div \frac{3}{4} = \frac{2}{4} \div \frac{3}{4} = 2 \div 3$ or $\frac{2}{3} = \frac{2}{3}$ (The dividend is equal to $\frac{2}{3}$ of a group of $\frac{3}{4}$).

The quotient $\frac{2}{3}$ may also show a ratio of $\frac{2}{3}$ between the dividend and the divisor.

$\frac{3}{8} \div \frac{3}{4} = ?$

Like-Fraction Method $\frac{3}{8} \div \frac{3}{4} = \frac{3}{8} \div \frac{6}{8} = \frac{3}{6}$ or $\frac{1}{2}$

Inversion Method $$\frac{3}{8} \div \frac{3}{4} = \frac{\overset{1}{\cancel{3}}}{\underset{2}{\cancel{8}}} \times \frac{\overset{1}{\cancel{4}}}{\underset{1}{\cancel{3}}} = \frac{1}{2}$$

The process of reducing the quotient to lowest terms is used in each method of computation.

In the *like-fraction method,* the reduction is done after finding the quotient ($\frac{3}{8} \div \frac{6}{8} = \frac{3}{6}$ or $\frac{1}{2}$).

In the inversion method, reducing to lowest terms is done by using cancellation before finding the quotient $\left(\frac{\overset{1}{\cancel{3}}}{\underset{2}{\cancel{8}}} \times \frac{\overset{1}{\cancel{4}}}{\underset{1}{\cancel{3}}} = \frac{1}{2}\right)$.

$$12\tfrac{2}{3} \div 40\tfrac{1}{2} = ? \quad 12\tfrac{2}{3} \div 40\tfrac{1}{2} = \tfrac{38}{3} \div \tfrac{81}{2} = \tfrac{76}{6} \div \tfrac{243}{6} = \tfrac{76}{243}$$

$$12\tfrac{2}{3} \div 40\tfrac{1}{2} = ? \quad 12\tfrac{2}{3} \div 40\tfrac{1}{2} = \tfrac{38}{3} \div \tfrac{81}{2} = \tfrac{38}{3} \times \tfrac{2}{81} = \tfrac{76}{243}$$

Generalized Rule and Conclusion

To find the quotient in division with fractions or mixed numbers, when the dividend is a number smaller than the fraction number in the divisor, divide the dividend by the divisor and notate the quotient as a fraction.

Important Conclusion: In division of fractions or mixed numbers, when the dividend is less than the divisor, the quotient will be less than one, or a fraction.

EXERCISE

Find the quotient for each example. Explain the thought process and the computation. Also explain the meaning of the quotient.

(*a*) $1\frac{1}{3} \div 3\frac{1}{2} = ?$

(*b*) $4\frac{3}{8} \div 8\frac{3}{4} = ?$

(*c*) $5\frac{3}{8} \div 10\frac{5}{6} = ?$

(*d*) $3\frac{3}{4} \div 8\frac{1}{2} = ?$

(*e*) $20\frac{2}{3} \div 30\frac{7}{8} = ?$

(*f*) $100\frac{1}{2} \div 200\frac{2}{3} = ?$

Summary of Meanings That Apply to Division of Fractions

Division may be used to find the ratio between two numbers, either or both of which may be integers, fractions, or mixed numbers. The dividend tells *how many* in all of the equal groups. The divisor tells *how many* in one of the equal groups. The quotient is a number telling how many groups with the numerical value of the divisor are equal to the dividend.

In a social situation the divisor may indicate the number in each equal group or the number of equal groups, and the quotient will tell how many in each equal group or how many equal groups.

The question asked by the example $4 \div \frac{1}{2}$ may be, "How many $\frac{1}{2}$'s = 4?" or "What number $\times \frac{1}{2} = 4$?" or "$4 =$ what number $\times \frac{1}{2}$?" In each case the answer or quotient is 8. The answer is determined by using knowledge gained in a study of multiplication.

The principle of computing with like units extends to computation used in dividing fractions. In the example $\frac{7}{8} \div \frac{1}{4} = ?$ the division method of computation consists of substituting $\frac{2}{8}$'s for $\frac{1}{4}$ and of rewriting the example $\frac{7}{8} \div \frac{2}{8} = ?$ Then if the question is considered as being "How many $\frac{2}{8}$'s $=$ $\frac{7}{8}$'s?" the answer can be computed by finding how many 2 ($\frac{1}{8}$'s) $=$ 7 ($\frac{1}{8}$'s). Three 2's and $\frac{1}{2}$ of another group of 2 ($\frac{1}{8}$'s) $=$ 7 ($\frac{1}{8}$'s). 7 ($\frac{1}{8}$'s) $\div$ 2 ($\frac{1}{8}$'s) $= 3\frac{1}{2}$. $3\frac{1}{2} \times \frac{2}{8} = \frac{7}{8}$.

A more abstract method of finding the answer to the example $\frac{7}{8} \div \frac{1}{4} = ?$ is the inversion method. In this method the dividend, $\frac{7}{8}$, is multiplied by the reciprocal of $\frac{1}{4}$. $\frac{7}{8} \times \frac{4}{1} = \frac{28}{8} = 3\frac{4}{8} = 3\frac{1}{2}$.

Diagnosing Pupil Growth—Test A

1. Draw a circle around the numerator in the fraction $\frac{7}{8}$.

2. How many fractional units are shown by the fraction $\frac{5}{6}$?

3. Draw a circle around the denominator in the fraction $\frac{3}{4}$.

4. How many even divisions of 1 are shown by the fraction $\frac{2}{3}$?

5. How many units are expressed by the mixed number $5\frac{3}{8}$?

6. How many fractional units are notated by the improper fraction $\frac{14}{4}$?

7. What is the equivalent, in lowest terms, for the fraction $\frac{9}{12}$?

8. Change these fractions to sixteenths: $\frac{1}{2}$, $\frac{3}{4}$, $\frac{7}{8}$.

9. What is the measurement size of each fractional unit expressed by the fraction $\frac{3}{4}$ ft?

10. What is the fraction that shows the ratio of 7 to 8?

11. What is the fraction that shows the ratio of 12 to 9?

12. Write the fraction for seven-fifteenths of 1.

13. Write the mixed number for nine and one-third.

14. Construct a drawing to show that $\frac{3}{4}$ rectangle is equal to $\frac{9}{12}$ rectangle.

15. Draw and mark a number line to show the relationship between integers and common fractions.

Diagnosing Pupil Growth—Test B

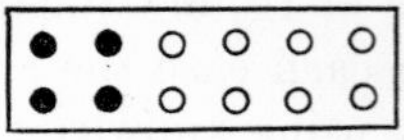

1. Draw a rectangle and shade $\frac{3}{8}$ of it.

2. What fraction of the circles in the box are black?

3. Which of these pieces of string is the shortest? $\frac{1}{2}$ yd $\frac{1}{4}$ yd $\frac{1}{6}$ yd $\frac{1}{3}$ yd.

4. Draw a line under the fractions that are like fractions $\frac{2}{3}$, $\frac{3}{4}$, $\frac{1}{8}$, $\frac{1}{3}$, $\frac{5}{8}$, $\frac{1}{4}$, $\frac{2}{8}$, $\frac{2}{5}$, $\frac{7}{8}$.

5. Construct a drawing to show the mathematical meaning for: (*a*) $\frac{3}{4} \div \frac{5}{6} = ?$ (*b*) $\frac{7}{8} \div \frac{1}{2} = ?$ Explain each thought step.

6. Construct a drawing to illustrate the mathematical statement, $\frac{2}{3} \times 2\frac{1}{2}$ rectangles $= 1$ and $\frac{2}{3}$ rectangles.

7. Construct a drawing to show the mathematical meanings involved in finding the answer to the question: $4 \times \frac{3}{8} = ?$

8. Construct drawings to illustrate the meaning of the mathematical statement: $3\frac{1}{2}$ rectangles $\div \frac{2}{3}$ rectangle $= 5\frac{1}{4}$.

9. Construct drawings to illustrate the meaning of the statement: $\frac{2}{3}$ is the equivalent for $\frac{6}{9}$.

10. Construct drawings to illustrate the mathematical meaning of the statement: $\frac{1}{2} \div \frac{3}{4} = \frac{2}{3}$.

Summary

Abstractly as notated on paper a fraction symbol shows the relationship between two numbers, and may therefore be considered as a ratio. However, the fraction symbol is used to express ideas which develop out of various situations. It is a number.

To illustrate:

1. A fraction may identify one or more than one of the equal parts of an object.

2. A fraction may identify one or more than one of the equal divisions of a group of objects.

3. A fraction may indicate an incompleted division.

4. A fraction may indicate the ratio of one group to another group.

When the ratio of numerator to denominator is less than one, the fraction is considered as a proper fraction. An improper fraction notates a ratio equal to one or more than one. A complex fraction notates the ratio between two fractions or between fraction units and decimal units.

Each fraction has a numerator and a denominator. The denominator notates the number of even divisions of an object, the number of even divisions of a group of objects, or the size of one group of objects. In each case the denominator indicates the total number of even divisions. The numerator notates the number of fractional units being considered. The figures 1, 2, 3, 4, 5, 6, 7, 8, and 9, which indicate the frequency of decimal units of ones, tens, hundreds, and so forth, are used as numerators to indicate the frequency of the fraction units being considered. The numerator may also notate the size of a group of objects when ratio relationship to the denominator is to be determined.

Fractions with a fewer number of larger units may be substituted for those fractions with numerators and denominators divisible by 2, 3, 4, or larger numbers. To illustrate: $\frac{1}{2}$ may be substituted for $\frac{2}{4}$, $\frac{3}{6}$, $\frac{4}{8}$, and so forth. Fractions with a larger number of smaller units may be substituted for any fractions. To illustrate, $\frac{2}{4}$, $\frac{3}{6}$, $\frac{4}{8}$, etc., may be substituted for $\frac{1}{2}$.

The principle of computing with like units, which applies in addition, subtraction, multiplication, and division of integers, applies to the addition, subtraction, multiplication, and division of fraction units. When the fractions being computed have like denominators, the fractions are called *like fractions.* When the fractions being computed have unlike denominators, the fractions are called *unlike fractions.* Before computing with unlike fractions, the fractions should be rewritten as equivalent fractions, all with a common denominator. When the denominators are alike, the computation of the numerators is the same as the computation of integers.

SUGGESTED QUESTIONS FOR TEACHER SELF-EVALUATION

1. When is a fraction a number?

2. When is a fraction an expression of relation?

3. When a fraction is a number, what is the meaning of the denominator? Of the numerator?

4. What is the meaning of a proper fraction? Of an improper fraction?

5. How is the measurement size of a fraction to be found?

6. What is the meaning of a fraction equivalent for a fraction?

7. Why are $\frac{3}{4}$ and $\frac{9}{12}$ equivalent in numerical value?

8. What thought process and mathematical operation are involved when changing a fraction to lower terms? To higher terms?

9. How should pupils interpret the meaning of reduction of fractions to lower terms? To higher terms?

10. What thought process is required to change an improper fraction to a mixed number? To change a mixed number to an improper fraction?

11. How should pupils interpret the terms: "like fractions"? "unlike fractions"?

12. What meanings related to addition and subtraction of integers can be used in addition and subtraction of fractions and mixed numbers?

13. Read the mathematical statement: $\frac{3}{4} \div \frac{1}{2} = 1\frac{1}{2}$. (*a*) What is the meaning of the dividend? Of the divisor? (*b*) How should the quotient $1\frac{1}{2}$ be interpreted? (*c*) What is the difference in meaning between the divisor $\frac{1}{2}$ and the $\frac{1}{2}$ in the quotient?

14. Explain the thought process and the computation involved when using the *like-fraction method* in division. When using the *inversion method.*

15. Why is the *like-fraction method* in division of fractions more consistent with the meanings of division than the *inversion method?*

16. Can you explain the meaning and use of cancellation when used in the *inversion method?*

17. In what type of examples in division of fractions or mixed numbers will the quotient be a fraction?

18. What two questions are answered by the application of multiplication with fractions or mixed numbers?

19. What is a reciprocal of an integer? Of a fraction?

20. Read the example, $\frac{7}{8} \div \frac{3}{4} =$? What fraction is the dividend? How should the sign $\div$ be interpreted?

21. Read the statement: $4 \times \frac{2}{3}$ ft $= 2\frac{2}{3}$ ft. There are how many groups with a numerical value of $\frac{2}{3}$ ft? How should the product be interpreted? What is the meaning of the sign, $\times$?

22. How should pupils think of the term, "lowest common denominator?"

23. Explain the similar and different meanings related to integers, to fractions, and to mixed numbers.

24. Explain the meaning and computation process to be understood for the generalized rules:

(*a*) To find the sum of two or more fractions.

(*b*) To find the difference between two fractions or two mixed numbers.

(*c*) To find the product of two or more fractions. Two or more mixed numbers.

(*d*) To find the product when the multiplier is a fraction.

(*e*) To find the quotient in division of fractions. Of mixed numbers.

(*f*) To find the quotient when the dividend is a number smaller than the divisor.

PRACTICE EXERCISE

Write the answer to each example below and be ready to explain your thinking.

Addition of Fractions

1.	$\frac{3}{5}$	$\frac{4}{7}$	$\frac{3}{8}$	$\frac{7}{10}$	$\frac{2}{3}$	$\frac{3}{8}$	$\frac{4}{5}$	$\frac{3}{10}$
	$+\frac{1}{5}$	$+\frac{2}{7}$	$+\frac{3}{8}$	$+\frac{1}{10}$	$+\frac{1}{3}$	$+\frac{5}{8}$	$+\frac{4}{5}$	$+\frac{9}{10}$

2.	$4\frac{1}{8}$	$3\frac{1}{5}$	$6\frac{7}{10}$	$9\frac{2}{5}$	$8\frac{6}{7}$	$7\frac{3}{4}$
	$+\frac{7}{8}$	$+4\frac{3}{5}$	$+8\frac{1}{10}$	$+6\frac{3}{5}$	$+4\frac{3}{7}$	$+2\frac{3}{4}$

3.	$\frac{1}{4}$	$\frac{1}{2}$	$\frac{3}{10}$	$2\frac{3}{8}$	$5\frac{1}{6}$	$9\frac{5}{8}$
	$+\frac{1}{2}$	$+\frac{1}{10}$	$+\frac{4}{5}$	$+\frac{1}{2}$	$+3\frac{7}{12}$	$+3\frac{3}{4}$

4.	$\frac{1}{2}$	$\frac{1}{3}$	$\frac{1}{4}$	$2\frac{3}{4}$	$8\frac{1}{2}$	$5\frac{1}{4}$
	$+\frac{2}{5}$	$+\frac{1}{2}$	$+\frac{4}{5}$	$+2\frac{1}{3}$	$+9\frac{3}{5}$	$+3\frac{5}{6}$

Subtraction of Fractions

1.	$\frac{4}{5} - \frac{1}{5}$	$\frac{5}{8} - \frac{3}{8}$	$6\frac{3}{8} - \frac{3}{8}$	$5\frac{7}{8} - 2\frac{3}{8}$	$1 - \frac{5}{6}$	$5\frac{1}{7} - 2\frac{5}{7}$
2.	$6\frac{3}{10} - 2\frac{7}{10}$	$\frac{2}{3} - \frac{5}{9}$	$\frac{7}{12} - \frac{1}{4}$	$4\frac{5}{6} - \frac{1}{12}$	$9\frac{3}{8} - 3\frac{1}{4}$	$1\frac{1}{3} - \frac{5}{6}$
3.	$7\frac{1}{6} - \frac{2}{3}$	$8\frac{1}{8} - 2\frac{3}{4}$	$6\frac{1}{2} - 4\frac{7}{8}$	$\frac{5}{8} - \frac{1}{3}$	$\frac{2}{3} - \frac{2}{5}$	$1\frac{1}{5} - \frac{1}{2}$
4.	$7\frac{1}{2} - \frac{4}{5}$	$6\frac{1}{3} - 3\frac{4}{5}$	$8\frac{2}{3} - 3\frac{8}{9}$	$5\frac{1}{8} - 3\frac{1}{3}$	$4\frac{3}{7} - 1\frac{1}{2}$	

Multiplication of Fractions

1. $3 \times \frac{1}{4} = ?$ $2 \times \frac{3}{8} = ?$ $6 \times \frac{3}{4} = ?$ $5 \times \frac{2}{3} = ?$ $6 \times \frac{5}{8} = ?$

2. $2 \times 3\frac{1}{3} = ?$ $4 \times 2\frac{1}{2} = ?$ $\frac{1}{2} \times 10 = ?$ $\frac{3}{4} \times \frac{2}{3} = ?$

3. $\frac{5}{6} \times 2\frac{1}{4} = ?$ $2\frac{2}{3} \times 6 = ?$ $4\frac{3}{8} \times 2\frac{2}{3} = ?$ $\begin{array}{r} 27\frac{3}{8} \\ \times 12 \\ \hline \end{array}$

Division of Fractions

1. $\frac{8}{15} \div \frac{2}{15} = ?$ $\frac{9}{10} \div \frac{7}{10} = ?$ $\frac{2}{3} \div \frac{2}{9} = ?$ $\frac{9}{10} \div \frac{1}{2} = ?$

2. $3\frac{3}{4} \div \frac{3}{4} = ?$ $5\frac{1}{8} \div 2\frac{1}{3} = ?$ $4 \div \frac{2}{3} = ?$ $3\frac{1}{5} \div 2 = ?$

3. $\frac{3}{5} \div \frac{4}{5} = ?$ $\frac{3}{4} \div 1\frac{3}{8} = ?$ $4 \div 6\frac{1}{2} = ?$ $3\frac{1}{4} \div 1\frac{1}{3} = ?$

SUGGESTED ACTIVITIES

1. Prepare a summary of the mathematical meanings teachers should help pupils to learn about common fractions.

2. Examine the new textbooks in arithmetic to observe the methods used to help pupils to discover and to understand the meanings and use of common fractions.

3. Prepare diagnostic tests to diagnose the pupils' understanding of the meanings of common fractions.

4. Prepare a summary of the meanings teachers should help pupils to learn for addition, subtraction, multiplication, and division of common fractions.

5. Prepare:

(*a*) A diagnostic test to determine the pupils' understanding of the meanings involved in computation with common fractions.

(*b*) A diagnostic test to appraise the computational level and skills in addition, subtraction, multiplication, and division of fractions.

SELECTED REFERENCES

1. Brueckner, Leo J., and Grossnickle, Foster E., *How to Make Arithmetic Meaningful.* Philadelphia: John C. Winston Company, 1947.

2. Buckingham, B. R., *Elementary Arithmetic: Its Meaning and Practice.* Boston: Ginn & Company, 1947.

3. Clark, John R., and Eads, Laura K., *Guiding Arithmetic Learnings.* Yonkers, N. Y.: World Book Company, 1954.

4. Eads, Laura K., "We Eat Fractions," *Grade Teacher,* April, 1956.

5. Johnson, J. T., "Common Versus Decimal Fractions," *The Arithmetic Teacher,* November, 1956.

6. Latino, Joseph J., "Take the Folly Out of Fractions," *The Arithmetic Teacher,* November, 1955.

7. Morton, Robert Lee, *Teaching Children Arithmetic.* Morristown, N. J.: Silver Burdett Company, 1953.

8. Polkinghorne, Ada R. "Young Children and Fractions," *Childhood Education,* May, 1935.

9. Ulrich, Louis E., Sr., *Streamlining Arithmetic.* Chicago: Lyons & Carnahan, 1943.

8

Meaning and Use of Decimal Fractions and Mixed Decimals

Introduction

Decimal fractions have no written denominator. The decimal fraction, .7, consists of the symbol 7 and the decimal point (.). The first position to the right of the decimal point is for tenths, so the indicated denominator for .7 is tenths. Seven is a numerator representing the idea that 7 tenths are being considered.

Mixed decimals are composed of an integer and a decimal fraction. The mixed decimal, 5.4 consists of the integer 5, which represents the idea of 5 ones and the decimal fraction .4, which represents the idea of 4 (one-tenths). The decimal point indicates the need for thinking of figures to its right as representing decimal units smaller than ones.

Exploratory Questions

Teachers may find it helpful to appraise their understanding of the mathematical meanings and structure of decimal fractions and mixed decimals by answering each question below. They are encouraged to decide upon answers they plan to help pupils discover and understand.

1. What are the mathematical meanings to be understood for a decimal fraction?

2. What meanings that are related to integers and common fractions may be applied to decimal fractions?

3. What mathematical and social questions are answered by using decimal fractions and computation with decimal fractions?

4. Can you explain the decimal value of decimal fractions based on an extension of the Hindu-Arabic System of notation to the right of the ones' place?

5. What mathematical meaning should pupils understand for the terms: (*a*) an integer, (*b*) a decimal fraction, (*c*) a mixed decimal?

6. How is the denominator of a decimal fraction expressed? How is the numerator of a decimal fraction expressed?

7. What mathematical meanings and what other thought process are involved when substituting a decimal fraction for a decimal fraction with higher or lower terms?

8. What mathematical meanings and thought process are involved when substituting a common fraction for a decimal fraction or in substituting a decimal fraction for a common fraction?

9. How may the mathematical meanings used in addition and subtraction of integers and common fractions be applied when adding decimal fractions and mixed decimals? What new mathematical meanings need to be used?

10. How may the mathematical meanings used in multiplication and division of integers and common fractions be applied to multiplication and division of decimal fractions and mixed decimals? What new mathematical meanings need to be used?

11. What mathematical terms should pupils understand if they are to interpret and communicate accurately their ideas about decimal fractions and decimals?

12. What are the developmental levels of examples that teachers should observe when helping pupils to learn the mathematical sequence in each computation process with decimal fractions and mixed decimals?

13. Why is correct comprehension of mathematical thought processes used by pupils when working with decimal fractions and mixed decimals as important as accuracy in computation?

14. What diagnostic procedures may teachers use to determine the understandings, progress, and needs of pupils as related to decimal fractions and mixed decimals?

Continuity in Teaching and Learning

Mathematics is a logically and sequentially developed system of notation and computation. Teachers have the opportunity to help pupils to discover the structure of the sequential development in the mathematical system so that each learner develops a similar sequence in his psychological understanding and use of mathematics as a thought process.

Continuity in meaningful learnings is obtained when pupils discover and understand the relationship and extension of meanings previously learned to new meanings and operations to be learned.

Some of the mathematical meanings about integers and common fractions that should be related to the meanings for decimal fractions and mixed decimals are:

1. The Hindu-Arabic system of notation is based on a system of place value of one, ten, and powers of ten.

2. The decimal value of a number depends upon the place value of each digit of the number (234 or 2 hundreds + 3 tens + 4 ones).

3. Only units of like decimal value may be added, subtracted, multiplied, or divided.

4. An integer is a number that notates or stands for a group of decimal units.

5. A common fraction is a number that notates or stands for a group of fractional units ($\frac{3}{4}$ or 3 one-fourths of one).

6. Addition is a thought process of combining a given number of addends and notating the sum with one number.

7. Subtraction is a thought process of finding the difference between two numbers and notating the difference with one number.

8. Multiplication is a thought process of finding the sum or product of a given number of like integers or fractions and notating the total with one number (the product).

9. When the multiplier is a fraction, multiplication is also a thought process, that of finding a part of a given integer or fraction.

10. Division is a thought process of finding the ratio relationship between two integers or two fractions.

11. The questions that the mathematical signs (+, −, ×, ÷) ask about integers and common fractions also apply to decimal fractions and mixed decimals.

12. The methods used to verify accuracy in computation with integers and common fractions may be used to verify accuracy of computation with decimal fractions and mixed decimals.

Numerical Value of Decimal Fractions

The numerical value of decimal fractions is based on the division of one into 10 even divisions or 100 even divisions or divisions of $(\frac{1}{10})^N$. The center of the Hindu-Arabic system of notation is the place position *one*. The place value of decimal fractions is an extension of place position to the right of the position *one*. The first place position to the right of one indicates a decimal value of one-tenth ($\frac{1}{10}$) of one. The second place position to the right of the ones place indicates a decimal value of one-hundredth ($\frac{1}{100}$) of one; it also indicates a decimal value of one-tenth of one-tenth ($\frac{1}{10} \times \frac{1}{10}$) of one. In a similar way each place position to the right of the ones place indicates a value in an order series of one-tenth ($\frac{1}{10}$) of one and one-tenth to the N power $(\frac{1}{10})^N$ of one.

	10,000 $(10)^4$ 10,000 Ten Thousand	1000 $(10)^3$ 1000 Thousand	100 $(10)^2$ 100 Hundred	10 $(10)^1$ 10 Ten	1 $(10)^0$ 1 One	$\frac{1}{10}$ $(10)^{-1}$ .1 Tenths	$\frac{1}{100}$ $(10)^{-2}$ .01 Hundredths	$\frac{1}{1000}$ $(10)^{-3}$ .001 Thousandths	$\frac{1}{10,000}$ $(10)^{-4}$ .0001 Ten Thousandths
(*a*)		6	4	3	7				
(*b*)						2	2	5	
(*c*)		8	7	5	6	4	0	8	

(*a*) The number 6437 is an integer 6(1000) + 4(100) + 3(10) + 7(1).

(*b*) The number .225 is a decimal fraction 2(.1) + 2(.01) + 5(.001).

(*c*) The number 8756.408 is a mixed decimal—an integer and a decimal fraction 8(1000) + 7(100) + 5(10) + 6(1) + 4(.1) + 0(.01) + 8(.001).

The decimal point (.) is an adopted symbol or sign to indicate the need for a change in thought from ones to tenths, hundredths, thousandths, etc. It is not a part of the decimal system of notation. The place position of the digits of a notated decimal fraction show the decimal value of the units represented by the notated decimal fraction or a mixed decimal.

1000. —1 thousand, no hundreds, no tens, no ones
100. —1 hundred, no tens, no ones
10. —1 ten, no ones
1. —1 one
.1 —1 one-tenth of one
.01 —1 one-hundredth of one
.001—1 one-thousandth of one

375 (3H + 7T + 5) .8 (8 tenths) .45 (4 tenths + 5 hundredths)

68.036 (6 tens + 8 ones and no tenths + 3 hundredths + 6 thousandths)

Kinds of Decimals

1. An integer is a decimal number having a place value of 1's, 10's, 100's, etc. (476).

2. A decimal fraction is a decimal number having a place value less than one (.25).

3. A mixed decimal is a decimal number having a combination of an integer and a decimal fraction (32.435).

The Hindu-Arabic system of notation is a decimal value system. Therefore all notated numbers may be properly called decimal numbers or decimals.

Reading Decimal Numbers

3587 is read or thought: three thousand five hundred eighty-seven

.026 is read or thought: twenty-six one-thousandths

43.005 is read or thought: forty three and five one-thousandths

48,700.6 is read or thought: forty-eight thousand seven hundred and six one-tenths

Different Forms for Writing Decimal Numbers

The generally accepted form used to write numbers is the notation form. 548 34.5 0.75 .36 .024

Pupils may find interest in using other forms to write numbers, such as:

1. A system of exponents to show decimal place value

$6(10)^3 + 7(10)^2 + 5(10)^1 + 2(10)^0$ (6752)

$8(10)^2 + 4(10)^1 + 3(10)^{-1}$ (840.3)

$4(10)^{-1} + 6(10)^{-2}$ (.46)

$7(10)^{-1} + 0(10)^{-2} + 8(10)^{-3}$ (.708)

2. A system that combines integers and common fractions

$27\frac{4}{10}$ (27.4)

$8\frac{364}{1000}$ (8.364)

Decimal Place Value and Measurement Size of Decimal Fractional Units

The decimal place value of the units of a notated decimal fraction is shown by the place position in which the digits are written. In .3 each of the three units has a decimal value of one-tenth of one. In .27 each unit shown by 2 has a decimal value of one-tenth of one. Each unit shown by 7 has a decimal value of one-hundredth of one. The decimal fraction (.27) as notated stands for 2 tenths and 7 hundredths. It may be interpreted to be 27 hundredths of one.

The decimal .10 shows 1 tenths and no hundredths; however, it must be interpreted to represent 10 hundredths. When .1 is substituted for .10 the decimal fraction shows 1 tenth (.1 is equivalent to .10).

The measurement size of a decimal fractional unit, like common fractional units, depends on the size of the base number and the number of even divisions that have been made or thought to have been made in the base number.

4 yards—The measurement size of each unit of 1 is 1 yard.

.4 yard—The measurement size of each unit is found by thinking of 1 yard or 36 inches divided into 10 even divisions. Each of the tenths has a measurement size of .1 yard or 3.6 inches.

.04 yard—The measurement size of each unit is found by thinking of 1 yard or 36 inches divided into 100 even divisions. Each of the hundredths has a measurement size of .01 yard or .36 inches.

The Terms of a Decimal Fraction

The decimal fraction .8 possesses two identification terms, the numerator and the denominator. The 8 is the numerator and represents a group of eight fraction units. The place position—tenths—is the denominator and shows that each fraction unit is one-tenth of one.

The decimal fraction .36 can be thought of as having a numerator and a denominator. The numerator 36 represents a group of 36 hundredths notated as 3 tenths and 6 hundredths. The denominator is hundredths and shows that the fractional units were based on one divided into 100 even divisions.

The decimal fraction .36 mile shows a numerator and a denominator and also the numerical size of one. The numerator shows 36 fraction units notated as 3 tenths and 6 hundredths. The denominator shows that the unit 1 mile was divided or thought to be divided into 100 even divisions. The measurement size of each of the 36 decimal fraction units is $\frac{1}{100}$ mile or $\frac{1}{100}$ of 5280 feet. The total measurement size of all the 36 decimal fraction units is found by multiplication, 36×52.80 ft $=$ 1900.80 ft.

Teachers may help pupils to understand the meaning of the numerator, denominator, and measurement size of the decimal units by using materials to be measured and then divided into fraction units of tenths, hundredths, or thousandths. These materials may be used effectively to help pupils interpret the mathematical and thought relationship between decimal fraction units and notated decimal fractions.

Generalization to Be Derived

1. The numerator of a decimal fraction is the notated number.

2. The denominator of a decimal fraction is shown by the number of place positions.

3. The notated decimal fraction must be interpreted by using the last place position (.45 is interpreted to be 45 hundredths).

Substituting a Decimal Fraction for Another Decimal Fraction in Higher or Lower Terms

The meanings and process for substituting for a common fraction another fraction with higher terms or lower terms can be applied with minor change to decimal fractions. The generalizations are:

1. Substituting a fraction with higher terms: As the number of even divisions of one (the denominator) is increased, the number of fraction units (the numerator) will be increased in the same ratio.

2. Substituting a fraction with lower terms: As the number of even divisions of one (the denominator) is decreased, the number of fraction units, the numerator, will be decreased in the same ratio.

Changing to higher terms (decimal fractions)

(*a*)		(*b*)		(*c*)		(*d*)
.1	or	.10	or	.100	or	.1000

In (*a*) (.1) the denominator is tenths and the numerator is 1.

In (*b*) (.10) the denominator is hundredths and the numerator is 10.

In (*c*) (.100) the denominator is thousandths and the numerator is 100.

In (*d*) (.1000) the denominator is ten-thousandths and the numerator is 1000.

The total decimal value of (*a*), (*b*), (*c*), and (*d*) is the same.

Substituting a fraction with lower terms (decimal fractions)

(*a*)	(*b*)	(*c*)	(*d*)
.1000	.100	.10	.1

In (*a*) (.1000) the denominator is ten-thousandths and the numerator is 1000.

In (*b*) (.100) the denominator is thousandths and the numerator is 100.

In (*c*) (.10) the denominator is hundredths and the numerator is 10.

In (*d*) (.1) the denominator is tenths and the numerator is 1.

The total decimal value of (*a*), (*b*), (*c*), and (*d*) is the same.

Generalization or Principle

(*a*) When substituting a decimal fraction with higher terms each zero added to the right of the number shows that the number of divisions of the integer, one, has been multiplied by 10.

(1) .6 (2) .60 (3) .600 (4) .6000

(*b*) When substituting a decimal fraction with lower terms each time a decimal position is dropped the number of even divisions of the integer, one, has been divided by 10.

(1) .8000 (2) .800 (3) .80 (4) .8

EXERCISE

1. Write the decimal fractions as hundredths, then as thousandths.

.1 .5 .8 .7 .3 .2

2. Write the decimal fractions as thousandths, then as hundredths, then as tenths.

.4000 .8000 .7000 .1000 .3000 .5000

Equivalents, Decimal Fractions, and Common Fractions

Decimal fractions and common fractions are numbers.

The value of the denominators of decimal fractions is based on tenths and multiples of tenths. The value of the denominator of common fractions is based on $\frac{1}{2}$, $\frac{1}{3}$, $\frac{1}{4}$, and so forth, but there is not a multiple series. Another difference is in the form of notation. Decimal fractions have a numerator that is a number and the denominator is expressed by positions that are related to an extension of the decimal system to the right of the ones' position (.1, .8, .25). The denominator of a common fraction is generally written under a line below the numerator ($\frac{1}{2}$, $\frac{2}{3}$, $\frac{3}{4}$, $\frac{5}{8}$).

Equivalents

Decimal Fraction			*Common Fraction*		
1 or 1.0			$\frac{1}{1}$		
.1			$\frac{1}{10}$		
.5			$\frac{5}{10}$	or	$\frac{1}{2}$
.8			$\frac{8}{10}$	or	$\frac{4}{5}$
.25	.75		$\frac{1}{4}$	$\frac{3}{4}$	
.33$\frac{1}{3}$	.66$\frac{2}{3}$		$\frac{1}{3}$	$\frac{2}{3}$	
.12$\frac{1}{2}$	.37$\frac{1}{2}$		$\frac{1}{8}$	$\frac{3}{8}$	

The decimal fraction .1 is interpreted as 1 one-tenth of one; .5 is interpreted as 5 one-tenths of one; .25 is interpreted as 25 one-hundredths of one. The equivalent of a decimal fraction, when written as a common fraction, is a common fraction that has a numerator that is the same as the numerator of the decimal fraction and that has a denominator of 10, 100, or 1000 depending on the decimal value of the decimal fraction. When the equivalent is written as a common fraction, the fraction is generally expressed in lowest terms (.5 or $\frac{5}{10}$ or $\frac{1}{2}$, .75 or $\frac{75}{100}$ or $\frac{3}{4}$).

The common fraction $\frac{3}{4}$ is interpreted as 3 one-fourths of one. The fraction $\frac{3}{8}$ is interpreted as 3 one-eighths of one. When $\frac{3}{4}$ is changed to the decimal equivalent, .75, the thought process is to think that $\frac{1}{4}$ of 1.00 is .25; therefore, $\frac{3}{4}$ is 3 × .25 or .75. When .37$\frac{1}{2}$ is substituted for $\frac{3}{8}$, the thought process is to think that $\frac{1}{8}$ of 1.00 is .12$\frac{1}{2}$, therefore, $\frac{3}{8}$ is 3 × .12$\frac{1}{2}$ or .37$\frac{1}{2}$.

The generalized rule used to notate the decimal fraction equivalent to a common fraction is to divide the numerator by the denominator.

Generalized Rules for Writing Equivalents

1. To change a decimal fraction to a common fraction, write the numerator over 10 or a power of 10 and reduce to lowest terms when required (.25 or $\frac{25}{100}$ or $\frac{1}{4}$).

2. To substitute a decimal fraction for a common fraction, divide the numerator by the denominator. The quotient is the equivalent decimal fraction. When the division is uneven, express the remainder as a fraction ($\frac{3}{4}$ or .75, $\frac{1}{3}$ or .33$\frac{1}{3}$, $\frac{1}{8}$ or .12$\frac{1}{2}$, $\frac{1}{6}$ or .16$\frac{2}{3}$).

Exercise: Write the equivalent. Explain the process to find the equivalent.

1. $\frac{1}{2}$ or ______, $\frac{1}{4}$ or ______, $\frac{3}{4}$ or ______, $\frac{2}{3}$ or ______, $\frac{5}{6}$ or ______, $\frac{7}{8}$ or ______.
2. .5 or ______, .8 or ______, .25 or ______, .80 or ______, $62\frac{1}{2}$ or ______, $58\frac{1}{3}$ or ______.

Addition

The meanings and thought processes related to adding integers and common fractions apply to the addition of decimal fractions.

1. Add only numbers which express units of like value or size.
2. Substitute one unit of the next larger value or size when required.
3. The sum is the number that notates all the addends as one number (all thought of as one group).

Integers

4	27	87
+5	+46	+49
9	73	136

Fractions

$$\begin{array}{rcr} \frac{3}{4} & \text{or} & \frac{6}{8} \\ \frac{3}{8} & & \frac{3}{8} \\ +\frac{1}{2} & \text{or} & +\frac{4}{8} \\ \hline & & \frac{13}{8} \text{ or } 1\frac{5}{8} \end{array}$$

(a)

Decimals

.4	.27	.87
+.5	+.46	+.49
.9	.73	1.36

(b)

	One	tenths (*t*)
		7
+		8
	1	5

	tenths (*t*)	hundredths (*h*)
	0	7
+	0	8
	1	5

(c) (d) (e)

.77	.007
+.88	+.008
1.65	.015

T	O	Tenth (*t*)	Hundredth (*h*)	Thousandths (*th*)
	7	7	7	7
+	8	8	8	8
1	6	6	6	5

In example (*a*), the question asked is "How many are 7 tenths and 8 tenths together?" These are like decimal units; therefore, they can be added and notated by one number. The addition fact, $7 + 8 = 15$, is used. There are 15 tenths in all, but to notate the sum, 1 must be substituted for 10 tenths. The sum as notated is 1.5 (1 one and 5 tenths).

In example (*b*) the similar question is asked, but the units are hundredths. To find the answer or sum, a person thinks, "7 hundredths and 8 hundredths are how many hundredths in all?" Since the fraction units are alike, the addition fact, $7 + 8 = 15$, is used. There are 15 hundredths in all, but to notate the sum, 1 tenth is substituted for 10 hundredths. The answer is .15 (1 tenth + 5 hundredths).

In example (*c*) the thought process is to find the sum of the addends in each place position. The smaller decimal fraction units are added first; 7 hundredths + 8 hundredths equal 15 hundredths. Substitute 1 tenth for 10 hundredths. Write 5 in the hundredths place and remember the 1 tenth. Then 7 tenths and 8 tenths equal 15 tenths plus the 1 tenth remembered equal 16 tenths. Substitute 1 for 10 tenths and write 6 in the tenth place and 1 in the ones place. The sum is 1.65.

Study (*c*) and (*d*). What are the steps taken in thinking to find each sum? What have you discovered to be the major difference between addition of integers, addition of decimal fractions, and addition of mixed decimals?

Column Addition

(*a*)

O	*t*
	3
	4
+	2
	9

(*b*)

O	*t*	*h*
	4	4
	7	6
+	0	8
1	2	8

(*c*)

O	*t*	*h*	*th*
	0	4	5
	7	0	6
+	8	7	4
1	6	2	5

(*d*)

T	*O*	*t*	*h*	*th*
	3	8	4	7
	9	0	4	6
	7	4	2	1
2	0	3	1	4

In example (*a*) the question asked is, "What number equals the sum of all the tenths?" The first step is to think, $3 + 4 = 7$. The second step is to think $7 + 2 = 9$. There are 9 tenths in all so 9 is written in the tenth's place in the answer or sum.

In example (*b*) the thought process used to find the sum is more complex for the reason that use is made of needed addition facts, and substitution of one unit in the next higher place position for 10 units in the lower place position. The thought steps are: First, think $4 + 6 = 10$; substitute 1 tenth for 10 hundredths and remember 1 tenth; since only eight is left, write 8 in the hundreds place in the answer. Second, think, $4 + 7 = 11 + 1$ (remembered) equal 12, then substitute 1 one for 10 tenths and write 2 in the tenths place and 1 in the ones place. The answer or sum is 1.28 (1 one + 2 tenths + 8 hundredths).

Similar meanings and thought processes are used to find the sums for examples (*c*) and (*d*). Study each example and answer shown in grids (*c*) and (*d*). Explain each thought step taken to find the answer for each example.

Generalization to Be Derived

1. Addition of decimal fractions and mixed decimals involves meanings and thought processes similar to those used in addition of integers.

2. Only like decimal units may be added.

3. When adding decimal fractions or mixed decimals, begin by finding the sum of the addends in the smallest place position.

4. One unit in the next higher place position may be substituted for 10 units in any place position when required.

5. The sum is a decimal fraction or a mixed decimal equal to all the addends combined.

6. Care must be observed in writing decimal fractions or mixed decimals so that units of like decimal value will be in the same place position.

7. The decimal point is used to show separation between integers and decimal fractions.

8. The accuracy of the sum may be verified by repeating the addition.

EXERCISE

Compute the sum for each of the examples. Construct a decimal grid before adding. Explain each thought step in computation:

(*a*)	(*b*)	(*c*)	(*d*)
.3	.02	.431	4.072
+.5	+.07	+.258	+1.928

(*e*)	(*f*)	(*g*)	(*h*)
5.76	.243	48.01	387.435
2.43	.920	50.72	800.203
+8.05	+.875	+81.27	+517.348

Subtraction

The meanings and thought processes used in subtraction of integers apply to subtraction of decimal fractions and mixed decimals.

1. Subtraction is the thought process used to find the difference between two numbers.

2. When there are more units in any decimal place in the subtrahend than in the corresponding place in the minuend, rewrite the minuend by taking 1 of the next larger units, substituting for it 10 smaller units and adding them to the figure in the place to the right.

3. The accuracy of the answer may be determined by adding the difference or answer to the subtrahend to see if it equals the number in the minuend.

Integers

(*a*) $9 - 2 = ?$

$$\begin{array}{r} 9 \\ -2 \\ \hline 7 \end{array}$$

(*b*) $76 - 49 = ?$

T	*O*
6	16
~~7~~	~~6~~
−4	9
2	7

Fractions

(*c*) $\frac{7}{8} - \frac{2}{8} = ?$

$\frac{7}{8}$ 7 one-eighths

$-\frac{2}{8}$ 2 one-eighths

$\frac{5}{8}$ 5 one-eighths

(*d*) $4\frac{1}{2} - 1\frac{3}{4} = ?$

$$\begin{array}{rcrcr} 4\frac{1}{2} & \text{or} & 4\frac{2}{4} & \text{or} & 3\frac{6}{4} \\ -1\frac{3}{4} & \text{or} & -1\frac{3}{4} & \text{or} & -1\frac{3}{4} \\ \hline & & & & 2\frac{3}{4} \end{array}$$

(*e*) $.9 - .2 = ?$

	O	t
		9
−		2
		7

(*f*) $.76 - .49 = ?$

	O	t	h
		6	16
		7	~~6~~
−		4	9
		2	7

(*g*) $.875 - .350 = ?$

	O	t	h	th
		8	7	5
−		3	5	0
		5	2	5

(*h*) $4.50 - 1.75 = ?$

	O	t	h
		4	10
	4	~~5~~	~~0~~
−	1	7	5
	2	7	5

In examples (*a*) and (*e*) the thought process is the same in finding the answer. In example (*a*) the addends are ones; in example (*e*) the addends are tenths.

In examples (*b*) and (*f*) the thought process used to find the answer is similar; the significant difference is that in (*b*) there are integers and in (*f*) there are decimal fractions. The same subtraction facts and substitutions are used in (*b*) and (*f*).

Study examples (*c*) and (*g*). What is the difference in the question asked by each example? What thought steps and subtraction facts are used to find the answer?

Study examples (*d*) and (*h*). What is the difference in the numbers? What is the difference in the question asked?

(*i*)

	O	T	h	th
			9	10
		3	~~10~~	
		~~4~~	~~0~~	~~0~~
−		3	2	6
			?	

(*j*)

	H	T	O	t	h
		8	7	4	2
−		1	9	3	5
			?		

(*k*)

	Th	H	T	O	t	h	th
	9	0	3	2 .	0	7	8
−	6	7	1	0	4	5	9
			?				

In example (*i*) the question asked is, "What is the difference between .400 and .326?" There are no units in the hundredths and thousandths place in the minuend. Thus the minuend is rewritten by substituting 10 hundredths for 1 tenth and then substituting 10 thousandths for one of the ten tenths (.400 is rewritten as $3t + 9h + 10th$). The difference between units in each place value is then computed. Can you interpret the similarity of the thought process used when subtracting decimal fractions and when subtracting integers?

Study carefully examples (*j*) and (*k*). What kinds of decimals are to be compared? What is each thought step to be used in finding the answers to each example?

EXERCISE

Read the question asked by each example. Explain the thought process used to find each answer.

(*a*)	(*b*)	(*c*)	(*d*)
.58	.48	.076	.700
−.23	−.19	−.024	−.487
?	?	?	?

(*e*)	(*f*)	(*g*)
887	40.75	500.65
−309	−12.75	−387.96

Generalization to Be Derived

1. A decimal fraction is a number.
2. The value of a decimal fraction is less than 1.
3. The terms related to a decimal fraction are: (1) numerator and (2) denominator.
4. The numerator shows the number of decimal units.
5. The denominator shows the decimal value of the units.
6. A mixed decimal shows an integer and a decimal fraction.
7. Integers, common fractions, decimal fractions, and mixed numbers denote groups of units.
8. Substitution of one larger unit for ten smaller units is required to find the sum for addends when the sum in any place position is ten or more.
9. Substitution of ten smaller units for one next larger unit is required to find the answer in subtraction when the units in any place position in the subtrahend are larger than the units in the same place position in the minuend.

Multiplication of Decimals

Decimal Fractions

The meanings and computation processes related to multiplication of integers and common fractions apply to the thought process in the multiplication of decimal fractions and also to mixed decimals. The primary difference to be understood is the place value or decimal value of the numbers.

1. Multiplication is the thought and computation process of finding the product or (sum) of two or more numbers that notate equal-sized groups of integers or fractions.
2. The product is one notated number that shows the total amount when the given numbers have been combined or thought to be combined in one group.
3. Only integers or fractions that identify like things or like numerical value can be combined by multiplication.
4. When finding partial products, if the number of units or number in any value position equals ten or more, then one unit of the next larger positional value must be substituted for a group of ten.
5. When the multiplier is an integer, the thought process is to combine a given number of like numbers or fractions in a total group.
6. When the multiplier is a fraction, the thought process is to find a part of an integer or a fraction or a mixed number.

$$\begin{array}{r} 8 \\ \times 5 \\ \hline 40 \end{array} \qquad \begin{array}{r} 87 \\ \times 6 \\ \hline 42 \\ 48 \\ \hline 522 \end{array} \qquad \begin{array}{r} \frac{3}{8} \\ \times 2 \\ \hline \frac{6}{8} \text{ or } \frac{3}{4} \end{array} \qquad \begin{array}{r} \frac{3}{4} \\ \times 14 \\ \hline \frac{42}{4} = 10\frac{2}{4} = 10\frac{1}{2} \end{array} \qquad \begin{array}{r} \frac{2}{3} \\ \times \frac{1}{2} \\ \hline \frac{2}{6} \end{array} \qquad \begin{array}{r} \frac{5}{8} \\ \times \frac{3}{4} \\ \hline \frac{15}{32} \end{array}$$

Multiplication of Decimals— Multiplier a One-Place Integer

$$\begin{array}{c} (a) \\ \begin{array}{r} .3 \\ \times 2. \\ \hline .6 \end{array} \end{array} \qquad \begin{array}{c} (b) \\ \begin{array}{r} .8 \\ \times 4. \\ \hline 3.2 \end{array} \end{array} \qquad \begin{array}{c} (c) \\ \begin{array}{r} .03 \\ \times 2. \\ \hline .06 \end{array} \end{array} \qquad \begin{array}{c} (d) \\ \begin{array}{r} .03 \\ \times 4. \\ \hline .12 \end{array} \end{array} \qquad \begin{array}{c} (e) \\ \begin{array}{r} .34 \\ \times 8. \\ \hline .32 \\ 2.4 \\ \hline 2.72 \end{array} \end{array}$$

In example (*a*) 2 × .3 = ? the question asked and to be answered is, "What number equals two groups of 3 one-tenths?" The answer is the number .6.

In example (*b*) 4 × .8 = ? the question asked is, "What number equals four groups of 8 one-tenths?" The answer is 32 one-tenths or 3 ones and 2 tenths (3.2).

In example (*c*) the question to answer is, "What number is equal to 2 × .03?" The number .06 is the product. In example (*d*) the question is, "4 × .03 = ?" Four groups of .03 (four groups of 3 one-hundredths equal one group of 12 one-hundredths or 10 one-hundredths and 2 one-hundredths or 1 tenth and 2 hundredths (.12). In example (*e*) the product is found by first thinking "8 × .04 = ?" or .32, and then thinking 8 × .3 = ? or 2.4. The product is the sum of the partial products (.32 + 2.4 or 2.72).

Multiplication with a Two-Place Multiplier

(*a*)	(*b*)	(*c*)
.4	.04	.28
×24.	×24.	×36.
1.6	.16	.48
8.	.8	1.2
9.6	.96	2.4
		6.
		10.08

In example (*a*) 24 × .4 = ? the first step is to think, "4 ones × .4 are 16 tenths or 1 and 6 tenths." The second step is to think, "2 tens × .4 is 80 tenths or 8." The sum of the partial products 1.6 and 8 is 9.6.

In example (*b*) 24 × .04 = ? the first step is to think, "4 ones × .04 are 16 hundredths or 1 tenth and 6 hundredths (.16)." The second step is to think, "2 tens × .04 are 80 hundredths or 8 tenths (.8)." The sum of the partial products (.16 + .8) is .96."

In example (*c*) 36 × .28 = ? the first step is to think, "6 ones × .08 are 48 hundredths or 4 tenths and 8 hundredths (.48)." The second step is to think, "6 ones × .2 are 12 tenths or 1 and 2 tenths (1.2)." The third step is to think, "3 tens × .08 are 24 tenths or 2 ones and

4 tenths (2.4)." The fourth step is to think, "3 tens × .2 are 60 tenths or 6 ones (6.)." The sum of the partial products is 10.08. The example (*c*) may be computed by a short mental process that eliminates showing the second and fourth partial products.

(*c*-1)	(*c*-2)	(*c*-3)
.28	.28	.28
×36.	×36.	×36
.48	1.68	168
1.2	8.4	84
2.4	10.08	10.08
6.		
10.08		

The thought process required to find the product in example (*c*-1) has been explained above. In finding the product to example (*c*-2), the first step is to think, "6 × .08 is .48." Write the .08 and remember the 4 tenths. Then, 6 ones × .2 are 12 tenths plus the 4 tenths equal 16 tenths or 1.6." The second step is to think, "3 tens × .08 are 24 tenths or 2 ones and 4 tenths. Write the 4 in the tenths place and remember the 2 ones. Write 8 in the ones position." Then find the sum of the two partial products.

The abstract rule method is shown in the computation for example (*c*-3). The multiplier, 36, is written beneath the decimal fraction, .28. The thought process is to multiply as with integers and then place in the product, 1008, as many decimal places as are shown in the multiplicand and the multiplier. Since there are two decimal places in the multiplicand, two decimal places are indicated in the product, beginning from right to left, 1008 is written, 10.08.

The authors present the view that the process of multiplication in which numbers are left in their correct value positions is more meaningful and no longer than the *abstract rule method*. Pupils who develop an understanding for the abstract rule method should be permitted to use it.

EXERCISE

Find the product for each example, leaving the numbers in their proper value position. Explain the thought process in finding the product.

	(a)	(b)	(c)	(d)	(e)	(f)
A.	.2 ×4. ?	.7 ×6. ?	.03 ×3. ?	.08 ×9. ?	.24 ×3. ?	.76 ×8. ?
B.	.6 ×12. ?	.05 ×24. ?	.36 ×18. ?	.72 ×48. ?		

C. Compute the product for these examples by the *abstract rule method.* Explain the thought process involved.

(*a*) 8 × .6 = ? (*b*) 7 × .24 = ? (*c*) 15 × .38 = ? (*d*) 78 × .65 = ?

Multiplication of Decimals—Two- or Three-Place Decimal Fractions as the Multiplicand and the Multiplier is a Two- or Three-Place Integer

The thought process required to find each partial product in each example is shown to the right of each partial product.

(*a*)

.36	
×24.	
.24	4 ones × .06 = .24
1.2	4 ones × .3 = 1.2
1.2	2 tens × .06 = 1.2
6.	2 tens × .3 = 6.
8.64	Product = 8.64

(*b*)

.246	
×38.	
.048	8 ones × .006
.32	8 ones × .04
1.6	8 ones × .2
.18	3 tens × .006
1.2	3 tens × .04
6.	3 tens × .2
9.348	Product

Multiplication of Decimals—Multiplier Is an Integer—Multiplicand Is a Mixed Number

A mixed number is composed of an integer and a decimal fraction (38.52).

(*a*)		(*b*)	
24.3		378.46	
×54.		×84.	
1.2	4 ones × .3	1513.84	4 ones × 378.46
16.	4 ones × 4 ones	30276.8	8 tens × 378.46
8	4 ones × 2 tens	31790.64	
1215.	5 tens × 24.3		
1312.2	Product		

Generalized Rules

1. Correct Place Value Method or Grid Method

Write the numbers for the multiplicand and the multiplier in their proper decimal value positions. Find the partial products by multiplying the digits or numbers in the multiplicand by the integer that is the multiplier. Then add the partial products to find the total product or the number whose value equals all the decimal fractions combined.

2. Abstract Rule Method

Write the multiplier under the multiplicand. Multiply as with integers to find the product. Then place the decimal point in the product. There should be as many places to the right of the decimal point in the product as in the multiplicand.

EXERCISE

Find the product for each example, first by the *place value method* or *grid method* and then by the *abstract rule method*. Explain the thought process involved in finding the product.

	(a)	(b)	(c)	(d)	(e)
A.	.3	.07	.48	.046	.704
	×8.	×5.	×9.	×6.	×27.
	?	?	?	?	?

B. 33 × 8.76 = ? 25 × 34.15 = ? 50 × .875 = ?
324.87 × 506.95 = ?

C. Construct a decimal grid. Compute the product for each example in row B. Write to the left of the grid the thought process involved in finding each partial product.

Division of Decimals

The meanings and computation process related to the division of integers and common fractions can be applied to division of decimal fractions and mixed numbers. The primary difference to be understood is the decimal value of the numbers.

1. Division is a mathematical and thought process used to answer these questions.

(*a*) How many groups of equal size are formed when a number has been changed or is thought to be changed into numbers of a known value?

(*b*) What is the value of one of the numbers when a known number has been changed or thought to be changed into a given number of groups of equal size?

(*c*) What is the ratio between two given numbers?

2. Division requires the comparison in ratio of like value numbers or like value numbers that identify like things.

3. The divisor is used as the number to find how many numbers like the divisor are equal to the dividend.

4. When there is an uneven division, the remainder may be expressed as a number left or as a fraction indicating what part of another number is like the divisor.

5. The multiplication facts are essential in finding partial quotients and the total quotient in division.

6. When the dividend is smaller than the divisor, the quotient will be less than 1.

7. The accuracy of the quotient in division may be verified by multiplying the divisor by the quotient and adding the remainder, if the division is uneven.

Division—Dividend a Decimal Fraction and Divisor a Decimal Fraction

(*a*)	(*b*)	(*c*)	(*d*)	(*e*)
$.3\overline{).9}$	$.2\overline{).7}$	$.03\overline{).08}$	$.004\overline{).008}$	$.004\overline{).009}$

1. In example (*a*) the question asked is, "How many 3 tenths equal 9 tenths? [? $\times$ .3 = .9]." The answer or quotient is 3, or 3 groups of 3 tenths equal 9 tenths.

2. In example (*b*) the question asked is, "How many 2 tenths equal 7 tenths?" Since the division is uneven the answer or quotient is three groups of 2 tenths and $\frac{1}{2}$ of another group of 2 tenths (.7 $\div$ .2 = 3 and $\frac{1}{2}$).

3. In example (*c*) the question is, "How many 3 hundredths equal 8 hundredths? [.08 $\div$ .03 = ?]." The quotient is 2 groups of 3 hundredths and two-thirds of another group of 3 hundredths (.08 $\div$ .02 = $3\frac{2}{3}$).

4. In example (*d*) the question asked is, "How many 4 thousandths equal 8 thousandths?" The answer or quotient is 2 (.008 $\div$ .004 = 2).

5. In example (*e*) the question asked is, "How many 4 thousandths equal 9 thousandths?" The quotient is 2 groups and $\frac{1}{4}$ of another group of 4 thousandths. In example (*f*) the quotient may be expressed as a decimal as shown at the right. The answer shows that 2 groups of 4 thousandths and 25 hundredths of another group of 4 thousandths. 2 $\times$ .004 = .008 + .25 $\times$ .004 = .008 + .001 = .009.

(*f*)

$$\begin{array}{r} 2.25 \\ .004\overline{).009} \\ \underline{.008} \\ .0010 \\ \underline{.0008} \\ .00020 \\ \underline{.00020} \end{array}$$

Generalized Rule

When dividing like decimal fractions when the dividend is larger than the divisor, the quotient will be one or more groups. If the division is unequal, the quotient will be an integer and a fraction or a decimal fraction.

Division—Dividend an Integer and Divisor a Decimal Fraction

(*a*)	(*b*)	(*c*)	(*d*)
$.3\overline{)6.}$	$.8\overline{)16.}$	$.04\overline{)12.}$	$.006\overline{)36.}$

1. The division example (*a*) asks the question, "How many 3 tenths equal 6 ones?" Since the number in the dividend is unlike in value to the number in the divisor, the dividend is thought of as 60 tenths. The example 6.0 ÷ .3 = ? asks the question, "How many 3 tenths equal 60 tenths?" The quotient is 20. It shows that there are 20 groups of 3 tenths in 60 tenths (20 × .3 = 6.0 or 6).

2. In example (*b*) the example 16 ÷ .8 = ? asks the question, "How many 8 tenths equal 16 ones?" The dividend is thought of as 160 tenths. 16.0 ÷ .8 = ? The quotient is 20. It shows that there are 20 groups of 8 tenths in 160 tenths or 16 ones (20 × .8 = 16.0 or 16).

3. In example (*c*) the example 12. ÷ .04 = ? asks the question, "How many 4 hundredths equal 12 ones?" Since the divisor is hundredths and the dividend is 12 ones, the dividend is thought of as 1200 hundredths. 12.00 ÷ .04 = ? The numbers in the divisor and the dividend now are alike in decimal value. Thus 12.00 ÷ .04 = 300. There are 300 groups of 4 hundredths in 1200 hundredths (300 × .04 = 12.00 or 12).

4. In (*d*) the example 36 ÷ .006 = ? asks the question, "How many groups of 6 thousandths equal 36 ones?" The dividend is thought of as 36,000 thousandths. The ratio between 36,000 thousandths and 6 thousandths is 6000 to 1. The quotient shows that 6000 groups of .006 equal 36,000 thousandths (36.000 ÷ .006 = 6000) (6000 × .006 = 36.000 or 36).

(*e*)

```
     ?                1 54 and 4R or 154 4/24
.24)37.  or  .24)37.00
                  24          154 × .24 + 4R = 154 4/24 × .24 = ?
                 ----
                  13 0
                  12 0
                 ----
                   1 00
                     96
                   ----
                     4 Remainder
```

Derived Generalization

When dividing an integer by a decimal fraction, think of the integer or dividend as a number that shows position value like the number in the divisor. Then divide to find a number or quotient that shows how many groups the size of the divisor equal the number that is the dividend. If the division is uneven, express the remainder as a common fraction or as a decimal fraction. To check the accuracy of the quotient, multiply the divisor by the quotient, and add the remainder if the division is uneven.

The Abstract Rule Method

```
(e)   ?              154 R4 or 154 4/24
.24)37   or   24)3700
                 24
                ---
                130
                120
                ---
                 100
                  96
                 ---
                   4
```

In computing the quotient for the example 37 ÷ .24, both the divisor and the dividend were multiplied by 100 to make the divisor an integer. When the divisor and the dividend in division are both multiplied by 10 or a multiple of 10, the ratio between the dividend and the divisor is unchanged.

EXERCISE

Compute the quotient by the *correct place value method* and also by the *abstract rule method*. Explain the thought process used in finding the quotient by each method.

	(*a*)	(*b*)	(*c*)	(*d*)	(*e*)
1.	$.2\overline{)8}$	$.3\overline{)9}$	$.04\overline{)16}$	$.006\overline{)24}$	$.375\overline{)2625}$
	(*f*)	(*g*)	(*h*)	(*i*)	(*j*)
2.	$.5\overline{)27}$	$.25\overline{)160}$	$.175\overline{)55}$	$.026\overline{)142}$	$.705\overline{)2115}$

Division—Dividend and Divisor Are Mixed Numbers

(*a*)	(*b*)
$2.64\overline{)158.4}$	$37.523\overline{)789.46}$

(*a*)

$$\begin{array}{r} 60 \\ 2.64\overline{)158.40} \\ 158.4 \\ \hline 0 \end{array}$$

(*b*)

$$\begin{array}{r} 21 + R1.477 \\ 37.523\overline{)789.460} \\ 750\ 46 \\ \hline 39\ 000 \\ 37\ 523 \\ \hline 1\ 477R \end{array}$$

1. In example (*a*) the value of the dividend is in tenths (158.4) and the value of the divisor is in hundredths (2.64). When a zero is placed to the right of the 4 tenths in the dividend, the smallest value is hundredths and the smallest value in the divisor is hundredths. The quotient is 60 (60 groups of 2.64 equal 158.40 or 158.4).

2. In example (*b*) similar meanings and computation apply. The smallest value in the divisor is thousandths and the smallest value in the dividend is hundredths. The dividend is changed by adding a zero to the right of 6 so that the smallest value is now thousandths. After computation, the quotient is found to be 21 and the remainder 1477. The quotient has not been computed to one or two decimal places for the reason that the meanings involved have not as yet been introduced (21 groups of 37.523 plus 1.477 equal the dividend, 789.460 or 789.46).

Finding the quotient for each example by the *abstract rule method* requires both the dividend and the divisor in example (*a*) to be multiplied by 100. The new example becomes 15840 ÷ 264. The ratio between the dividend and divisor remains the same but the given numbers have been changed. In example (*b*) the dividend and divisor must be multiplied by 1000 to make the divisor an integer. The new example becomes $37{,}523\overline{)789{,}460}$ = ? The quotient, after being found, in each example must be related to the numbers in the given example. Therefore, the *correct value method* requires mathematical thinking consistent with the question asked by the division example.

EXERCISE

Compute the quotient for each example by the two methods. Explain the mathematical question asked and the mathematical thinking involved in computing the quotient.

	(*a*)	(*b*)	(*c*)
1.	3.42)410.4	14.76)3642.4	4.056)14601.6
	(*d*)	(*e*)	(*f*)
2.	8.07)465.1	38.04)2784.3	4.056)278.4

Division—Dividend Is a Number Smaller Than the Divisor

```
  (a)           (b)              (c)

     .5              .5                  .75
 .4).2          2.4)1.2         24.4)18.3
     .20             1.20             17.08      .7 × 24.4 = 17.08
                                       1.22     .05 × 24.4 = 1.220
                                       1.220
```

In example (*a*) the question .2 ÷ .4 = ? involves another interpretation of division. The question asked is, "The 2 one-tenths in the dividend equal what decimal part of the 4 tenths in the divisor?" The quotient, a decimal fraction, shows that .5 of .4 = .20 or .2.

In example (*c*) the dividend is a mixed number that is smaller than the divisor. The quotient when computed is .75. It shows that .75 of 24.4 is 18.3. The first decimal figure in the quotient shows that .7 of 24.4 is 17.08 which, when subtracted from 18.3, leaves 1.22. The second decimal figure in the quotient shows that .05 of 24.4 is 1.220 or 1.22. Since the division is even, the quotient, .75, shows that 18.3 is .75 of 24.4.

The quotient in example (*c*) can be computed by the *abstract rule method.* Both the divisor and the dividend have been multiplied by 10 to make the divisor an integer. Since 244 is greater than the dividend (183) the quotient will be less than one or a decimal fraction. The question to answer is, "183 is what decimal part of 244?" The computation given for example (*c*) shows that .75 of 244 is 183. However, the given example asked the question, "18.3 is what decimal part of 24.4?" When the quotient is computed without changing the divisor to an integer it shows correctly the mathematical relationship between 18.3 and 24.4.

```
                              .75
24.4)18.3 or 244)183.
                 170.8
                 -----
                  12.2
                  12.20
                  -----
```

EXERCISE

Compute the quotient for each example by both methods. Explain the thought process used in each computation and in the interpretation of the quotient.

	(*a*)	(*b*)	(*c*)	(*d*)	(*e*)
1.	.8).4	1.4).7	4.8).96	.08).032	14.5)4.35

	(*f*)	(*g*)
2.	38.74)21.69	504.6)52.866

Generalized Rule

When the dividend is smaller than the divisor, the quotient will be less than one or a decimal fraction. It shows what decimal part of the divisor equals the dividend. The quotient is computed by first determining how many tenths of the divisor are equal to or near to the dividend. Then find what hundredth part of the divisor is equal to or near the remainder left when the first partial product has been subtracted from the dividend.

Diagnosing Pupil Growth—Test A

I. Questions to be asked by the teacher

1. What is the difference between an integer and a decimal fraction?
2. What place value is the center of the decimal system of rotation?

3. What is the function of the decimal point when notating decimal fractions and mixed decimals?

4. What is the meaning of the numerator of a decimal fraction?

5. What is the meaning of the denominator of a decimal fraction?

6. What thought process is used when changing a common fraction to a decimal fraction?

7. What is the mathematical meaning of a mixed decimal?

8. What question is asked by a multiplication example when the multiplier is a decimal fraction?

9. What question is asked and is answered by subtraction of decimal fractions and mixed decimals?

10. What change must be made in interpreting a decimal fraction when a zero is added to the right?

11. Under what conditions in division will the quotient always be a decimal fraction?

12. What thought process is used when changing a decimal fraction to an equivalent common fraction?

13. In a multiplication example, when the multiplicand is a decimal fraction and the multiplier is an integer, what does the multiplier show? What question is asked by the example?

14. In a division example, when the divisor is a decimal and the dividend is a mixed number, what change must be made in the dividend before the quotient can be computed?

15. Can you tell why decimal fractions are based on an extension, to the right of the ones' place, of the Hindu-Arabic system of notation?

16. What mathematical meanings and generalizations related to integers and common fractions can be applied to decimal fractions?

17. Why are decimal fractions and mixed decimals so important in business?

Diagnosing Pupil Growth—Test B

1. Use the digits 5 and 7. Notate the largest possible two-place decimal fraction.

2. Use the digit 3 and the place holder (0). Notate the smallest possible three-place decimal fraction.

3. Draw a line under the numerator of the decimal fraction .825.

4. Draw a circle around the integer in the mixed decimal 65.25.

5. Change the decimal .650 to lowest terms.

6. Write the common fraction equivalent to the decimal fraction .875.

7. Use the digits 8, 5, 1, 2, and write the smallest possible four-place mixed decimal.

8. Write the decimal fraction equivalent to $\frac{3}{4}$.

9. Draw a circle around the decimal fraction in the mixed decimal 803.45.

10. What number is .125 of 64?

11. What is the answer to the example 4 ÷ 8 = ?

12. What is the answer to the example 24 ÷ .25 = ?

13. Write $12\frac{37}{1000}$ as a mixed decimal.

14. If the dividend and divisor have the same decimal fraction, the quotient will be ______ ?

15. Notate the following decimals and mixed decimals:

(*a*) 28 hundredths
(*b*) $25\frac{3}{4}$ hundredths
(*c*) $8\frac{1}{2}$ tenths
(*d*) 47 thousandths
(*e*) 860 ten-thousandths
(*f*) 500 and 75 hundredths
(*g*) 1000 and 3 one-thousandths
(*h*) eleven thousand, eleven hundred, eleven and eleven hundredths

16. Change .8 to thousandths.

17. Construct a decimal grid. Compute the quotient and explain each thought step for the example: 21 ÷ .875 = ?

Diagnosing Pupil Growth—Test C

Addition of Decimal Fractions and Mixed Decimals

.6	.7	.08	.86	.008	6.985
+.3	+.9	+.08	+.95	+.005	+5.768

.3	.6	.54	.032	.3965	37.7658
.2	.5	.65	.709	.8754	29.6743
+.3	+.8	+.78	+.865	+.7643	+95.7247

Subtraction of Decimal Fractions and Mixed Decimals

.7	.16	.17	.78	.63	.78	.57
−.2	−.07	−.05	−.08	−.07	−.65	−.30

.60	.85	.86	7.25	8.68	6.80	1.26
−.20	−.27	−.79	−.24	−.95	−.45	−.79

4.03	7.35	8.39	49.0	71.7	9.00	700.26
−.68	−2.24	−2.65	−28.6	−47.8	−1.56	−378.18

Multiplication of Decimal Fractions and Mixed Decimals

.4	.9	.03	.05	.84	.5	.76
× 2	× 6	× 2	× 6	× 8	×24	× 85

.376	35.3	485.76	695.078
× 49	× 64	× 84	× 95

Division of Decimal Fractions and Mixed Decimals

$.4\overline{).8}$ $.2\overline{).9}$ $.04\overline{).08}$ $.03\overline{).07}$ $.003\overline{)00.5}$ $.004\overline{).009}$

$.2\overline{)6.}$ $.7\overline{)14.}$ $.05\overline{)25.}$ $.008\overline{)32.}$ $.32\overline{)45.}$

$3.8\overline{)165.9}$ $62.425\overline{)586.45}$ $3.75\overline{)165.30}$ $46.232\overline{)929.720}$

$.6\overline{).2}$ $3.4\overline{)1.7}$ $.06\overline{).36}$ $72.2\overline{)31.5}$

Summary

The understandings developed in a study of integers and fractions can be used in thinking about and computing with decimal fractions and mixed decimals. Decimal units with a place value smaller than one have the same 1 to 10 relationship as decimal units with a place value of one or units larger than ones. The questions asked by addition, subtraction, multiplication, and division examples in which the numbers represent decimal fractions or mixed decimals ask the same questions asked by addition, subtraction, multiplication, and division examples in which the numbers represent integers.

The ideas of computing with like units apply to computation of decimal fractions and mixed decimals. In the addition, subtraction, and multiplication of decimal fractions and mixed decimals, first the smallest and then the successively larger units are computed. In division of decimal fractions or mixed decimals, the dividend can be separated into partial dividends. The first partial dividend will have figures equal to or larger than the figure in the divisor.

The new idea that is utilized in computing with decimal fractions or mixed decimals is that a decimal point (.) represents the point at which we stop thinking about integers and begin thinking about decimal fraction units.

Examples in addition, subtraction, multiplication, and division of decimal fractions and mixed decimals may be taught in accordance with developmental levels determined by the complexity of the examples. These levels are very similar to those in examples in which there are integers.

SUGGESTED QUESTIONS FOR TEACHER SELF-EVALUATION

1. Why is the system of decimal fractions frequently called an extension to the right of the decimal system of notation?

2. What mathematical meanings should teachers help pupils to learn for decimal fractions? For mixed decimals?

3. What mathematical meanings can be applied to integers, common fractions, and mixed decimals?

4. What are the different questions that can be answered by multiplication of decimals?

5. What are the developmental levels of examples teachers should use when helping pupils to learn the mathematical sequence when adding, subtracting, multiplying, and dividing decimal fractions?

6. What are the meanings and computational steps pupils should understand about division of decimal fractions? Of mixed decimals?

7. How may teachers help pupils to understand the mathematical thought process when changing decimal fractions to higher or lower terms?

8. What is the correct thought process pupils should use when computing the answers to these examples:

(*a*) .805 + .360 + .031 = ? (*d*) .44 × 86 = ?

(*b*) 5.00 − 3.74 = ? (*e*) 144 ÷ .24 = ?

(*c*) 24 × .45 = ? (*f*) .12 ÷ .9 = ?

PRACTICE EXERCISES

Write the answer to each example below and be ready to explain your thinking.

Addition of Decimals

1.

.3	.04	.7	1.4	6.8	.98	.3	.04
.6	.05	.6	.3	.6	.05	.2	.06
						.3	.07
						.1	.08

2.

.53	.85	2.7	.29	9.78	57.6	9289.7	74.865
.45	.72	1.8	.47	.89	45.6	8654.3	86.758
	.91	3.3	.32			7478.7	92.875
		1.2	.86			9643.9	86.924

Subtraction of Decimals

1.

.9	.15	4.9	5.7	6.2	.66	.86	7.25
−.4	−.07	−.6	−.7	−.7	−.34	−.29	−.14

2.

.968	6.90	12.6	8.04	.516	80.0	9.2987
−.074	−.35	−7.9	−.68	−.376	−12.5	−4.3998

Multiplication of Decimals

1.

.04	6.0	8.2	.26	.68	93.7	79.6	950.4
×2	×3	×.4	×.03	×.5	×.07	×.009	×.008

2.

4.1	.83	.68	3.9	.28	84.3	7.642	62.7
×5.1	×.30	×.41	×8.2	×.73	×45	×.047	×49.6

Division of Decimals

1. .2).8 .15).75 .003)9.000 .4)8.4 .05)7.50

2. 6).3 8.5).51 32.7)98.1 3.6)4.50 4.5)96.8522

SUGGESTED ACTIVITIES

1. Prepare a summary of the mathematical meanings that teachers should help pupils to learn about decimal fractions and the computational processes with decimal fractions.

2. Examine the new textbooks in arithmetic to determine the meanings and methods given for teaching understanding and computational skills for decimal fractions and mixed decimals.

3. Prepare diagnostic tests that teachers may use:

(*a*) To appraise the pupils' understanding of decimal fractions.

(*b*) To determine the ability of pupils to compute with decimals.

(*c*) To illustrate the mathematical meanings of decimal fractions and the computational process with decimal fractions.

SELECTED REFERENCES

1. Arnold, Frank C., "The Decimal Is More Than a Dot." *The Arithmetic Teacher*, October, 1955.

2. Brueckner, Leo J., and Grossnickle, Foster E., *How to Make Arithmetic Meaningful.* Philadelphia: John C. Winston Company, 1947.

3. Clark, John R., and Eads, Laura K., *Guiding Arithmetic Learnings.* Yonkers, N. Y.: World Book Company, 1954.

4. Grossnickle, Foster E., "Some Factors Affecting a Test Score in Division of Decimals," *Journal of Educational Research*, January, 1944.

5. Haraph, H. L., and Mapes, C. E., "The Learning of Decimals in an Activity Program." *Journal of Educational Research*, May, 1936.

6. Marth, Ella, "Building Concepts in Decimal Fractions," *Grade Teacher*, April, 1956.

7. Morton, Robert Lee, *Teaching Children Arithmetic.* Morristown, N. J.: Silver Burdett Company, 1953.

8. Spitzer, Herbert F., *The Teaching of Arithmetic*, 2d ed. Boston: Houghton Mifflin Company, 1954.

9. Ulrich, Louis E., Sr., *Streamlining Arithmetic.* Chicago: Lyons & Carnahan, 1943.

9

Use of Arithmetic in Home, Business, and Industry

Introduction

The American producer and consumer are becoming increasingly dependent upon money as the medium of exchange for raw materials, finished products, and services. The American citizen, whether a householder, businessman, or industrialist, needs to know how to use percentage; prepare budgets; keep accounts of expenditures; offer or take advantage of discounts; buy or sell on the installment plan; compute interest, taxes, and public utility bills. He needs to be able to read, understand, and use financial data, whether presented on charts, tables, or graphs. Schools must accept the responsibility of helping pupils become competent in practical financial matters.

Exploratory Questions

Teachers may appraise their present understanding of the meanings, thought processes, and skills used in the family, in business, and in industry by deciding upon answers to the following questions.

1. What is the meaning of "percent"? What is the relationship between percent, decimal fractions, and fractions?

2. How may teachers help pupils to learn to (*a*) add percents, (*b*) subtract percents, (*c*) substitute decimal fractions for percents,

(*d*) substitute percents for decimals, (*e*) substitute fractions for percents, (*f*) substitute percents for fractions?

3. What understandings and skills are used in (*a*) finding the percent of a whole quantity, (*b*) finding the percent that one number is of another, (*c*) finding the whole quantity when a part and the percent of the whole quantity are known?

4. What understandings and skills are used in finding the percent of increase? In finding the percent of decrease?

5. How is an understanding of percents applied to answering questions involving subjects such as interest, profit and loss, stocks and bonds, discounts, budgets, commission, taxes?

6. What kinds of mathematical ideas can be best presented through the use of charts and graphs?

7. What are the meanings and skills that teachers should help pupils to understand regarding the interpretation and construction of graphs?

8. What is the consumer economic importance of graphs?

9. What is the functional value of (*a*) straight-line graphs, (*b*) bar graphs, (*c*) circle graphs, (*d*) pictographs?

Percent as a Way of Thinking

Percents and percentages are essential in modern business and industry. The intelligent consumer needs to be able to interpret advertisements in which percents may be a prominent part of the advertising copy. Sportswriters spend considerable time reducing scores and averages to percents. Writers in the social studies and other school subjects like to express data in percents. Despite the increasing use of percents and percentages in written communication, many persons confess a complete lack of understanding of what is meant by the % sign, percent of increase, percent of decrease, percent of discount, rate of interest, and so forth.

This lack of understanding may have several bases. In the past, the subject of percent was deferred until the seventh or even eighth grades. Teachers in lower grades sometimes purposely avoided any discussion of the subject so as to avoid taking the "frosting" from this topic. By the time the children had an opportunity to study percent they had learned to stand in awe of it as being something very difficult. Teachers sometimes failed to see the relationships among percent, decimals, and fractions. As a result they were unable to help children see the relationships and tended to teach percent in isolation.

At the present time many teachers are giving children an opportunity to lay the groundwork for their study of percent long before it is introduced as a formal topic in the curriculum. In the third or fourth grade, for example, children can be helped to understand that if a savings bond earns 3% interest, the government will pay $3 interest for each $100 invested. They can be helped to understand that if a merchant advertises a 25% reduction in price, the merchant plans to sell articles for less than the usual price. The 25% is simply his way of letting his customers know how many cents out of each $1 (100 cents) they can expect to save if they buy his goods on sale.

As the children become more mature, they can be helped to see that percent is a means of expressing the fraction relationship (ratio) between two numbers. The second term of the ratio (denominator of the fraction) must be hundredths. If not, then a ratio with a denominator of hundredths must be substituted for the ratio of the two numbers. Illustration: $\frac{1}{2}$ expresses the relation of 1 to 2. $\frac{1}{2} = \frac{50}{100}$ and $\frac{50}{100}$ expresses the relation of 50 to 100. The ratio of 50 : 100 may be expressed 50%. $\frac{3}{4} = \frac{?}{100}$. $\frac{3}{4} = \frac{75}{100}$. $\frac{75}{100} = 75\%$.

Three percent expresses the relationship of 3 to 100; 5% expresses the relationship of 5 to 100; $12\frac{1}{2}\%$ expresses the relationship of $12\frac{1}{2}$ to 100.

From previous experience, children have learned to think of ratios in terms of common fraction units and decimal fraction units. Such expressions as $\frac{3}{100}$ or .03 are common symbols whose meaning must be understood by children before they begin a formal study of percent. But children who understand the use of the fraction line (—) [slant (/)] to show the relationship between 3 and 100, and the use of the decimal point together with place value to show the relationship of 3 of the hundred equal parts of 1 to 100 of the hundred equal parts of 1 will have a background to aid them in learning to think of a % sign as just another symbol used to show relationship between two numbers. The sign % identifies hundredths.

They can use this background to help them understand that $\frac{3}{100}$, or .03, or 3% all mean that some quantity has been divided or has been thought of as being divided into 100 equal divisions and that 3 of the 100 equal parts are under consideration. Thinking about percent and percentage is not different from thinking about fractions and fractional units. The percent symbol is new but the ideas of how to use percent are based on ideas already taught.

Equivalent Common Fractions, Decimals, and Percent

$\frac{1}{2}$ is a fraction with a denominator of 2 and a numerator of 1; .50 is a decimal fraction with a denominator of hundredths (expressed by place value) and a numerator of 50; 50% is a percent with a denominator of hundredths (expressed by the % sign) and a numerator of 50.

In the illustration shown below, $\frac{1}{2}$ shows that an undivided unit, a

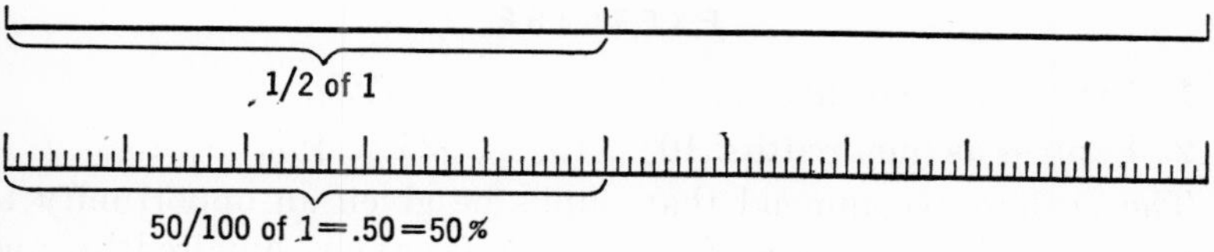

line segment, was divided into two equal divisions and one of the equal fractional parts is being considered. The fraction, $\frac{50}{100}$, shows that an identical undivided unit, a line segment, was divided into 100 equal divisions and that 50 of the equal parts are being considered. On the second line each fractional unit is $\frac{1}{50}$ as large as the fractional unit notated by $\frac{1}{2}$.

To solve $\frac{1}{2} = \frac{?}{100}$, think: There are 50 times as many hundredths as halves in lines of equal length. $\frac{1}{2} = \frac{50}{100}$. $\frac{1}{2} = .50$. $\frac{1}{2} = 50\%$. To solve $\frac{3}{4} = \frac{?}{100}$, think: The denominator, hundredths, indicates 25 times as many fractional units as the denominator, fourths. Each $\frac{1}{4} = \frac{25}{100}$. Three of the $\frac{1}{4}$'s $= \frac{75}{100}$.

The shortcut rule used in finding a decimal fraction equivalent to a common fraction is to divide the numerator by the denominator, as $\frac{1}{5} = \begin{array}{r} .20 \\ 5\overline{)1.00} \end{array}$. To substitute a percent for hundredths, simply rewrite the decimal fraction as an integer and substitute the percent sign for the decimal place value, hundredths.

The fraction, $\frac{20}{100}$, can be reduced to lower terms by dividing both numerator and denominator by 20. $\frac{20}{100} = \frac{1}{5}$, so .20 or $20\% = \frac{1}{5}$.

Writing Percents

Percents smaller than 1% may be expressed as a common fraction or as a decimal. $\frac{1}{2}$ of 1 hundredth may be written as $\frac{1}{2}$% or .5%. To express a decimal such as .875 as percent we think of the number as composed of 87 hundredths and 5 thousandths ($\frac{1}{2}$ of 1 hundredth). The 87 hundredths is notated as 87%. The .005 may be notated as $\frac{1}{2}$% or .5%. .875 = 87$\frac{1}{2}$% or 87.5%. Numbers larger than tenths are expressed as ones, tens, and so forth. Thus 2.50 is written, 250% (2 = $\frac{200}{100}$+ $\frac{50}{100}$ = 200% + 50% = 250%). Percents may be rewritten as decimals by dividing the percent by 100. This is accomplished by dropping the percent sign and rewriting the number as hundredths. 75% = .75. 12$\frac{1}{2}$% = .12$\frac{1}{2}$. .5% = .005.

EXERCISE

1. Express as percent: $\frac{5}{100}$, $\frac{33}{100}$, $\frac{15}{100}$, $\frac{3}{1000}$, $\frac{375}{1000}$.

2. Express as hundredths: 10%, 12$\frac{1}{2}$%, 325%, $\frac{1}{4}$%.

The authors recommend that pupils be given an opportunity to construct their own table of equivalent fractions, hundredths, and percents. A representative table follows:

TABLE OF EQUIVALENTS

$\frac{1}{2}$ = .50 = 50%	$\frac{1}{3}$ = .33$\frac{1}{3}$ = 33$\frac{1}{3}$%	$\frac{4}{5}$ = .80 = 80%
$\frac{1}{4}$ = .25 = 25%	$\frac{2}{3}$ = .66$\frac{2}{3}$ = 66$\frac{2}{3}$%	$\frac{1}{10}$ = .10 = 10%
$\frac{3}{4}$ = .75 = 75%	$\frac{1}{6}$ = .16$\frac{2}{3}$ = 16$\frac{2}{3}$%	$\frac{3}{10}$ = .30 = 30%
$\frac{1}{8}$ = .12$\frac{1}{2}$ = 12$\frac{1}{2}$%	$\frac{5}{6}$ = .83$\frac{1}{3}$ = 83$\frac{1}{3}$%	$\frac{7}{10}$ = .70 = 70%
$\frac{3}{8}$ = .37$\frac{1}{2}$ = 37$\frac{1}{2}$%	$\frac{1}{5}$ = .20 = 20%	$\frac{9}{10}$ = .90 = 90%
$\frac{5}{8}$ = .62$\frac{1}{2}$ = 62$\frac{1}{2}$%	$\frac{2}{5}$ = .40 = 40%	$\frac{2}{2}$ = 1 = 100%
$\frac{7}{8}$ = .87$\frac{1}{2}$ = 87$\frac{1}{2}$%	$\frac{3}{5}$ = .60 = 60%	$\frac{4}{4}$ = 1 = 100%

Adding and Subtracting Percents

(a)	(b)	(c)	(d)	(e)	
3%	37%	112$\frac{1}{2}$%	75%	100 % =	99$\frac{3}{3}$%
+4%	+45%	+65 %	−10%	−16$\frac{2}{3}$%	−16$\frac{2}{3}$%
7%	82%	177$\frac{1}{2}$%	65%		83$\frac{1}{3}$%

In example (*a*) the question asked is, "What % equals the sum of 3% and 4%?" The answer is 7%. In example (*b*) and (*c*) the addition is done as with other numbers by first computing the sum of the smaller and then of successively larger units. Since each addend represents percent, the sum represents percent.

In examples (*d*) and (*e*) the solution depends upon thinking of a number which represents the difference between the subtrahend and the minuend. In example (*d*) first ones and then tens are subtracted. In example (*e*) $\frac{3}{3}$% was substituted for 1% in the minuend and the minuend rewritten as $99\frac{3}{3}$%. Then fractions, ones, and tens were subtracted.

Generalizations to Be Understood

1. Percents are equivalent to decimal fractions or common fractions with denominators of 100.

2. The percent sign (%) can be substituted for the slant (/) and stated denominator in fractions having a denominator of hundredths or for the decimal point in a decimal fraction written as hundredths.

The Three Cases of Percent or Three Kinds of Questions About Relationships

A number such as 5% arises out of a situation in which some quantity, for example $500, was separated into 100 equal parts and 5 of the equal parts are being considered. In the equation, 5% of $500 = $25, 5% tells how many *percent;* $500 tells how many in the *whole quantity,* and $25 tells how many in the fractional part which is known as the *percentage.*

If any two of the three factors in such equations as 5% of $500 = $25 are known, the missing element can be computed. In the example, 5% of $500 = ? the percentage is unknown. The example asks the question, "What number equals 5 of the 100 equal parts of $500?" Five of the 100 equal parts of $500 = $25. In the example just discussed, the whole quantity, $500, may be considered as the base (*b*), the percent (5%) may be considered the *rate* (*r*), the percentage ($25) may be considered as the percentage (*p*). The formula for finding percentage is $p = rb$ (percentage = rate × base). In examples where it is necessary to find the percentage, we are using the *first case of percent* or one question answered by percent.

In some situations the whole quantity and the percentage are known and it is necessary to find the percent. Situations of this kind are considered the *second case of percent.* A representative question, which can be answered by using the second case of percent, is "\$25 = what percent of \$500?" Since percent represents a special kind of fraction, this question can be rephrased, "\$25 = what fraction of \$500?" and the example can be written, ?% = $\frac{25}{500}$. To answer the question, divide $500\overline{)25.00}$ (quotient $.05 = 5\%$). The answer to the question asked by the example, "25 = what percent of \$500?" is "\$25 = 5% of \$500." If \$500 is considered as the base (*b*) and \$25 as the percentage, then the formula becomes $r = \frac{p}{b}$.

EXERCISE

Answer these questions: 7 = ?% of 14 ?% of 20 = 5 25 = ?% of 125 ?% of 3.5 = 14?

Occasionally the percent and the percentage are known but the whole quantity is unknown. Examples in which the whole quantity is unknown illustrate the third use of percent. In the example, 20% of ? = \$50, the question asked is, "\$50 = 20% of what number?" To answer the question we can think, "\$50 = $\frac{1}{5}$ of the number. Then $\frac{5}{5}$ = 5 × \$50 or \$250." The answer is "\$250." If we prefer to work with decimals we can think, "\$50 = .20 of the number. Then .01 = \$50 ÷ .20, which equals \$2.50. 100% = 100 × \$2.50 = \$250." The answer to the question asked by the example, "\$50 = 20% of what number?" is "\$50 = 20% of \$250." The answer is \$250. If \$50 is considered as the percentage (*p*) and 20% is considered as the rate (*r*), then the formula becomes $b = \frac{p}{r}$.

EXERCISE

Answer these questions: 15 = 30% of ? $66\frac{2}{3}$% of ? = 90 \$25 = 3% of ?

Percent Decrease and Percent Increase

The label on a bolt of material might indicate, "Maximum shrinkage, 2%." To find how long a 10-yard piece of material would be after shrinking might be done in two ways as shown at the right. In Method 1, the decrease in yards is computed by using the first case of percent and then the amount of decrease in yards is subtracted from the original length. In Method 2, the decreased length of material is 98% of the original length. The subtraction of percents preceded the multiplication. The percent of decrease is 2%. The decreased length is 98% of the original length.

Method 1

10 yd	10. yd
× .02 yd	− .20 yd
.20 yd	9.80 yd

Method 2

100% − 2% = 98%

10 yd
× .98
9.80 yd

The *increase* in value or size may be expressed as percent. To illustrate, a storekeeper might plan to increase prices by 25%. If he does, then an article originally priced at \$8 would be increased \$2 (25% of \$8 = $\frac{1}{4}$ of \$8 = \$2). The increased price would be \$10 (\$8 + \$2 = \$10). Another method of determining the new price is to add the percents (100% + 25% = 125%). The new price is 125% of \$8 ($1\frac{1}{4}$ × \$8 = \$10). The percent of increase is 25%. The new price is 125% of the original price.

Cash Accounts and Budgets

The intelligent expenditure of money for goods and services is dependent upon numerous knowledges and skills together with the skills of computation. Before money can be wisely spent, wants and needs, quality as well as quantity, style, and depreciation should all be considered. The record of expenditures and receipts is important to the intelligent consumer. One of the simplest kinds of records is the *cash account.* Several forms may be used, but in each form there will be a place to record *income* and a place to record *expenditures.* The difference between these items is the *balance.* Cash accounts may be balanced at any time but are usually balanced at least once a month. The difference between total monthly receipts (which include balance brought forward from the previous month) and expenditures is recorded with the expenditures. The total expenditures and receipts will then be equal. Double lines are drawn beneath the sums in both columns and the balance is recorded again as an item of income in the income column.

After careful records have been kept for a period of time an analysis of them may reveal a certain spending pattern. Then the income and the expenses may be predicted rather accurately. If this is possible, a budget may be prepared. A budget is simply a plan to use in spending available income.

The amount of money spent for each major item of expense may be computed as a percent of the total income. To illustrate, if an individual has an income of \$80 a week and has had an average expenditure of \$20 a week for food, he has been spending 25% of his income for food ($\frac{20}{80} = \frac{1}{4} = 25\%$). By determining allowances in percent rather than limiting oneself to expressing amounts in dollars and cents, the plan for the budget can be used even though there are minor fluctuations in income. If, however, income increases or decreases sharply, some percents may have to be adjusted to meet changing conditions.

The second use of percent; i.e., finding what percent one number is of another, is used in setting up budget allowances. The first use of percent; i.e., finding the percentage, is used in computing the actual amount to allow for each item in the budget. If, for example, 20% is allowed for rent, then the weekly rent can be 20% of \$80 or \$16.

Discounts

Customers are often induced to enter stores because of promises of discounts; i.e., reductions from the usual price. Discounts may be expressed as fractions, percents, or as the difference between the regular price and the sale price. It is common practice to show both the list price and the sale price and the buyer is expected to find the difference between these prices if he wants to know the amount of discount. In computing the amount of discount when the fraction or percent of discount is known, multiply the original price by either the fraction or percent to find the amount of discount. The sale price is then determined by subtracting the amount of discount from the original price. The formula to use in finding the discount (d) when the rate (r) and base (b) are known is as follows: $d = rb$.

In modern merchandising, many stores offer cash discounts or trade-in allowances which, in effect, are discounts. The rate of the discount can be computed by using the second case of percent. If a store offers a \$2 reduction on a \$10 item, the percent of discount is 20%: $\left(\frac{\$2}{\$10} = \frac{1}{5} = 20\%\right)$.

Wholesalers and some retailers offer *successive discounts*. These discounts may be given as a regular trade discount to any purchaser, as a special discount because of the size of the order, and as a cash discount if payment is made within a stated period of time. The successive discounts are sometimes called a discount series. Discounts of 25%, 10%, and 2% are a representative discount series.

When two or more discounts are allowed, the first discount is computed as a percent (or fraction) of the list price, and the amount of discount is subtracted from the original list price. The amount left is the base upon which the second discount is computed. The amount of the second discount is then subtracted from the second base price. If there are more discounts, each successive discount is computed as a percent of what remains after the preceding discount has been subtracted.

If a radio is priced at \$125 with discounts of 10% and 2%, the actual price to the customer is \$110.25 (10% of \$125 = $\frac{1}{10}$ of \$125 = \$12.50. \$125 − \$12.50 = \$112.50. 2% of \$112.50 = \$2.25. \$112.50 − \$2.25 = \$110.25). A second procedure might be to multiply \$125 by 90% and to then multiply the product by 98%. Explain why this method is a good one. How much less than \$110.25 would the radio have cost if the discounts had been added and the sum of the discounts used as a single discount on the original base price?

EXERCISE

Complete the following table.

	List Price	Percent of Discount	Discount	Sale Price
1.	\$25	30%	?	?
2.	\$60	?	\$10	?
3.	\$15	?	?	\$12
4.	\$500	25%, 10%, 2%	?	?

Buying on the Installment Plan

The practice of paying a certain amount down and the balance in equal payments spread over a period of time is becoming increasingly common. The down payment may be expressed as a percent, such as "10% down." To determine the amount of the down payment the buyer uses the first case of percent. If a $225 television set can be purchased for a down payment of 10%, the amount of the initial payment is 10% of $225 or $22.50.

Installment buying is often spoken of as "buying on terms." In a recent year (1955) 65% of the new cars purchased were bought on terms. A rule of thumb used by most finance companies is that there is danger in any monthly car payments that exceed 25% of the family's monthly income. To keep the cost of installment buying at a minimum and to keep the monthly payments relatively low, intelligent consumers make the largest possible down payment on merchandise bought under the installment plan. It is perfectly possible to purchase goods that will have completely lost their value before the series of payments has been completed. Then the purchaser has burdensome payments for which he can see no tangible benefits.

The installment price is higher than the cash price because it must include a finance charge, which often adds several hundred dollars to the price of an expensive item such as a car. The computation of the actual cost of installment buying is complicated because of the finance charge, interest, insurance, and brokerage fees, which must all be added to the list price of the car before the amount of the monthly payments is determined.

After the difference between the cash price and the installment price is computed, the *percent of increase* in price can be determined by using the second case of percent. If the total installment price of an article is $150 and the cash price is $125, the amount paid for the privilege of buying on the installment plan is $25. This represents an increase of 20% over the cash price ($\frac{25}{125} = 20\%$).

Interest

For various reasons, people are willing to pay for the use of money and others are willing to loan their money if they get paid for making the loan. The amount paid is called *interest*, the amount borrowed or loaned is called *principal*, and the *rate* of interest per year is stated as a percent of the principal. Interest is really a special application of percent because principal and rate as well as time must be considered in computing interest costs.

The principal is the *whole quantity*. The rate is the *percent*, and the amount of interest is the *percentage*. The method of finding the interest on $300 at 3% for 1 year is shown at the right. Since the time is for 1 year, it can be disregarded in the computation because 1 × $9.00 = $9.00. If the time had been less than 1 year, the amount of time would have been expressed as a fraction of a year and the interest for 1 year ($9.00) multiplied by the fraction. If the $300 had been borrowed at 3% for 4 months, the time would be expressed as $\frac{1}{3}$ of a year ($\frac{1}{3}$ of $9.00 = $3.00). Three dollars is the amount of interest on $900 borrowed at the rate of 3% for a period of 4 months.

$$\begin{array}{r} \$300 \\ \times .03 \\ \hline \$9.00 \end{array}$$

SIMPLE INTEREST FOR $100

Bankers and others engaged in the business of lending money use interest tables to simplify their work. Following is a portion of one kind of interest table.

	1 day	7 days	1 month	3 months	6 months	1 year
2%	$.00556	$.03889	$.16667	$ .50000	$1.00000	$2.00000
2½%	.00694	.04861	.20833	.62500	1.25000	2.50000
3%	.00833	.05833	.25000	.75000	1.50000	3.00000
3½%	.00972	.06806	.29167	.87500	1.75000	3.50000
4%	.01111	.07778	.33333	1.00000	2.00000	4.00000
4½%	.01250	.08750	.37500	1.12500	2.25000	4.50000
5%	.01389	.09722	.41667	1.25000	2.50000	5.00000
5½%	.01528	.10694	.45833	1.37500	2.75000	5.50000
6%	.01667	.11667	.50000	1.50000	3.00000	6.00000
6½%	.01806	.12639	.54167	1.62500	3.25000	6.50000
7%	.01944	.13611	.58333	1.75000	3.50000	7.00000
8%	.02222	.15556	.66667	2.00000	4.00000	8.00000
9%	.02500	.17500	.75000	2.25000	4.50000	9.00000
10%	.02778	.19444	.83333	2.50000	5.00000	10.00000

Note: The above table is from *Information Please Almanac*, planned and supervised by Dan Golenpaul Associates. The Macmillan Company, New York.

To find the interest for any amount of money, move the decimal point of that amount two places to the left and multiply by the figure obtained from the table.

For figuring simple interest, the year is considered to have 360 days.

When the period of time during which money has been borrowed is over 1 year, the time may be expressed as a decimal number or as an improper fraction, which is used as a multiplier with the interest for 1 year being the multiplicand. If \$500 is borrowed at a rate of 5% for 1 year and 6 months, the first step in computing the interest is to multiply: 5% × \$500 = \$25. The next step is to think of 1 year 6 months as $1\frac{1}{2}$ ($1\frac{1}{2} = \frac{3}{2}$ and $\frac{3}{2} \times \$25 = \frac{75}{2} = \$37.50$).

The interest formula is interest (i) = rate of interest (r) × principal (p), × time (t) or $i = rpt$. When the question asked is, "What is the interest?" the answer is computed by finding the product of the principal multiplied by the rate. The product is multiplied by the time expressed in years.

EXERCISE

Use the interest formula or the above table to find the interest on the following:

1. \$1000 at 2% for 60 days

2. \$1000 at 6% for 14 days

\$300 at $4\frac{1}{2}$% for 1 year

\$600 at 10% for 2 years

Compound Interest

Many people who save money do not withdraw the interest earned by their savings. This interest can then be considered the same as a new deposit and immediately becomes part of the principal and begins to earn interest at the same rate as the original principal. Interest paid on the original principal plus interest is called compound interest. The portion of the compound interest table on page 227 shows that \$1 will more than double itself in 20 years if the rate is 4%. How much interest would \$1 earn in 20 years if the rate were 4% and the interest were withdrawn each year? The plan of withdrawing interest each year is considered *simple interest* (see the table on page 225).

COMPOUND INTEREST

Amount of $1 with Compound Interest

Years	$\frac{1}{2}$%	1%	$1\frac{1}{2}$%	2%	3%	4%
1	1.00500	1.01000	1.01500	1.02000	1.03000	1.04000
2	1.01003	1.02010	1.03023	1.04040	1.06090	1.08160
3	1.01508	1.03030	1.04568	1.06121	1.09273	1.12486
4	1.02015	1.04060	1.06136	1.08243	1.12551	1.16986
5	1.02525	1.05101	1.07728	1.10408	1.15927	1.21665
6	1.03038	1.06152	1.09344	1.12616	1.19405	1.26532
7	1.03553	1.07214	1.10984	1.14869	1.22987	1.31593
8	1.04071	1.08286	1.12649	1.17166	1.26677	1.36857
9	1.04591	1.09369	1.14339	1.19509	1.30477	1.42331
10	1.05114	1.10462	1.16054	1.21899	1.34392	1.48024
15	1.07768	1.16097	1.25023	1.34587	1.55797	1.80094
20	1.10490	1.22019	1.34686	1.48595	1.80611	2.19112
25	1.13280	1.28243	1.45095	1.64061	2.09378	2.66584

It is possible to compute compound interest by using the interest formula, providing the interest earned each period is added to the previous principal. However, interest tables are readily available and it is probably of more value to teach pupils to use the tables than to have them go through the rather laborious practice of computing compound interest in isolated examples. Constructing and then using a compound interest table is a profitable experience for many learners.

In the example shown here, the *amount* (interest plus principal) at the end of a period = 105% of the money on deposit during the preceding period (100% = the amount actually on deposit and 5% = interest. 100% + 5% = 105% = 1.05). In constructing a table such as that shown above, pupils would not be expected to extend it beyond 5 decimal places.

```
      $1
     ×1.05
     $1.05 (1st yr)
     ×1.05
      5.25
     105
   $1.1025 (2d yr)
     ×1.05
    5 5125
  110 25
 $1.157625 (3d yr)
```

EXERCISE

Expand the interest table on page 227 to include a column for 5%.

Other Uses of the Interest Formula

Finding the rate of interest involves the use of the second case of percent. The yearly rate will equal the interest divided by the principal. The rate for a period of more or less than a year will equal the yearly rate divided by the time in years expressed either as an integer, proper fraction, or improper fraction. The formula used in finding the rate is, $r = \frac{i}{pt}$. In actual practice, the first step is to multiply the time × the principal. The second step is to divide the interest by the product of the time × the principal.

EXERCISE

Find the rate when:

1. Interest = \$4, principal = \$100, time = 2 years.
2. Interest = \$2.25, principal = \$100, time = 6 months.
3. Interest = \$1.50, principal = \$100, time = 3 months.

The question "What is the amount of the principal?" can be answered if the interest, rate, and time are known. Answering the question requires the use of the third case of percent. In the initial step the time may be disregarded and the principal may be considered as an amount borrowed for 1 year. If the interest is \$2 and the rate 4%, the principal is \$50. If we know the money was borrowed for 6 months rather than a year, then the principal must have been twice \$50 or \$100. Interest of \$2 paid at the end of 6 months at the rate of 4% would indicate that the principal borrowed was \$100. The formula to use is $p = \frac{i}{rt}$. Observe the computation at the right. The computation in the denominator is done before the division step is accomplished.

$$\$2.00 \div .04 = \$50$$

$$p = \frac{i}{rt} = \frac{\$2.00}{.04 \times \frac{1}{2}} = \frac{\$2.00}{.02} = \$100$$

EXERCISE

Find the principal when:

1. Rate = 3%, interest = \$9, time = 1 year.
2. Rate = 4%, interest = \$4, time = 3 months.
3. Rate = 6%, interest = \$36, time = 3 months.
4. Rate = 2%, interest = \$5, time = 1 year 4 months.

Other Application of Percent

When the principles of percent are understood, the use of the principles in various applications is similar. However, in each application there are certain vocabulary difficulties that must be mastered. In problems involving profit and loss, commissions, buying and selling, stocks and bonds, taxation, social security, tariffs, and mortgages, a specialized vocabulary is used. However, in each problem where percents occur, the question will mean one of three things: "What is the percentage?" or "What is the whole quantity?" or "What is the rate?" The procedure to use in answering each question has been discussed in detail on preceding pages.

Additional Opportunities for Developing Business Experience

Many children are denied the business experience that comes from going shopping with parents or from doing shopping on their own. Even those children who do get the opportunity to shop for or with their parents actually receive little experience in the wise expenditure of money. Teachers and pupils can establish classroom stores equipped with containers in which many kinds of goods are sold. The practice of reading labels to discover the symbols indicating quality, the actual ingredients, and the capacity of the container should be encouraged. By dividing the price by the number of ounces or other unit of measure indicating contents, the pupils can determine the price per unit of measure. The price per unit of measure may be more important than the price tag on the container itself.

Experiences when acting as seller can include preparing sales slips, making change, and even repricing merchandise using discounts. Pupils or pupil committees may make a habit of stopping in at selected stores to watch for weekly fluctuations in prices. They may take these fluctuations into account when doing their own pricing so that they keep their prices on a competitive basis.

School savings plans give children a reason to study the services of banks. In studying these services, the pupils will learn about the kinds of savings accounts, how to make deposits, and the use of the passbook. They will develop an understanding of how to open a checking account, how to fill out deposit slips, how to write out checks, how to complete the check stub, and how to endorse a check. Many banks welcome field trips from children who have been well prepared to ask intelligent questions.

The services of a post office are of interest to children and young people. The cost of various classes of mail, the basis for determining parcel post rates, and the sending of money by using money orders are all subjects that can be investigated by pupils. A comparison of present-day rates with those of earlier days is a worthwhile arithmetic activity. Post offices as well as banks often welcome field trips from the pupils.

The Services and Cost of Government

With ever-increasing demands upon the various governments for more and better schools, for highways and streets, for protection, for social security, for welfare, and many other services, the proportion of each wage earner's salary used to pay for these services must increase. Pupils need to understand the relationship of services to the cost. They can be helped to understand that governments as well as individuals and families prepare budgets. The money required to meet these budgets comes from taxes.

Some of the taxes, notably the sales taxes, are stated in percents. In a state with a 3% sales tax, certain items may be exempted but for many purchases an amount equal to 3% of the list price is added as tax. Computing this tax in-

\$15	\$15.00		\$15
× .03	+ .45	or	× 1.03
\$.45	\$15.45		\$15.45

volves using the first case of percent. If the list price of an article is given as $15 and the tax is 3%, the total price is $15.45. Observe that the tax can be computed and then added to the list price or the percents can be added and the list price multiplied by the sum of the addition (100% + 3% = 103% = 1.03).

Another source of income for governments is the income tax. This is a graduated tax, meaning that the rate increases as the income increases. Individuals with relatively small incomes can compute their taxes by using tax tables. These may be made available to young people who will need assistance in learning how to prepare their own income tax returns. The U. S. Treasury Department has been issuing bulletins for use with pupils.

The property tax is another source of governmental revenue. The tax rate is computed by dividing the amount of money to be raised from this source by the *assessed valuation.* The rate may be expressed as mills per dollar of assessed valuation, or as dollars and cents per hundred or per thousand dollars of assessed valuation. In doing the computation, the assessed valuation may be considered the whole quantity and the amount to be raised may be considered the percentage. To compute the percent the second case of percent is used. The example below shows the computation of the tax rate when the assessed valuation is $10,575,000 and the amount of the budget is $433,575.

```
                     .0409
$10,575,000)$433,575.000
             423,000 000
              10 575 0000
```

.0409 = 41 mills per dollar = $4.10 per hundred = $41.00 per thousand.

The tax rate is $.0409 per dollar of assessed valuation. This is usually expressed as a tax of 40.9 mills. In actual practice the rate would probably be rounded off to 41 mills. The examples below show how the tax is computed when (*a*) the rate is expressed as mills, (*b*) the rate is expressed as dollars and cents per hundred, and (*c*) the rate is expressed as dollars and cents per thousand. It would be more accurate to use the rate as the multiplicand and the assessed valuation as the multiplier inasmuch as the tax rate is determined as a specific amount per dollar of valuation.

(a)	(b)	(c)
$8,500	$85 hundred	$8.5 thousand
×.041	×4.10	×41
8 500	850	8 5
340 00	340	340
$348.50	$348.50	$348.50

EXERCISE

Determine the tax on the following:

1. House and lot assessed at $4250. Tax rate, 21 mills.
2. House and lot assessed at $3785. Tax rate, $3.90 per hundred.
3. Store building assessed at $41,500. Tax rate, $19 per thousand.

Various tariffs and excise duties are charged on products entering this country. In situations where pupils live in a city where there is a customs office, a fine appreciation teaching unit can be developed around the work of a customs officer.

Determining the Cost of Utilities

The cost of utilities such as gas, electricity, and water is often the sum of a fixed charge plus the cost of the actual amount of gas, electricity, or water used. Gas is commonly measured in cubic feet and the rate is expressed as an amount per hundred cubic feet (CCF). Electricity is commonly measured in watts and the rate is expressed as an amount per thousand watt-hours (Kilowatt Hours—KWH). Water is often measured in cubic feet and the rate expressed in hundreds of cubic feet. In each case the rate per unit of measure usually decreases somewhat as the number of units used increases.

Most public utility companies are willing to give schools a schedule of rate charges. Pupils will enjoy reading meters at the beginning and end of a month and using the schedule of rate charges in computing the monthly cost of each kind of service.

Using Graphs to Show Mathematical Relationships

Modern techniques of presenting data lean heavily upon the use of graphs, which are an excellent means of showing relationships between numbers. The individual constructing the graph has done the thinking about the relationships, and the reader of the graph can see the answers to some of his questions without taking time to compute them. The computation, in effect, has been done for the reader.

Graphs have several advantages over word problems and charts, both of which may be used to express mathematical data. To illustrate a problem may express data in this form: "A school library circulated 49 books on Monday, 30 books on Tuesday, 45 books on Wednesday." The question in the problem is to determine a mathematical relationship between either the numbers (addends) and their sum, or between the numbers (addends). A disadvantage of using a problem to present data is that the question asked by a problem serves as a limiting factor in the amount of information that can be given.

Tables may be used to present mathematical data and, providing they have appropriate titles, the data can be easily read. A variety of different questions can be answered directly from the table, but in a table all data are presented with equal emphasis. With nothing highlighted, the reader is forced to examine the table closely to find the information he needs.

Graphs are one of the best means of presenting certain kinds of data. They have eye appeal, which causes the reader to focus attention on them. Answers to questions can often be determined with a minimum of effort because the bars, broken lines, pictures, or segments of a circle are in proportion to the numbers they represent. The proportions can be seen quickly and at least an approximate answer to a specific question can be seen.

The constructor of the graph presupposes that the reader will have specific questions that he may want to answer as he looks at the graph. He constructs the graph with the intention of helping the reader find the answer to his question or questions with a minimum of time and effort.

Kinds of Graphs

The following graphs illustrate various means of presenting the same data.

The accompanying graphs (*a*) to (*d*) each present the same data and accordingly have the same title. The circle graph is so constructed that its outline encompasses the entire sum of 200 books. The segments of the circle each represent component parts of the sum. Observe that the segments are in proportion to the numbers they represent. The larger the number represented, the larger the segment. The difference in the size of the segments shows at a glance that some represent greater amounts than the others. Questions that can be easily answered by looking at graph (*a*) are: On what day was the circulation highest? On which day was it lowest? About what fraction of the books were circulated on Friday?

A considerable amount of computation preceded the construction of the graph. The circle represents 360°. The Monday circulation of 45 books is $\frac{45}{200}$ of the total circulation. Thus $\frac{45}{200}$ of $360° = 81°$, which is the angular measurement of the segment labeled Monday. The angular measurement of each of the other segments is computed in similar manner. Determine the angular measurement of each of the other segments in graph (*a*).

On graph (*b*) the peaks and valleys of circulation are indicated by the location of the dots on the broken line. Since all squares on the graph are equal, the greater the vertical distance of the dot from the horizontal base line, the proportionally greater the number of books represented by the space below it. The numerical value of the distance on the vertical line is indicated by the horizontal equidistant lines, which are numbered or can be thought to be numbered in sequence. This numerical value represents exactly the circulation of books on a given day.

Observe that graph (*b*) has a vertical scale, a horizontal scale, and squares that are equal to each other. Representative questions that can be answered by using graph (*b*) are: On which day were 49 books circulated? How many books were circulated on Monday? When was circulation highest? When was it lowest?

On graph (*c*), the bar graph, the outline of each bar can be considered as encompassing an addend, providing each bar is thought of as representing one of the parts of the total book circulation for

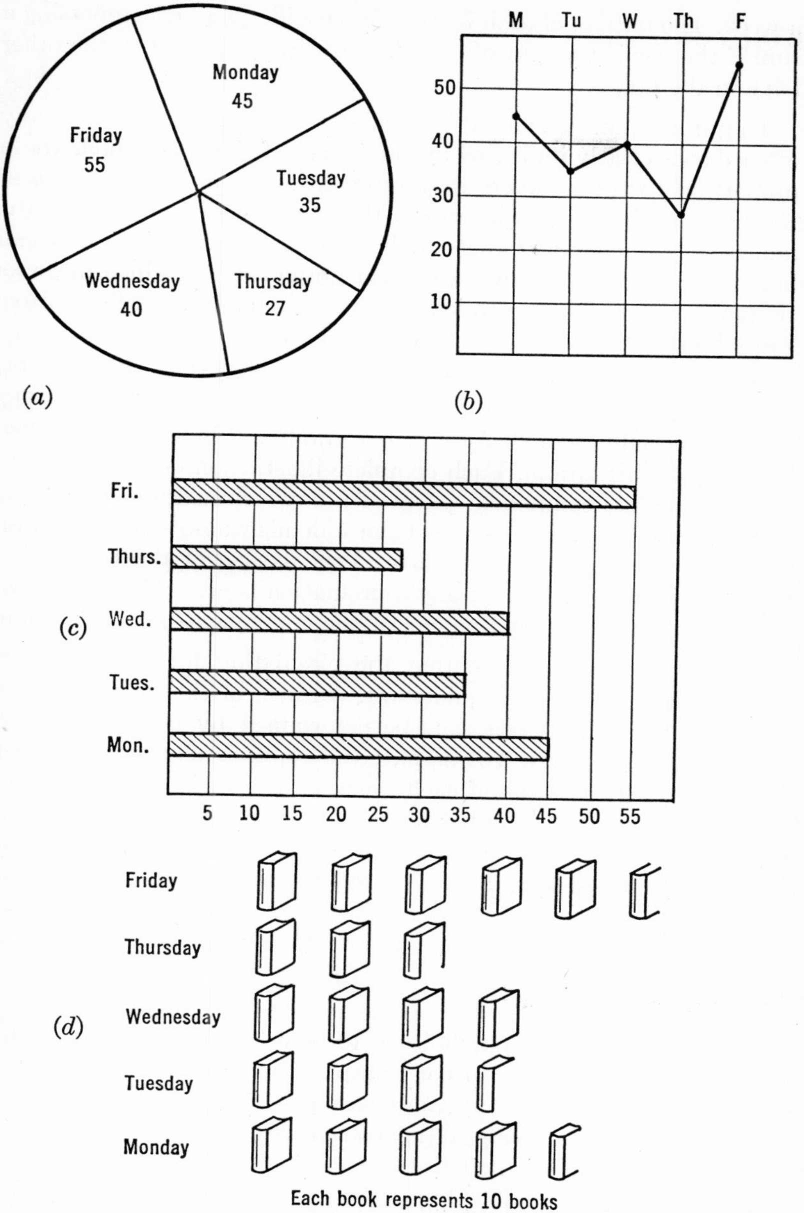

Books Circulated by Lincoln School, Oct. 1-5

a week. The outline of each bar can be considered as encompassing a sum if the bar is thought of in isolation without regard to the other bars on the graph.

The proportion of one day's circulation to the circulation of any other day is clearly indicated by the length of the bars, which are in proportion to the numbers they represent. The numerical value of the horizontal line that intersects the end point of any bar is the numerical value of the bar itself. Representative questions that can be quickly answered by using the bar graph are: On which day was circulation greatest? On which day was circulation smallest? How many books were circulated on Wednesday?

On graph (*d*), the picture graph on page 235, the ratio between each drawing of a book and each book circulated is as 1 is to 10. The graph is actually another form of bar graph and is sometimes called a Multiple Unit Graph. Each complete illustration of a book represents one of the component parts of a day's circulation. If a day's circulation is considered as one of the addends whose sum is the total weekly circulation, each illustrated book is one of the component parts of an addend. If each day's circulation is considered individually, each illustrated book is one of the component parts of a sum.

The illustrations representing the circulation for each day are identical in size and are equidistant. An idea of the days on which circulation is highest can thus be determined by observing which line of books is longest. To compute the exact circulation for a given day the numerical value of each illustrated book is considered as a multiplicand and the number of books as the multiplier. Questions that can be answered by using line or bar graphs can be answered by using the picture graph.

Constructing Graphs

A good way to help pupils learn to understand graphs is to give them an opportunity to construct graphs using data which they have compiled themselves. Many times so much energy is used in ruling squared paper or in trying to separate circles into segments that the actual experience of constructing the graphs seems to be of secondary importance to the pupils. Pupils should be provided with squared paper and with circles already marked around the circumference in

5° or 10° divisions so that they can devote their energies to constructing graphs. After graphs have been constructed, pupils should be given an opportunity to discuss them and to evaluate their work.

EXERCISE

Gather data and construct graphs as follows:

1. Make a line graph to show temperature fluctuations over a 10-hour period.

2. Check the price of some commodity such as eggs on each of 10 days and then make a bar graph to show the fluctuations.

3. Make a circle graph to show how you spend an average 24-hour day.

4. Make a picture graph to show the daily attendance on each of 5 days.

Exhibiting Graphs

An excellent project in which pupils may engage is the collection and exhibition of various kinds of graphs. To emphasize the idea that each graph presents data that can be used in answering a great number of questions, a list of questions should be posted beside each of the exhibited graphs. Pupils will discover that the steps in reading a graph are:

1. Reading the title to find what the graph is about.
2. Observing the scale.
3. Finding the part of the graph that specifically relates to the question the reader wishes to answer.
4. Finding the answer to the question.
5. Doing the necessary computation providing the question is such that computation is required.

Pupils enjoy constructing and reading graphs after having had sufficient experience to do so with ease.

Diagnosing Pupil Growth

Many of the ideas developed by pupils in their study of the use of arithmetic in home, business, and industry can be clarified during discussion periods. Representative questions that teachers may use to stimulate discussion include:

1. What is the businessman's way of expressing hundredths?

2. Why is it correct to say that 100% of a quantity is equal to the whole quantity? Prove your answer is correct by using graph paper.

3. What method is used when writing numbers greater than 100%? Less than 1%?

4. What do you do when you want to rewrite a decimal fraction as a percent?

5. What do you do when you want to rewrite a percent as a decimal fraction?

6. What procedure is used when it is necessary to substitute a percent for a common fraction? For a mixed number?

7. What do you do to find the percentage when you know the rate or percent and the whole quantity?

8. How do you find the rate when you know the percentage and the whole quantity?

9. How do you find the whole quantity when you know the rate and the percentage?

10. What are some reasons for keeping personal cash accounts?

11. In what ways are budgets valuable to individuals? To governments?

12. What are some advantages and disadvantages of installment buying?

13. What are some reasons why people are willing to spend money for insurance?

14. In what ways can money be invested so that it will earn interest?

15. What case of percent is used when finding interest? Discount? Commission?

16. What case of percent is used when finding rate of interest? Rate of discount? Tax rate?

17. What are graphs? Describe four different kinds.

18. What are the advantages of using graphs to present information?

Test items such as the following may be included on pencil and paper tests:

Part I—Meanings

1. In business, hundredths are usually written as a (decimal, percent, fraction).

2. In the statement, "5% of \$50 = \$2.50," the number representing the whole quantity is (5%, \$50.00, \$2.50).

3. The percent equal to a whole quantity is (10%, 50%, 100%).

4. The correct way to write .12½ as a percent is (125%, 12½%, ⅛%).

5. The correct way to write 125% as a decimal fraction is (.125, 1.25, 125).

6. The percent equivalent of ⅓ is (.33⅓, 33.3%, 33⅓%).

7. The arithmetic process usually used in finding the amount of discount is (multiplication, addition, division).

8. The arithmetic process usually used in finding a batting average is (subtraction, division, multiplication).

9. Electric current is measured in (cubic feet, kilowatt hours, foot pounds).

10. The mathematical difference between receipts and expenditures on a cash account is called the (balance, profit, loss).

11. Money paid for the use of money is called (insurance, installments, interest).

12. The kind of account on which banks pay interest is a (savings account, checking account, government bonds).

13. The blanks filled out when money is deposited in a bank are called (checks, stubs, deposit slips).

14. The kind of graph best suited for showing the relationship between parts and a single whole quantity is the (line graph, circle graph, pictograph).

Part II—Computation

Put the correct number on each blank.

1. Weekly income, \$80. Food allowance, \$20. Percent allowed, ______.

2. Monthly income, \$320. Rent allowance, 20%. Amount of rent, ______.

3. Cash on hand, \$250.50. Receipts, \$185.19. Expenditures, \$92.75. Balance, ______.

4. List price, \$199.50. Rate of discount, $33\frac{1}{3}\%$. Discount, ______. Net cost, ______.

5. Down payment, \$10. Monthly payments, \$5. No. of payments, 6. Time payment price, ______.

6. Installment price, \$250. Cash price, \$212.50. Cost of installment buying, ______.

7. List price, \$750. First discount, 20%. Second discount, 5%. Net price, ______.

8. Cost price, \$.98. Selling price, \$1.25. Overhead, ______.

9. Cost price, \$2.10. Profit, \$.50. Percent of profit, ______.

10. Amount of sales, \$800. Commission, 25%. Amount of commission, ______.

11. Principal, \$200. Rate of interest, 2%. Time, 3 years. Interest, ______.

12. Principal, \$500. Interest, \$30. Time, 2 years. Rate, ______.

13. Interest, \$10. Rate, 3%. Time, 1 year. Principal, ______.

14. Number of shares, 25. Price per share, \$35. Brokerage fee, \$21.50. Net cost of shares, ______.

15. Assessed valuation, \$5400. Tax rate, 29 mills. Tax, ______.

16. Amount of money to be raised, \$215,500. Assessed valuation, \$12,750,000. Tax rate, ______.

Summary

Percent and percentage are essential ways of thinking in modern business and industry. For this reason, all intelligent readers of advertisements, news articles, books, and magazines need to develop an understanding of how to interpret percent. Interpreting the meaning of statements in which percents appear is impossible in some cases because many writers ignore the fact that percents are a way of expressing a relationship between quantities. In the statement, 6% of \$20 = \$1.20, the percent and the size of the two quantities are known so the meaning is clear. But in statements such as, "The population increased by 6%," there is little meaning because the whole quantity, i.e., former population, is not given. Unless this is known, the population increase cannot be computed. Because of the widespread use of percent in written communication, children need instruction in the reading of percents before making the formal study of percent and percentage usually assigned as a part of the seventh grade curriculum.

Pupil readiness for percentage is developed in a systematic teaching of fractions and decimals. The relationships among percent, fraction, and decimals must be clearly understood. All can be used to express the idea of hundredths and all express a ratio relationship between two numbers. A percent, however, is a decimal fraction that indicates relationship in a specific quantitative situation. A fraction or a decimal fraction may express relationship in any number of quantitative situations. All percents represent either a fraction or a decimal fraction with a denominator of hundredths.

The decimal point has a different meaning when used with a percent sign than when it is used in a decimal fraction. .5% represents $\frac{5}{10}$ or $\frac{1}{2}$ of 1 percent; 12.5% represents $12\frac{1}{2}\%$ or 12.5%; 125.% represents 125%.

There are five quantitative situations in which it is necessary to understand the equivalent relationships among integers, fractions, decimal fractions, and percents. Examples illustrating each situation are (1) 1 = 100%; (2) $\frac{1}{2}$ = .50 = 50%; (3) .25 = 25%; (4) 500% = 5.00; (5) 2% = $\frac{2}{100}$ = $\frac{1}{50}$ = .02. Observe that rewriting decimal fractions as percents involves moving the decimal point two places to the right and placing a percent sign after the number. Rewriting a percent as a decimal fraction involves deleting the percent sign and placing a decimal point two places to the left.

As stated earlier, each percent expresses the relationship between two quantities. If the percent and larger of the two quantities is known, the smaller quantity (percentage), is computed by multiplication (if the percent is less than 100). When the two quantities are known but the percent is unknown, the percent is computed by division. When the percent and smaller quantity are known and the larger quantity is unknown, the smaller quantity is divided by the percent expressed as a decimal.

An application of percent, which has meaning to pupils, is its use in budgeting. The pupils can readily understand that their personal financial records as kept on cash accounts will tell them how much to allow for each item budgeted. If they know their total income, they can compute the percent allowed. If they know the percent allowed and the total income, they can compute the amount allowed. The understanding of the cases of percent as they apply in the study of budgets can be applied in the study of topics such as interest, taxes, discounts, commission, profit, loss, stocks, bonds, insurance.

Graphs may be of several kinds including circle graphs, bar graphs, line graphs, and pictographs. The various parts of the graphs are in proportion to the numbers they represent. For this reason, it is possible actually to *see* the number relationships shown by graphs. One of the best ways of learning to understand graphs is to construct some. When pupils engage in this activity, they should be provided with the proper materials; i.e., graph paper, circles marked in degrees, rulers, sharp pencils.

SUGGESTED QUESTIONS FOR TEACHER SELF-EVALUATION

1. What reasons can you give for helping pupils apply arithmetical ideas and operations in personal, family, and community economics?

2. What is your understanding of the meaning of percent?

3. What are some advantages and some disadvantages of using a percent rather than a fraction or place value to express hundredths?

4. What are some reasons for helping elementary school pupils develop an understanding of the meaning of percent even prior to their study of decimal fractions?

5. In the example, 5% of \$60 = \$3, what number represents the whole quantity? What number represents the percentage? What number expresses the relationship between the two quantities?

6. What are the three cases of percent?

7. What are the three percentage formulas used respectively in each of the three cases of percent, or what questions are answered by percent?

8. What arithmetical operation is used in answering the question in percentage examples of the first case? In percentage examples of the second case? In percentage examples of the third case?

9. What procedure would you use in helping children use what they have learned about decimal fractions and fractions when you are teaching them to understand percent?

10. What applications and uses of percentage are applied in home, business, and industry?

11. What are some advantages and some disadvantages of using graphs as a means of presenting data?

12. What are some of the meanings and skills used in reading circle graphs? Bar graphs? Line graphs? Pictographs?

SUGGESTED ACTIVITIES FOR TEACHERS

1. Prepare a list of practical meanings and skills that teachers should help pupils develop regarding (*a*) percent, (*b*) graphs.

2. Prepare a vocabulary list of words essential to a meaningful understanding of (*a*) interest, (*b*) insurance, (*c*) stocks and bonds, (*d*) profit and loss, (*e*) taxation.

3. Prepare in chart form the decimal and percent equivalents for: 2, $\frac{1}{4}$, $\frac{1}{2}$, $\frac{2}{5}$, $\frac{3}{4}$, $\frac{4}{5}$, $2\frac{1}{3}$, $\frac{9}{10}$, $1\frac{1}{8}$, $3\frac{3}{8}$.

4. Write two problems to illustrate each of the three cases of percent and solve the problems. Each problem should illustrate a different application of percent in home, business, or industry.

5. Prepare a display of various kinds of graphs and for each graph write two questions that could be answered by reading the graph.

SELECTED REFERENCES

1. Brueckner, Leo J., and Grossnickle, Foster E., *Making Arithmetic Meaningful.* Philadelphia: John C. Winston Company, 1953.

2. Buckingham, Burdette R., *Elementary Arithmetic—Its Theory and Practice.* Boston: Ginn & Company, 1947.

3. Spitzer, Herbert F., *The Teaching of Arithmetic*, 2d ed. Boston: Houghton Mifflin Company, 1954.

4. Wheat, Harry Grove, *How to Teach Arithmetic.* Evanston, Ill.: Row, Peterson & Company, 1951.

5. Wilson, Guy M., *et al.*, *Teaching the New Arithmetic* (2d ed.). New York: McGraw-Hill Book Company, Inc., 1951.

10

Meaning and Use of Measures and Measurement

Introduction

Measures and the process of measurement have been indispensable to man's progress in industry, business, and scientific research. The selection of appropriate measures and the application with precision measuring instruments are essential in various endeavors such as building a home, manufacturing a product, cooking food, and purchasing wearing apparel. A mistake in measurement can bring costly consequences to producer and to consumer. The study of measurement should enable pupils to learn understandings, values, and appreciations related to the high standards in production and commerce in American society.

Exploratory Questions

Read these questions to appraise your understanding of the meanings, thought processes, and application skills that teachers should motivate pupils to discover and learn about practical measurements.

1. How may the study of measurement help pupils to learn understandings of and appreciation for the unprecedented progress man has made in industry, commerce, and scientific research?

2. What changing needs of man have been served by the development, refinement, and standardization of units of measure and instruments for measuring: (*a*) time? (*b*) length? (*c*) area? (*d*) volume? (*e*) weight? (*f*) temperature? (*g*) speed? (*h*) capacity? (*i*) money? (*j*) value?

3. What should pupils learn about the need for standardization in measurement, governmental authority for standardization, and the role of the states in protecting the consumer?

4. How do you interpret the differences between counting numbers and denominate numbers?

5. What should pupils understand to be the one-to-one correspondence as to: (*a*) Continuous magnitude or quantity and a unit of measure? (*b*) The application of measurement and the idea of amount? (*c*) The idea of quantity and the notated denominate number?

6. What are the more commonly used units of measure in the United States system of measurement? In the English system of measurement?

7. What are the essential procedures that pupils should learn to apply when measuring to answer the question, "How much?"

(*a*) What criteria should be observed in selecting a unit of measure and a measuring instrument?

(*b*) What attention should be given to precision and accuracy?

(*c*) How should the answer to the question, "How much?" be expressed?

8. How does the measurement of time, temperature, and value differ from the measurement of length, surface, volume, and capacity?

9. What are the meanings that teachers should help pupils to learn about the metric system of measurement?

(*a*) Why is the metric system more scientific than the English and United States systems of measurement?

(*b*) What are the primary units of measure in the metric system?

(*c*) What is the relationship among the primary units of measure in the metric system?

(*d*) How is the system of place value in the metric system similar to the system of place value in the decimal number system?

10. What are some of the equivalents between the metric and the English and United States units of measure that pupils should understand and apply?

11. What are the meanings and skills that teachers should help pupils to discover and use?

(*a*) When computing the area of plane surfaces?

(*b*) When computing volume?

(*c*) When substituting larger units for smaller units or substituting smaller units for larger units?

(*d*) When computing the square root of any given number?

12. What meanings and skills involved in computation with discrete numbers may be applied in computation with denominate numbers?

Purpose of Measures

Measures have been designed as a means of answering questions such as: (1) How much length? (2) How much surface? (3) How much volume? (4) How much weight? (5) How much time? An awareness of the need for answering the question must precede a desire to find the measure and the procedure by which it may be answered.

Primitive man thought of quantities as piles or heaps. He had no basic reason for accurately answering the question, "How much?" until he began to encounter the need of exchange or trade of possessions with other men. As the need and desire to trade grew, primitive man found it necessary to establish some units of measure that would help him to know how much to buy or to sell. He began to select and to apply units of measure related to parts of his body, such as: the foot, the digit, the yard, the palm, and the cubit.

In later years, the use of square tiles to cover floors served as the means to create the idea and use of square units. The use of brick or stones in building served as the means by which man learned to answer "How much does it fill?" by counting the number needed to fill the solid space. The idea and use of a cubic unit became the accepted way to find the answer to the question, "How much volume?"

The mental and physical process of applying a selected unit of measure to a given quantity or object is the second step in answering the question: "How much is the measurement?" The accuracy of the answer depends on the precision of the measuring instrument and the care with which it is applied. Pupils need guidance and practice in discovering the meaning of an appropriate unit of measure and in developing skill in its application to any object or quantity. In measuring length, deciding when to select an inch, or a foot, or a yard, stimulates thinking and also understanding of precision in measurement. Mechanically constructed and electrically operated instruments are used in modern industry, business, and research to produce greater precision and accuracy in applied measurement. Pupils should be motivated to observe the different kinds of measuring instruments used in the community and to discuss their advantages to producer and consumer.

Measuring Length

In early civilization a person who desired to build a home of stones might have asked himself the question, "How long shall each wall be?" He could then use his foot as a unit of measure to find the answer. He could drive a stake in the ground to show where the wall was to begin. He then could walk in a straight line placing one foot directly in front of the other foot. When reaching a point or position far enough away from the starting stake or point to make one of the walls of sufficient length, he would drive another stake. By counting the number of times he placed one foot in front of the other foot, he would determine the measured length of one of the walls. In a similar way, he could determine the measurement length of the wall that was to be the width of the home. In determining the height of the walls, he could use as a unit of measure, a palm, a span, a cubit or the length of his body. Early man by using body units of measure could answer to his satisfaction and need the questions, "How long?" "How wide?" or "How high?"

As man's need for measuring length increased, different units of measure were developed such as: (1) the foot—the length of a man's foot, (2) an inch—the length from the joint to the tip of the thumb, (3) a cubit—the length of the forearm, (4) a yard—the length of an outstretched arm, measured from the nose, (5) a pace—the length of a step, (6) a rod—the distance covered by 16 men standing in line so that the toe of each man's left foot touched the heel of the man's foot in front of him, (7) a mile—the length of a thousand paces.

Diversity in the physical size of men created the need for standard units to measure length. The authority to formulate standard units to measure length was given to the chief of the tribe; later to the priest and the church; and then assigned to governments. The measures used today have been accurately determined and defined. The British Imperial yard was defined in 1878 as the distance between two transverse lines on two gold plugs in a bronze bar kept in Westminster. This bronze bar is known as the "No. 1 Standard Yard." In the United States the standard yard is the same as the Imperial yard. The foot unit of measure is equivalent to one-third of the length of the yard. The inch unit of measure is a length that is equivalent to one-twelfth of a foot or one thirty-sixth of the yard.

Pupils should understand that a unit of length is the distance between two points on a line as measured by an inch, a foot, a yard, a rod, or a mile. They should have practical experience in using the standard unit of length from which to derive a mental concept of the standardized length of each measuring unit. Important is the mentally derived meaning that 3 feet are equivalent to a yard in total length only when they are thought to be end to end. One inch is a single unit of length. The concept that 1 foot is equivalent to 12 inches is dependent on the recognition that the 12 inches are placed end to end. The meaning that 3 feet is equivalent in length to 1 yard depends on the mental abstraction that 3 feet, end to end, may be substituted for 1 yard. In a similar thought process, 1 inch is equivalent in length to $\frac{1}{12}$ of 1 foot when 12 inches, end to end, are thought to have been substituted for 1 foot. What mental interpretation of length should pupils apply in thinking the answer to these questions:

1. 1 yard is equivalent to __?__ feet?
2. 1 foot is __?__ part of 1 yard?
3. 1 foot is equivalent to __?__ inches?
4. 1 inch is __?__ part of 1 foot?
5. 1 mile is equivalent to __?__ feet? __?__ yards?
6. 1 foot is __?__ part of 1 mile? 1 yard is __?__ part of 1 mile?

Derived Generalizations About Length

1. Length is the distance between two points on a line.

2. The magnitude of a line may be determined by applying a unit of measure created to measure length.

3. Diversity in measurement of length led to the establishment of standardized units such as: inch, foot, yard, rod, mile.

4. The amount of measured length is notated by a number and the name of the unit of measure (4 inches or 4 in, or 8 feet or 8 ft).

5. Precision in measuring length is dependent on the selection of an appropriate unit of measure and accuracy in applying it.

6. Standard units of length may be used in determining the length of a straight line, a broken line, or a curved line.

Measuring Area

The art of measuring with squares may have been discovered by the early Egyptian priests who needed to measure the area of farms before taxes were levied.[1] Their first clue to measuring area may have come from paving the floor with square tiles. Measuring with square tile consisted in laying tiles in a row and then making successive rows until the entire surface was covered. The answer to the question, "How much surface?" could be found by counting the number of square tiles in each row or by multiplying the number of tiles in the first row by the number of rows in the floor or surface.

A surface is a flat plane surrounded by a line. Its dimensions are length and width or base and height (depending on whether the plane is horizontal or vertical). When measuring the area of a surface, an area unit or a square unit must be selected and applied. The measures of surface or area are based upon linear units. A square inch is a square surface, each side being an inch in length. A square foot is a surface, each side being one foot. Likewise, a square yard is a surface with each side one yard in length, and a square mile is an area with a length of one mile on each side. A mental interpretation of the mathematical meaning of a square unit of measure can be more readily created when pupils have experience in constructing or drawing such square units as a square inch, a square foot, and a square yard, and then applying these measures to surfaces in the school or on the playground. They must develop the ability to select and apply appropriate square units of measure when finding the answer to the question, "What is the area of a given surface?"

---

[1]Lancelot Hogben, *The Wonderful World of Mathematics*, New York: Garden Citv Books, 1955.

Computing Area

Formulas have been mentally and mathematically derived as useful aids in computing areas of plane surfaces. These are illustrated below:

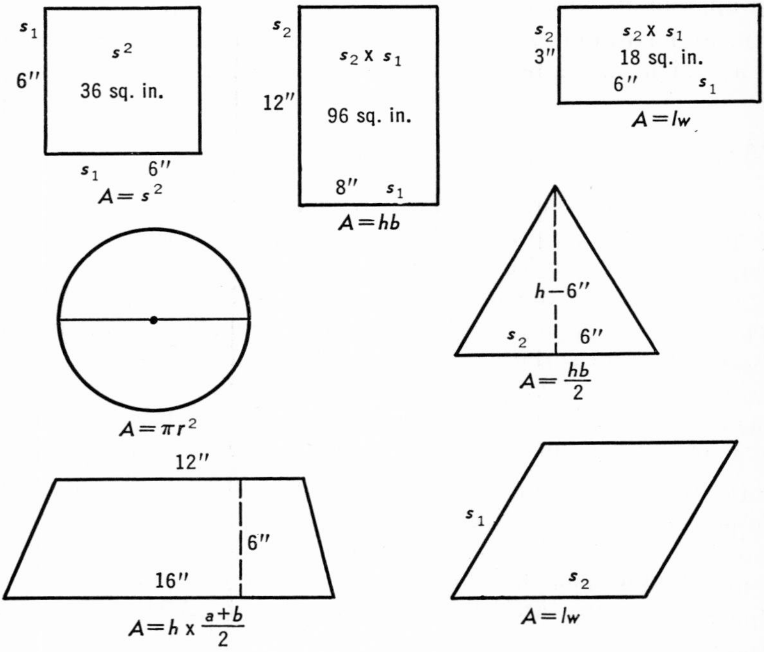

To find the area of the square shown on page 251, it is necessary to select and to apply a square unit, a square inch. The question is, "How many square inches are equivalent to the total surface?" The first mental act is to observe that 6 square inches will make a row along one edge. The second question is, "How many rows of 6 square inches will cover the entire surface?" The answer is "6 rows." Then to find the area of the surface think, "Six rows of 6 square inches equal 36 square inches." The area of the square is equal to 36 units, each 1 inch square.

Observe that the triangle and the square on this page both have an altitude and base of 6 inches. Why is the area of the triangle equal to 36 square inches divided by 2?

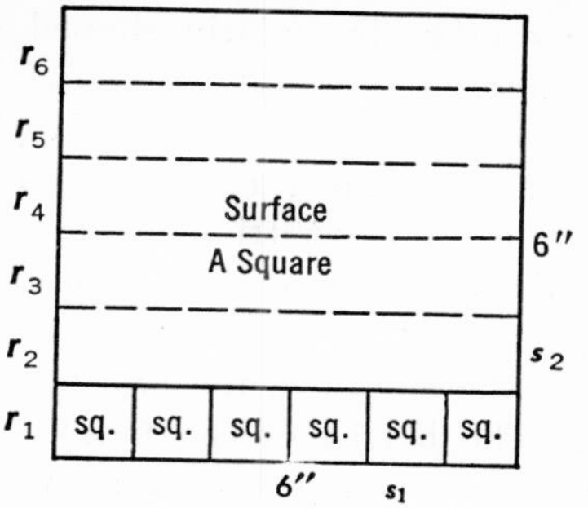

$A = s^2$
$A = 6$ rows x 6 sq. in.
$A = 36$ sq. in.

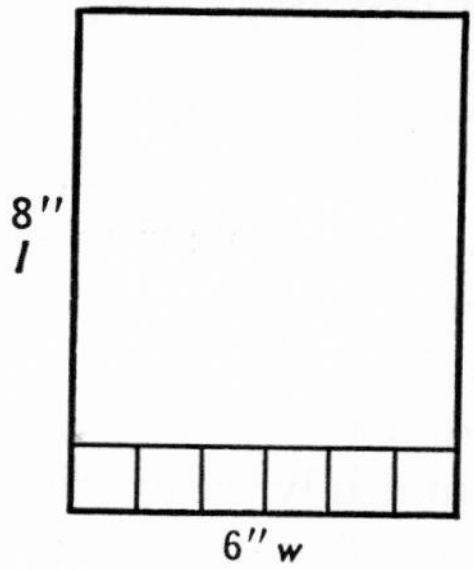

$A = lw$
$= 8 \times 6$ sq. in.
$= 48$ sq. in.

To find the area of the rectangle shown above, the first thought step is to select a square unit of measure. If it is a square inch, the question is, "The area of the surface is equal to what number of square inches?" The steps in mentally computing the area are identical to the steps used in finding the area of the square. Eight rows of 6 square inches each equal 48 square inches (8 × 6 sq in. = 48 sq in.). The area of the surface, a rectangle, is equal to 48 square inches.

In the parallelogram, shown below, the area can be determined by thinking of the parallelogram as a rectangle [move the triangle (*a*) to position held by triangle (*b*) and the shape of the parallelogram has been changed to a rectangle]. The area of the parallelogram is found to be 8 × 6 square inches. Observe that the formula used to find the area of a parallelogram is the same as the formula used to find the area of a rectangle.

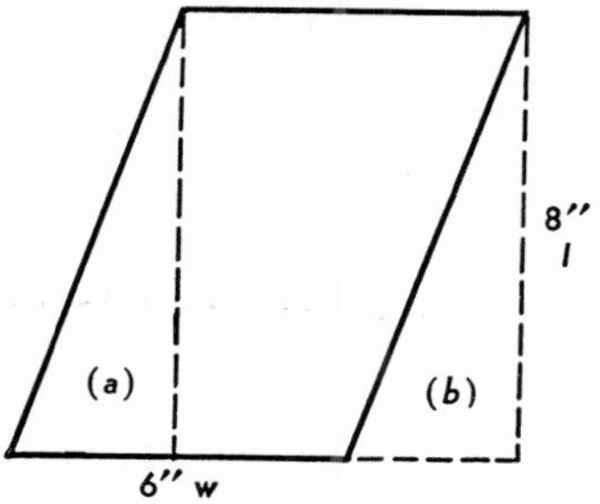

$A = lw$
$= 8 \times 6$ sq. in.
$= 48$ sq. in.

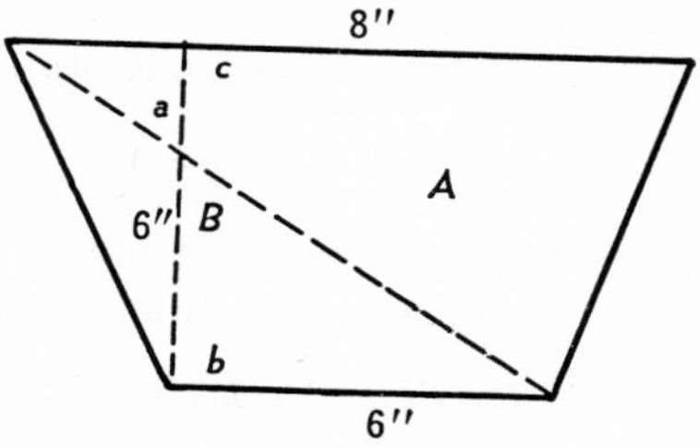

The area of a trapezoid or any other irregularly shaped plane surface with straight sides can be determined by first thinking of the surface as being divided into component triangles (see triangles A and B, previous page). The total area of the trapezoid is equal to the sum of the areas of the two component triangles, A and B ($\frac{1}{2}ab + \frac{1}{2}ac$). The altitude, a, is the same for each component triangle. The generalized rule that is used to find the area of any trapezoid is to find the average of the length of the two bases and then multiply it by the height. (The height of the parallelogram is identical with the altitude of each triangle.) The area of the illustrated trapezoid is, $6 \times \left(\frac{8'' + 6''}{2}\right)$ or 6×7 square inches = 42 square inches.

Measuring a Circle

The circumference, diameter, and radius of a circle are measured in linear units. If any one of the linear measurements of a circle is known, the other measurements can be found for the reasons: (1) The ratio of the circumference of a circle is constant with the diameter, and (2) a radius is equal to one-half the diameter. The ratio between the circumference and the diameter is called Pi (π); and has the numerical value of 3.14159+. The value of Pi that is used for many practical purposes is 3.1416. For approximations, Pi may be expressed as 3.14 or $3\frac{1}{7}$.

Pupils may more readily interpret the approximate value of Pi, $3\frac{1}{7}$, by comparing a string that is the length of the circumference with another string that is the length of the diameter. When they cut the string that is the length of the circumference into units which are the length of the diameter, they will discover that there are three units equal in length to the diameter and the remaining unit of the string is about $\frac{1}{7}$ of the diameter. This application of concrete material will serve as an aid in understanding the formulas: (1) $c = \pi d$, (2) $d = \frac{c}{\pi}$, and (3) $r = \frac{d}{2}$.

The formula, $c = \pi d$, expresses the mathematical ratio between the circumference and the diameter. *It states, The length of any circle is equal to the diameter multiplied by Pi* (π). The formula, $d = \frac{c}{\pi}$, is a mathematical statement: *The diameter is a length that equals the circumference divided by Pi* (π). The formula, $r = \frac{d}{2}$, is a mathematical statement: *The radius is a length that is equivalent to one-half the length of the diameter.*

EXERCISE

1. Measure the circumference of several circles. Find length of the diameter. Also the length of a radius.

2. Measure the diameter of several circles; compute the length of the circumference of each circle.

3. Use the formula, $c = \pi d$. If $d = 7$ inches, what is the length of c?

4. Use the formula, $d = \frac{c}{\pi}$. If $c = 132$ inches, what is the length of d?

5. Use the formula, $r = \frac{d}{2}$. If $d = 24$ inches, what is the length of r?

The Area of a Circle

The early Egyptians discovered that the area of a circle is a little more than three times as great as the area of a square with sides equal in length to the radius. The formula that is now used to find the area of a circle is πr^2. The area of a circle is 3.1416 or (approximately $3\frac{1}{7}$) times the area of a square with the side equal in length to a radius.

One method teachers may use to help pupils to understand the meaning of the formula, "Area of a circle $= \pi r^2$," is to have pupils execute these steps:

1. Draw a circle on a piece of paper or cardboard.
2. Draw a diameter on the circle.
3. Draw radii to make an equal number of sectors in each of the halves of the circle created by the diameter.
4. Cut the circle along the diameter.
5. Then cut the sectors formed by the radii in each of the half circles.

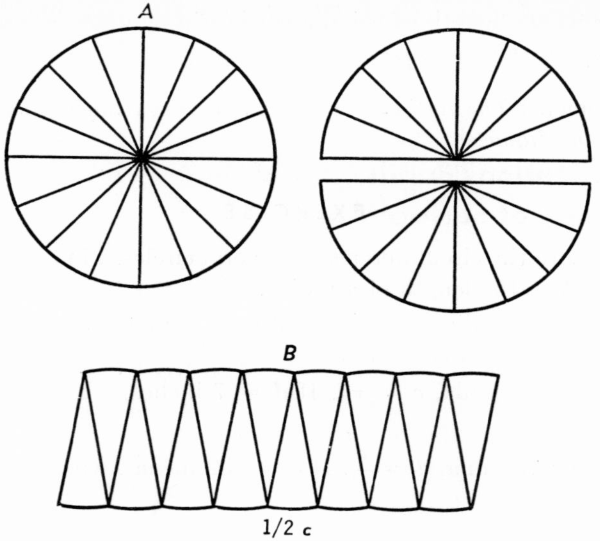

6. Place the sectors together to form an approximate parallelogram B. The area of the parallelogram equals the length of the base (which is $\frac{1}{2}$ of the circle A) multiplied by the height (which is equal to a radius of circle A). The base of the parallelogram is $\frac{1}{2}c$. The height is r. Then the area is equal to r times $\frac{1}{2}c$. Since the length of the circumference is πd and the base of the parallelogram is equal to $\frac{1}{2}$ of the circumference then by substituting $2r$ for d, the area of the parallelogram and of the circle is: r times $\frac{1}{2}(\pi 2r)$ or r times πr or πr^2.

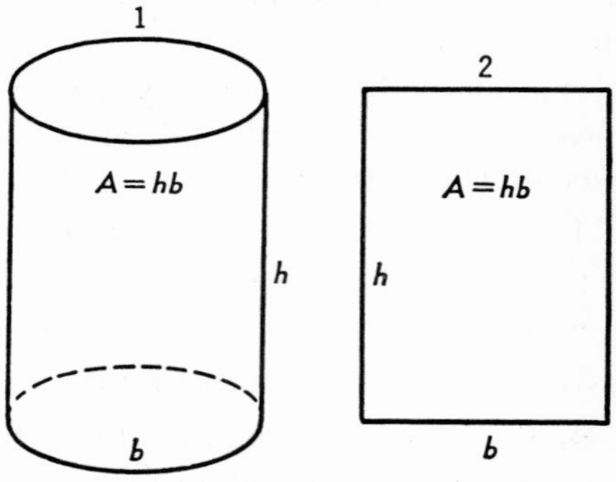

Area of a cylinder is determined by multiplying the circumference by the height, $A = hb$ or $A = hc$. The shape of the surface of a cylinder can be changed to equal the surface of a rectangle. This can be illustrated by removing the bottom from a tin can and then cutting the surface along a line from the bottom to the top. When the curved surface has been taken out it becomes a plane surface in the form of a rectangle. If the length of the diameter of a cylinder is known, the circumference can be found by multiplying the diameter by 3.1416 or $3\frac{1}{7}$ (Pi).

Generalizations Pupils Should Derive from Study of Surface Area

1. A plane surface has two dimensions, length and width or length and height.

2. A square unit of measure must be selected when computing area.

3. A square unit is a surface with the four sides equal in length.

4. The number that expresses width identifies the number of square units on the edge of the surface.

5. The number that expresses height identifies the number of rows of square units to cover the surface.

6. The area of a rectangle or a parallelogram is computed by the formula, $A = hb$ (height × base) or $A = lw$ (length × width).

7. The area of a trapezoid is computed by the formula, $A = h \times \frac{B_1 + B_1}{2}$ (height × average length of base_1 and base_2).

8. The area of a circle is computed by the formula, $A = \pi r^2$ (pi × radius^2).

9. The area of a cylinder is computed by the formula, $A = hc$ or $A = hb$ (height × circumference) or (height × base of equivalent rectangle).

EXERCISE

1. Draw a circle with a diameter of 12 inches on a piece of cardboard. Then change the shape of the circle to an approximate parallelogram and find the area of the parallelogram.

2. Find the area of a circle with a diameter of 18 inches.

3. Find the area of a circle with a radius of 8 inches.

4. Find the area of a circle with a circumference of 63 inches.

5. Find the area of a cylinder with a diameter of 10 inches and height 8 inches.

Measuring Volume

Measures of volume are expressed in cubic inches, cubic feet, cubic yards, and even cubic miles. A cubic unit of measure has three dimensions; length, width, height. The units of measure are cubes with a length, a width, and a height of 1 inch, or 1 foot, or 1 yard, or 1 mile. To find the volume of the box at the right, the unit of measure is the cubic inch. The question to answer is, "The volume of the box with the dimensions—length 5 inches, width 3 inches, and height 4 inches—equals how many, or what number of cubic inches?" The thought steps used in finding the answer are: (1) A cubic inch is the unit of measure. (2) 5 cubic inches will make a row along one edge of the base. (3) 3 rows of 5 cubic inches will be needed to cover the base. (4) Then 4 layers of 15 cubic inches will be needed to fill the box. Four layers times 15 cubic inches equal 60 cubic inches. The volume of the box is equal to 60 units, each with a volume of 1 cubic inch.

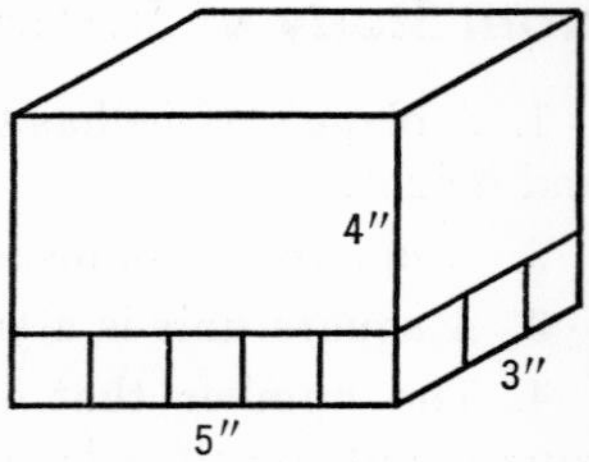

The abstract rule used in finding the volume of a rectangular solid is to multiply the length times the width times the height. The pupil can discover the meaning of the formula, $V = lwh$, by thinking that lw will give the number of cubic units of the bottom layer and h will show the number of layers. The formula for a cube is, $V = s^3$. The sides of a cube have the same dimension, s.

The principle of finding how many cubic inches are needed to cover the base and multiplying this number by number of rows of cubic units needed to fill the solid can be applied in finding the volume of a cylinder (see accompanying diagram). The number of cubic inches to cover the base will be $3\frac{1}{7} \times 4$ (cubic inches) or $12\frac{4}{7}$ cubic inches. The height, 6 inches, shows there will be 6 layers of $12\frac{4}{7}$ cubic inches each ($6 \times 12\frac{4}{7}$ cu in. $= 75\frac{3}{7}$ cu in.). The volume of the cylinder is equal to $75\frac{3}{7}$ cubic inches. The formula to find the volume of a cylinder is, $V = h\pi r^2$ (πr^2 is the base), therefore the formula may be written $V = hB$. Other formulas used in finding the volume of different shaped solids are:

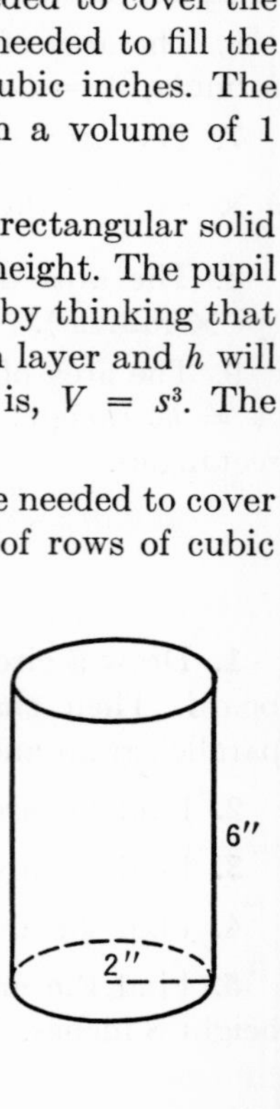

1. *Pyramid:* $V = \frac{hB}{3}$. B represents the area of the base and h is the height.

The volume of a pyramid equals one-third of a cylinder that has dimensions equivalent to the dimensions of the pyramid.

2. *Cone:* $V = \frac{hB}{3}$. B represents the area of the base and height represents the height.

The volume of a cone equals one-third of a cylinder that has the dimensions equivalent to the dimensions of the cone.

3. *Sphere:* The volume of a sphere $= \frac{4\pi r^3}{3}$.

EXERCISE

Find the volume of:

1. A cube with dimensions 6 inches.

2. A rectangular solid with dimensions: l = 8 inches, w = 4 inches, h = 3 inches.

3. A cylinder with dimensions: diameter 9 inches and height 6 inches.

4. A pyramid with dimensions: base = 9 inches, altitude = 15 inches, height = 30 inches.

5. A cone with dimensions: base = 6 inches, height = 15 inches.

6. A sphere with a diameter of 14 inches.

Measuring Capacity

The question, "How much does a container hold?" is answered in terms of the capacity of a smaller container. A large container may hold as much liquid as a stated number of smaller containers. The smaller containers, or unit of capacity measure, may vary from the gourds or bowls used in early times to the carefully defined unit of capacity measure used in modern times, such as pint, quart, and gallon.

In Great Britain the standard unit of capacity used for measuring both liquid and dry commodities is the British Imperial gallon. This unit of measure is defined as the volume of 10 pounds of pure water at 62°F. It contains 277.274 cubic inches. In the United States the standard unit used for measuring liquids is the gallon which contains 231 cubic inches.

The capacity of a container filled with a dry commodity is also determined by the use of smaller containers. These smaller units of measure are pint, quart, peck, and bushel. In Great Britain the gallon is the standard unit for measuring dry commodities and is 277.274 cubic inches. The bushel is defined as 8 gallons or 2218.192 cubic inches. In the United States the unit for measuring dry commodities is the bushel, which is defined as 2150.42 cubic inches. The United States gallon is about 17 percent smaller than the Imperial gallon. The capacity of a container in standard units of measure is determined by first finding the cubic inch volume and dividing this number by the number of cubic inches of the standard unit.

Measuring Weight

The answer to the question, "How much does an object weigh?" is expressed in terms of some referent that may be a pebble, a large stone, or a more accurately defined unit. In early times this unit was a grain of barley and present-day weights are often defined as a stated number of grains.

The present-day system of weights is complicated because of the existence of three kinds of weights: Avoirdupois weight, which is used for common purposes; troy weight, which is used for weighing gold and silver; and apothecaries' weight, which is used for weighing the content of prescriptions. One pound avoirdupois weight is the equivalent of 7000 grains. The troy apothecaries' pound is 5760 grains. The British Imperial pound (avoirdupois) is defined as the mass of a pure platinum cylinder kept by the Standards Department of the Board of Trade. In the United States the pound (avoirdupois) is defined in terms of the kilogram. Weight is the measure of the mass or gravity of an object.

Units of avoirdupois weight are the grain, dram, ounce, pound, hundredweight, and ton. The hundredweight used in the United States and Canada is the short hundredweight, 100 pounds. The long hundredweight, 112 pounds, is used in Great Britain. The short ton, 2000 pounds, is used in the United States and Canada. The long ton, 2240 pounds, is used in Great Britain.

Measuring Time

We cannot perceive time as we perceive many objects we measure, but we can perceive the changes that time makes. These changes can be measured and the result of the measurement expressed mathematically. To illustrate, primitive man could observe the change in the length of shadows that takes place from morning until evening. By observing the length of the shadow he could roughly determine how much of the day had passed.

Longer periods of time were probably measured by observing changes in the moon. Still longer periods of time could be recorded in terms of the change that takes place with the passing of a season, or in terms of the amount of time elapsed between the leafing out of the trees two successive times.

Originally the changes that occurred with the passing of time were probably recorded with tally marks. One tally mark could represent 1 day and another could represent 1 night. A different size or different kind of tally mark could represent 1 period between full moons. Still another kind could represent the period between seasons.

In more recent times clocks are used to measure time. As a tightly wound spring slowly unwinds, gears are turned, which move hands. As the hands move past numbers, time is recorded in seconds, minutes, and hours. Longer periods of time are measured in days, weeks, months, years, and centuries.

The conventional clock measures the passing of time over a 12-hour period, and each day is divided into periods between midnight and noon and between noon and midnight. In the armed forces clocks are graduated into 24 equal parts. Time for each 24-hour period is shown in hours and minutes after midnight. Thus 12 midnight is indicated, 2400, 1 A.M. is 0100, 11:30 A.M. is 1130, 2:45 P.M. is 1445. Observe that the left-hand pair of numbers indicates hours after midnight. The right hand pair of numbers indicates the number of minutes. To convert civilian time to time as recorded on the 24-hour clock, add 12 to the left-hand pair of figures if the time recorded is in terms of civilian time after 12 noon. To convert 24-hour clock time to 12-hour clock time, subtract 12 from the left-hand pair of figures if it is more than 12. If less than 12, no subtraction is necessary.

EXERCISE

Write the following times according to the 24-hour clock.

1:45 A.M. 10:00 A.M. 1:30 P.M. 5:00 P.M. 11:50 P.M.

Write the following times according to the 12-hour clock.

0255 1050 1345 1820 2220

Using Units of Circular Measure (Degrees) to Measure Time

The question, "How far apart are these cities?" can be expressed in miles, degrees, and if they are not on the same meridian, in terms of time. A degree is the principal unit of measure used in measuring arcs and angles. Each degree is $\frac{1}{360}$th of the circumference of a circle. The length of a degree is determined, therefore, by the length of the circumference.

The north-south angular distance between two cities is measured in degrees of latitude. Because of the flattened figure of the earth the meridians are not true circles, so the length of a degree of latitude varies somewhat on different parts of the meridians. A degree of latitude is 68.704 statute miles at the equator and 69.807 statute miles at the poles. All places on the same meridian are in the same time zone, so the north-south distance between cities is not expressed in terms of time.

The east-west angular distance between two cities is measured in degrees of longitude. The longitude of a place may be expressed as either degrees or as time. The longitude of New York is 74° or 4 hours 56 minutes west of Greenwich. Longitude can be expressed as time because the earth turns 15° in 1 hour ($\frac{1}{24}$ of $360° = 15°$). To change longitude in degrees to time, you simply divide the longitude in degrees by 15. In the case of New York, $74° \div 15° = 4$ hours and $\frac{14}{15}$ of another hour or 4 hours 56 minutes. The length of a degree of longitude varies greatly. At the equator each degree of longitude represents 69.65 statute miles. At 40° latitude it represents 53.43 miles.

For the sake of convenience in measuring time around the world, the world is divided into time zones, each of which is about 15° apart. The actual boundaries of the zones are usually drawn in such a way as to avoid the separation of large centers of population into two zones. The standard time in each zone is the same as the sun time for the meridian in the center of the zone.

The International Date Line, an imaginary line in the Pacific Ocean at approximately the 180° meridian, is a line at which the calendar day changes when one travels from east to west or west to east. In crossing the line on a westward journey, the date changes to one day later and a calendar day is omitted. On the return journey the date changes to one day earlier.

Measuring Temperature

Although temperature is not a tangible substance, its rise and fall can be measured by the changes in liquids, gases, or other substances, which change in volume or in some other characteristic in direct ratio to the temperature changes. Two kinds of thermometers are commonly used for measuring these changes. The one in everyday use is the Fahrenheit thermometer, which has as zero the temperature produced by mixing equal weights of snow and common salt, with "freezing point" at 32°, and which shows the boiling point of water as 212°. The other thermometer, commonly used in scientific work, is the centigrade thermometer, which has a scale with two standard points determined by the freezing point and boiling point of water at 760 millimeter barometric pressure. The space between these points is divided into one hundred equal parts. Accordingly, the freezing point is 0° and the boiling point of water is 100°.

It is sometimes necessary to express in degrees centigrade a temperature read from a thermometer with a Fahrenheit scale. On the Fahrenheit scale there are 180 divisions between the freezing point, 32°, and the boiling point, 212°. On the centigrade scale there are 100 divisions. Each division on the centigrade scale represents a greater change in the temperature and a relatively smaller number of degrees are needed to express temperature as centigrade rather than Fahrenheit degrees.

The first step in converting a Fahrenheit reading to a centigrade reading is to subtract 32° from the Fahrenheit reading. Then the starting point of both scales is at the freezing point of water. Each centigrade degree is $\frac{100}{180}$ or $\frac{5}{9}$ as large as each Fahrenheit degree. Step 2 is to multiply the difference between the Fahrenheit reading and 32° by $\frac{5}{9}$. $77° = ?°$ centigrade. Step 1: $77° - 32° = 45°$. Step 2: $\frac{5}{9} \times 45° = 25°$. $77°F = 25°C$.

When expressing a centigrade reading as a Fahrenheit reading there will be a greater number of degrees each with a smaller value than centigrade degrees. Step 1 is to multiply the centigrade reading by $\frac{9}{5}$. Step 2 is to add 32° to the product. 30°C = ?°F. $\frac{9}{5} \times 30° = 54°$. $54° + 32° = 86°$. 30°C = 86°F.

Measures of Value

The question, "What is the value?" can be answered in terms of money. The system of money in use in the United States is partly a decimal system with the dollar as the center of the system. See the decimal chart at the right. Each unit on the decimal grid is decimally related to the other units. Computation with decimal units that represent money is the same as computation with ones, tens, hundreds, etc.

$100	$10	$1	Dimes	Cents
7	5	4	3	2

$754.32

Money units of one denomination can be substituted for units of other denominations. It is therefore necessary to teach money equivalents other than decimal equivalents. The values of the nickel, quarter, and half dollar bear no decimal relationship between each other or between themselves and the other money units. An understanding of the money units that can be substituted for other money units is important in the making of change where the fewest possible coins are to be used.

Equivalent Measures

Computing with fewer but larger units is usually simpler than computing with many small units. To illustrate, adding, subtracting, multiplying, or dividing 4 feet is usually simpler than computing with its equivalent, 48 inches. Before 4 feet can be substituted for 48 inches it is necessary to think of the number of inches equal to 1 foot. This number, 12, is used as a divisor (48 in. ÷ 12 in. = 4 ft). Observe that the equivalent can be determined by finding the missing number in the proportion ($12 : 1 = 48 : X$).

Occasionally a number representing a greater number of smaller units is substituted for a number representing the larger units. To illustrate, 27 feet may be substituted for 9 yards. Since each yard is the equivalent of 3 feet, 9 yards are the equivalent of 9 × 3 feet or 27 feet.

Because of the lack of uniformity between units of measure in the English system of numbers, the learner must learn to apply tables of equivalent measures. Representative tables follow.

UNITS OF LENGTH

Unit	Comparison
Inch (in.)	
Foot (ft)	12 inches
Yard (yd)	36 inches 3 feet
Rod (rd)	16½ feet 5½ yards
Furlong (fur.)	660 feet 220 yards 40 rods
Mile (mi)*	5280 feet 1760 yards 320 rods 8 furlongs

* Known as statute mile.

UNITS OF AREA

Unit	Comparison
Square inch (sq in.)	
Square foot (sq ft)	144 sq in.
Square yard (sq yd)	1296 sq in. 9 sq ft
Square rod (sq rd)	272¼ sq ft 30¼ sq yds
Acre	43,560 sq ft 4,840 sq yd 160 sq rd
Square mile (sq mi)	27,878,400 sq ft 3,097,600 sq yd 102,400 sq rd 640 acres

UNITS OF VOLUME

Unit	Comparison
Cubic inch (cu in.)	
Cubic foot (cu ft)	1728 cu in.
Cubic yard (cu yd)	46,656 cu in. 27 cu ft
Cord (cd)	128 cu ft

UNITS OF CIRCULAR MEASURE

Unit	Comparison
Second (″)	
Minute (′)	60 seconds
Degree (°)	60 minutes
Right angle	90 degrees
Straight angle	180 degrees
Circle	360 degrees

UNITS OF CAPACITY

DRY MEASURE (U.S.)

Unit	Comparison	Cubic inches
Pint (pt)		33.6003
Quart (qt)	2 pints	67.2006
Peck (pk)	16 pints 8 quarts	537.605
Bushel (bu)	64 pints 32 quarts 4 pecks	2150.42

LIQUID MEASURE (U.S.)

Unit	Comparison	Cubic inches
Minim (min or m)*		.0038
Fluid dram (fl dr.)	60 min	.2256
Fluid ounce (fl oz)	8 fl dr	1.8047
Gill (gi)	32 fl dr 4 fl oz	7.2188
Pint (pt)	16 fl oz 4 gi	28.875
Quart (qt)	32 fl oz 8 gi 2 pt	57.75
Gallon (gal)	32 gi 8 pt 4 qt	231

* Approximately one drop.

UNITS OF WEIGHT OR MASS

Avoirdupois Weight

Unit	Comparison	Metric equivalent
Grain		.0648 gram
Dram (dr avdp)	27.3438 grains	1.7718 grams
Ounce (oz avdp)	16 drams 437.5 grains	28.3495 grams
Pound (lb avdp)	7000 grains 256 drams 16 ounces	.4536 kilogram
Hundredweight (cwt) *	100 pounds	45.3592 kilograms
Ton (tn) †	2000 pounds	.9072 metric ton

* Known as the short hundredweight, which is in use in the United States and Canada. Great Britain uses the long hundredweight (112 lb or 50.8024 kg).

† Known as the short ton, which is in use in the United States and Canada. Great Britain uses the long ton (2240 lb or 1.01605 metric tons).

Troy Weight

Unit	Comparison	Metric equivalent
Grain		.0648 gram
Pennyweight (dwt)	24 grains	1.5552 grams
Ounce (oz t)	480 grains 20 pennyweights	31.1035 grams
Pound (lb t) *	5760 grains 240 pennyweights 12 ounces	.3732 kilogram

* Declared illegal in Great Britain.

Apothecaries Weight

Grain		.0648 gram
Scruple (s ap or ℈)	20 grains	1.296 grams
Dram (dr ap or ʒ)	60 grains 3 scruples	3.8879 grams
Ounce (oz ap or ℥)	480 grains 24 scruples 8 drams	31.1035 grams
Pound (lb ap)	5760 grains 288 scruples 96 drams 12 ounces	.3732 kilogram

EXERCISE

Complete the statements below.

1. 6 pt = ? qt	4 gal = ? qt	3 hr = ? min
2. 7 qt = ? pt	8 pk = ? bu	6 gal = ? pt

Measuring Lumber

The standard unit of measure used in measuring lumber is the board foot. A board foot has a volume equal to that of a board 1 foot square and 1 inch thick or 144 cubic inches ($12 \times 12 \times 1 = 144$). In actual practice a board foot may have a volume of less than 144 cubic inches because of the fact that lumber is usually planed after it has been sawed. This may reduce the thickness of a 1-inch board by as much as $\frac{1}{4}$ inch. However the planed board is considered as being 1 inch thick for purposes of being measured in board feet. A board 1 inch thick, 12 inches wide, and 16 feet long is the equivalent of 16 board feet. A board 1 inch thick, 9 inches wide and 16 feet long is the equivalent of 12 board feet ($1 \times \frac{3}{4} \times 16 = 12$).

Generalized Rule

To find how many board feet are in a board, multiply the length expressed as feet, by the width expressed as feet, by the thickness expressed as inches.

The Four Fundamental Operations with Measures

Fractions are often avoided when numbers are written to express the result of a measurement. To illustrate, a man who is 73 inches tall might say, "I am 6 feet 1 inch" rather than, "I am $6\frac{1}{12}$ feet tall." For this reason it is necessary to teach the computation with measures expressed in different sized units. The following examples illustrate computation of measures when expressed in more than one kind of unit.

(*a*)	(*b*)	(*c*)	(*d*)
2 ft 5 in.	9 ft 2 in.	5 ft 6 in.	1 ft 6 in.
3 ft 5 in.	−5 ft 6 in.	×5	5)7 ft 6 in.
4 ft 8 in.	3 ft 8 in.	27 ft 6 in.	5 ft
10 ft 6 in.			2 ft 6 in. = 30 in.
			30 in.

The question asked by example (*a*) is, "What number of feet and inches equals all of the feet and all of the inches?" In computing the sum in example (*a*), first the numbers telling how many inches, the smallest units, are added. The sum is 18 inches or 1 foot 6 inches. 1 foot 6 inches are substituted for the sum with 1 foot remembered and 6 inches written. Then the numbers telling how many feet are added. The sum of the feet equals 1 foot remembered plus the sum of 2 + 3 + 4 or 10 feet. The total sum and answer to the question asked by example (*a*) is 10 feet 6 inches.

The question asked by example (*b*) is, "What is the difference between 9 feet 2 inches and 5 feet 6 inches?" In computing the answer, first the numbers telling how many inches are subtracted. The number in the subtrahend is more than the number in the minuend. The first step is to take one of the 9 feet and for it substitute 12 inches and add them to the 2 inches. The minuend can then be thought of as 8 feet and 14 inches. Then the numbers telling how many inches can be subtracted. The next step is that of finding the difference between the numbers that tell how many feet. The answer to the question asked by the example is, "3 feet 8 inches."

(*b*)

9 ft 2 in.	=	8 ft 14 in.
−5 ft 6 in.	=	5 ft 6 in.
		3 ft 8 in.

The question asked by example (*c*) is, "What number of feet and inches are equal to 5 groups of 5 feet 6 inches each?" The first step is to find the number of inches equal to 5 groups of 6 inches each. This number is 30 inches. For 30 inches substitute 2 feet 6 inches. The 2 feet are remembered and 6 inches written. The next step is to find the number of feet equal to 5 groups of 5 feet each. This number is 25 feet, and to it are added the 2 feet remembered. The total number of feet is 27. The answer to the question asked by the example is, "27 feet 6 inches."

(*c*)

5 ft 6 in.
×5
27 ft 6 in.

The question asked by example (*d*) is, "What is the length of each piece when a piece 7 feet 6 inches long is cut into 5 equal pieces?" The first step is to divide the 7, which represents feet, by 5. The answer is 1 foot with 2 feet remaining. For the 2 feet, 24 inches are substituted and they are added to the 6 inches. Then the sum is 30 inches. The next step is to divide the 30, which represents inches, by 5. The answer is 6 inches. The answer to the question in the example is, "1 foot 6 inches."

(*d*)

```
    1 ft 6 in.
5)7 ft 6 in.
  5 ft
  2 ft 6 in. = 30 in.
               30 in.
```

EXERCISE

5 ft 4 in. 6 ft 3 in. 4 ft 2 in.	6 gal 2 qt 8 gal 1 qt 2 gal 3 qt	12 hr 45 min −8 hr 20 min	9 yd 1 ft −6 yd 2 ft
10 ft 2 in. ×4	5 bu 2 pk ×5	3)15 ft 6 in.	9)15 yd 2 ft

Indirect Measurement

The early Greeks discovered certain facts and relationships about right triangles that enabled them to measure distances by means of computation rather than by actually applying the measuring unit to the distance being measured. One of the facts they discovered is that in a right triangle the square on the hypotenuse equals the sum of the squares on the other two sides. By using this knowledge they could find the length of any side of a right triangle if the length of the other two sides was known. To illustrate, if a right triangle has legs of 3 inches and 4 inches, the sum of the squares of the legs is 9 + 16 or 25. The length of the unknown side is the square root of 25, or 5 (see accompanying diagram).

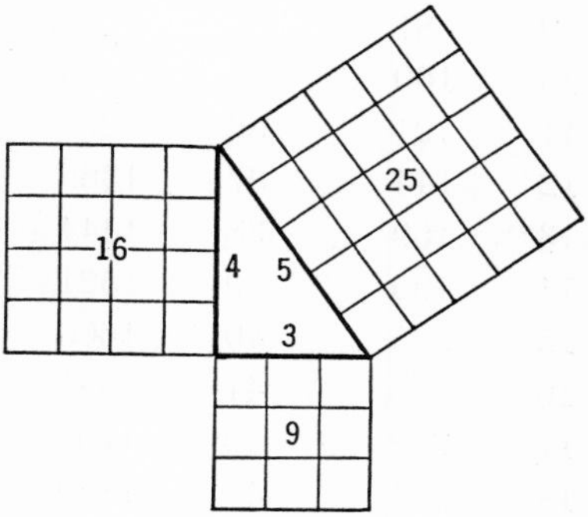

Squares and Square Roots

Finding the length of each side of a square when the area is known involves a process known as finding the square root. The sign $\sqrt{}$ means the *square root of*. The most common means of finding the square root of a number is through using a table of squares and square roots.

SQUARES AND SQUARE ROOTS

This table gives squares of numbers from 1 to 100:

No.	Square	No.	Square	No.	Square	No.	Square
1	1	26	676	51	2601	76	5776
2	4	27	729	52	2704	77	5929
3	9	28	784	53	2809	78	6084
4	16	29	841	54	2916	79	6241
5	25	30	900	55	3025	80	6400
6	36	31	961	56	3136	81	6561
7	49	32	1024	57	3249	82	6742
8	64	33	1089	58	3364	83	6889
9	81	34	1156	59	3481	84	7056
10	100	35	1225	60	3600	85	7225
11	121	36	1296	61	3721	86	7396
12	144	37	1369	62	3844	87	7569
13	169	38	1444	63	3969	88	7744
14	196	39	1521	64	4096	89	7921
15	225	40	1600	65	4225	90	8100
16	256	41	1681	66	4356	91	8281
17	289	42	1764	67	4489	92	8464
18	324	43	1849	68	4624	93	8649
19	361	44	1936	69	4761	94	8836
20	400	45	2025	70	4900	95	9025
21	441	46	2116	71	5041	96	9216
22	484	47	2209	72	5184	97	9409
23	529	48	2304	73	5329	98	9604
24	576	49	2401	74	5476	99	9801
25	625	50	2500	75	5625	100	10000

A portion of such a table is shown above. By looking at the table, it is possible to discover that the square root of 2116 is 46 and that the square of 46 is 2116.

The table can be used to find approximate square roots of numbers that are not perfect squares. To find the square root of 4504, the computation is as follows:

$67^2 = 4489$	$68^2 = 4624$	$135\overline{)15.000}$ = .111+
4624	4504	13 5
−4489	−4489	1 50
135	15	1 35
		150
		135

Step 1—Use the table to find the squares between which 4504 lies.

Step 2—Find the differences as shown above. The first difference is the difference between the squares and the second is the difference between the number, 4504, and the smaller square.

Step 3—Divide the smaller difference by the larger. The quotient is the decimal part of the square root.

The approximate square root of 4504 is 67.11.

EXERCISE

Use the table to find the square root of 1521; 9025; 875; 4995; 8245.

Since tables are not always available, it is necessary for pupils to learn how to compute squares and square roots. The first step in helping pupils learn to understand what is meant by squaring a number is to have them observe a diagram such as the diagram for 24^2.

	24	
	×24	
4 × 4	16	ones²
4 × 20	80	ones × tens
20 × 4	80	tens × ones
20 × 20	400	tens²
	576	Total Square

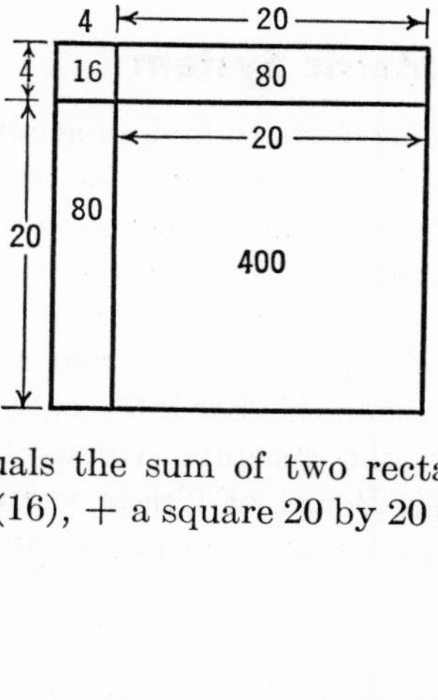

The number 24 when squared equals the sum of two rectangles each 20 × 4 (160), + a square 4 × 4 (16), + a square 20 by 20 (400). 16 + 160 + 400 = 576. 24^2 = 576.

The example $\sqrt{576}$ asks the question, "What number squared equals 576?" The above diagram can be used in showing how to find the answer. The first step is to find the largest square in 5 hundreds. It is 20. $20^2 = 400$. The next step is to find the width of the two rectangles and the small square. Their area, 176, is divided by 40 to find the approximate width. The approximate width is 4. The remainder, 16, represents the area of the small square. $\sqrt{16} = 4$ so the small square is 4 units wide and 4 units long. The dimensions of the large square are $20 + 4$ or 24 so the answer to the question, "What number squared equals 576?" is 24.

```
     4 r 16
40)176
   160
    16
```

The computation method used in finding the square root is shown at the right. Observe that 1764 is pointed off into periods of two figures, each beginning at the right. Think of the largest square in the first period at the left. The largest square in 17 hundreds in 16 hundreds. $\sqrt{16} = 4$. Write 4 in the answer and its square, 16, under 17. Subtract and bring down the next period, 64, to form a partial dividend. Divide the first two figures of the partial dividend (164) by twice the part of the square root already found, to find the next trial figure. (160 equals twice the product of the tens and ones). $16 \div 8 = 2$. Write 2 in ones place in the answer and also in the divisor, because the product of the ones in the answer and ones in the divisor should equal the square of the ones. Then multiply. $2 \times 82 = 164$, so you know 2 is the correct ones figure. The square root of 1764 is 42. To check, mult ply 42×42. The product is 1764.

```
    17'64)42
    16
82)1 64
   1 64
```

Find the square root of these numbers: 729, 1156, 5184.

The Metric System

Man's efforts to find an accurate standard unit of measure led him to establish the meter as the basis of an entire system of measurement. The meter was intended to be one ten-millionth of the distance measured on a meridian of the earth from the equator to the pole and is very nearly that distance. The meter used as a standard today is the distance between two lines on a certain platinum bar kept in Paris, when this bar is 0° centigrade or 32° Fahrenheit. In the United States, the accepted value of the meter is 39.37 inches, but the English Board of Trade value is 39.370113 inches. Copies of the Paris meter are kept elsewhere, and its value in wavelengths of light is known with very great exactness so the standard can be reproduced if the original standard is lost.

The metric system of weights and measures originated in France at the close of the eighteenth century and is the legal system of measures in France and the majority of other nations including the United States and England. One advantage of the system is that all units are related decimally. That is, each unit of measure is ten times the next smaller unit.

The basic unit of length is the meter (m), the basic unit of weight is the gram (g), and the basic unit of capacity is the liter (l). Each is used with the prefixes kilo, hecto, deka, meaning respectively thousand, hundred, and ten; and deci, centi, milli, meaning respectively tenths, hundredths, and thousandths.

Metric Measures of Length

In countries using the metric system, the question, "How much length?" is answered by applying the meter stick to the object being measured. As previously stated, the meter stick in the United States has a length of 39.37 inches. Shorter distances might be measured in decimeters (dm)—$\frac{1}{10}$ of 1 meter; in centimeters (cm)—$\frac{1}{100}$ of 1 meter; or in millimeters (mm)—$\frac{1}{1000}$ of 1 meter. The equivalent United States length of these smaller units is as follows: centimeter = $\frac{1}{10}$ of 39.37 = 3.937 inches; decimeter = $\frac{1}{100}$ of 39.37 inches = .3937 inch; millimeter = $\frac{1}{1000}$ of 39.37 inches = .0394 inch.

Distances longer than a meter might be measured in dekameters (dkm) 10 × 1 meter; in hectometers (hm)—100 × 1 meter; and kilometer (km) 1000 × 1 meter. The equivalent length of these longer units are as follows: dekameter = 10 × 39.37 inches = 393.7 inches; hectometer = 100 × 39.37 inches = 3937 inches or 328 feet 1 inch; kilometer = 1000 × 39.37 inches = 39370 inches or .62137 mile.

EXERCISE

Supply the missing numbers.

1. 15 ones = ? tens ? ones 15 meters = ? dm ? m 27 tens = ? hundreds ? tens

2. 27 meters = ? dm ? m 235 tenths = ? tens ? ones ? tenths 235 dm = ? dm ? m ? dm

Metric Measures of Area

In the metric system, the units of measure used in finding the areas are also based upon the meter. The square meter (m^2) is used for measuring areas of plane surfaces which, in the United States system of measures, would be measured with the square yard. The other metric units of square measure are designated by using the prefixes deka, hecto, kilo, for tens, hundreds, thousands; and deci, centi, and milli for tenths, hundredths, and thousandths. A square dekameter (dkm^2) is a unit of measure with dimensions of 10 meters on each side. A square decimeter (dm^2) is a unit of measure with dimensions of one tenth of a meter on each side. Specialized names are given to some units of measure used in measuring surface. See the accompanying table.

Unit	Metric Equivalent	U. S. Equivalent
Hectare	10,000 square meters (m^2)	2.47 acres
Are	100 square meters (m^2)	119.6 sq yd
Centare	1 square meter (m^2)	1550 sq inches

Metric Measures of Volume

The unit used to measure the volume of solids is a cube having dimensions of 1 meter on each side. This cube is called the cubic meter (m^3) and has an English equivalent of 35.3145 cubic feet. Smaller units of volume are: dm^3 with an English equivalent of 61.0234 cubic inches; cm^3 with an English equivalent of .061 cubic inch, and the mm^3 with an English equivalent of .00006 cubic inch.

Metric Measures of Weight

Just as the meter is the center of the metric decimal system of measures in measuring length, the gram (g) is the center of the decimal system of measures used in measuring weight. The gram was originally intended to be equal to the weight of one cubic centimeter of pure water at 4°C. A very small error in measurement was made, but for all practical purposes the

kg	hg	dkg	gram	dg	cg	mg
6	7	9	8	5	2	3

6798.523 kg.

measurement is sufficiently accurate. The decimal grid above shows the abbreviations for units larger than grams and for units smaller than grams. It shows that there are 8 grams, 9 dekagrams (dkg), 7 hectograms (hg), 6 kilograms (kg), 5 decigrams (dg), 2 centigrams (cg), and 3 milligrams (mg). Observe the use of the prefixes kilo, hecto, and deka to represent respectively thousands, hundreds, and tens; and the use of deci, centi, and milli to represent tenths, hundredths, and thousandths.

The standard for the kilogram (1000 grams) is a platinum-iridium cylinder, called the international standard of mass, which is kept at the International Bureau of Weights and Measures in France. If for some reason the standard were destroyed, it could be rediscovered by constructing a cube with dimensions of 1 centimeter, filling it with water at 4°C. and then multiplying by 1000 the weight of the water in the cube.

Metric Measures of Capacity

The liter (l) is the center of the metric decimal system of measures used in measuring capacity. The liter is defined as the volume of pure water at 4°C. that weighs one kilogram. The decimal grid at the right shows the decimal relationship between the metric units of capacity. Observe the use of the prefixes kilo, hecto, deka, deci, centi, and milli.

kl	hl	dkl	liter	dl	cl	ml
2	9	3	5	8	6	7

A cubic decimeter has the capacity of 1 liter. Since 1 decimeter equals 3.937 inches, you can find by multiplying that 1 liter equals 61.0234 cu. inches. A liter has the same capacity as 1.06 qt. One quart equals .95 liter.

EXERCISE

1. A gallon of milk equals how many liters?

2. How many gallons of gasoline equal 15 liters?

Some Useful Equivalents

With an increase in world trade and travel, it is useful to know some of the common equivalent metric and English units. A few of the more common equivalents are listed below.

1 millimeter	= .04 inch	1 yard	= .9144 meter
1 meter	= 39.37 inches or 3.28 feet or 1.094 yards	1 centimeter	= .39 inch
		1 kilometer	= .62 mile
		1 liter	= 1.06 quarts
1 kilogram	= 2.20 pounds	1 quart	= .946 liter
1 mile	= 1.609 kilometers	1 gallon	= 3.7853 liters

EXERCISE

Complete the statements below. (Hint: Mentally substitute thousand, hundred, or ten for kilo, hecto, and deka; and deci, centi, and milli for tenths, hundredths, and thousandths.)

1. 4 km 6 hm = ______ m 5 km 7 hm 3 m = ______ m

2. 762 m = ______ m ______ dkm ______ hm
3 km = ______ m = ______ cm

3. 12 m = ______ cm = ______ dm 5 m = ______ yd

4. 10 km = ______ mi 100 yd = ______ m

5. 5 l = ______ qt 10 qt = ______ l

6. 8 cm^3 = ______ mm^3 5 m^2 = ______ cm^2

7. 100 lb = ______ kg 100 gal = ______ l

Diagnosing Pupil Growth

Children need an opportunity to examine and discuss ideas developed in their study of measures. Representative questions that teachers may use to stimulate discussion include:

1. What are some objects you would measure with a ruler? A yardstick?

2. What events in your life might be measured in seconds? In minutes? In hours? In days? In weeks? In months? In years?

3. What events are sometimes measured in centuries?

4. What are some items in a grocery store that are sold by the ounce? By the pound? By the gallon? By the quart? By the pint? By the dozen?

5. What are some materials bought by the hundredweight? By the ton?

6. What are we actually measuring when we use a thermometer?

7. What is the purpose of time zones? Why is it necessary to have them?

8. What is the difference between A.M. and P.M.? Between civilian time and navy time?

9. What are some units of measure used in measuring area? Volume? How can the units be used?

10. What coins are the equivalent of $1? Of 50c?

11. What are some advantages of the metric system?

12. What are the three basic units of measure in the metric system?

13. What is meant by the prefixes milli, centi, deci, deka, hecto, kilo?

14. What units of measure in the metric system are most nearly equivalent to these units in the English system: yard, quart, pound?

Test items such as the following may be included on pencil and paper tests.

Part I—Meanings

1. You would probably measure the width of your book with a (yardstick, square inch, ruler).

2. The third month in the year is (February, March, April).

3. The time when school is most likely to commence is (9 A.M., 9 P.M., 10:30 A.M.).

4. When milk is 22c a quart, a sensible price for a half gallon would be (50c, 88c, 40c).

5. The Declaration of Independence was signed on (July 4, 1775 B.C., July 4, 1775 A.D.).

6. The length of the page in your arithmetic is most nearly (5 inches, 12 inches, 9 inches).

7. When it is cool enough for you to want to wear a sweater, the temperature is probably about (60°, 85°, 90°).

8. The time of day when the temperature is usually the highest is (7:00 A.M., 12 noon, 8:30 P.M.).

9. The unit of measure that is largest is the (square foot, square rod, square yard).

10. If you wish to substitute pints for gallons, multiply the number of gallons by (8, 4, 2).

11. If you wish to substitute tons for pounds, divide the number of pounds by (100, 1000, 2000).

12. The basic unit of length in the metric system is the (meter, gram, liter).

13. The width of a time zone in degrees is (15°, 45°, 90°).

14. The formula for finding the volume of a rectangular solid is ($V = s^3$, $V = Bh$, $V = \pi r^2$).

Part II—Finding Equivalents

What are the correct answers for these questions?

1. 1 gal = ? qt = ? pt	1 bu = ? pk = ? qt
2. 24 objects = ? doz	48 oz = ? lb
3. 1 mile = ? ft = ? yd	9 sq ft = ? sq yd = ? sq in.
4. A circle = ? degrees	1 m = ? dm = ? cm = ? mm
5. 5 kl = ? l = ? cl	500 cm = ? m = ? dkm
6. 50°C = ?°F	90°F = ?°C

Part III—Computation

1. Write the formula and then use it to find the area of each of the following:

(*a*) A square 9 in. on each side.

(*b*) A rectangle $6\frac{1}{2}$ ft by $12\frac{1}{2}$ ft.

(*c*) A triangle with a base of 10 in. and an altitude of 8 in.

(*d*) A parallelogram with a base of 12 yd and an altitude of 6 yd.

(*e*) A trapezoid with one base of $3\frac{1}{2}$ miles, a second base of $5\frac{3}{4}$ miles, and an altitude of 2 miles.

(*f*) A circle with a diameter of 49 ft.

2. Find the unknown dimension for each of the following:

(*a*) A square with an area of 144 sq in. s = ? in.

(*b*) A rectangle with an area of 35 sq ft and a length of 7 ft. $W = ?$

(*c*) A triangle with an area of 64 sq in. and an altitude of 10 in. $b = ?$

(*d*) A right triangle with a base of 9 yd and an altitude of 15 yd. Hypotenuse = ? yd.

3. Write the formula and find the volume for each of the following:

(*a*) A cube 6 in. on each side.

(*b*) A rectangular solid 3 ft long, 2 ft 6 in. wide, and 1 ft 4 in. deep.

(*c*) A cylinder with a radius of 7 ft and a height of 32 ft.

4. Find the answers for each of the following.

6 yd 1 ft 5 yd 2 ft 2 yd 2 ft	3 hr 15 min −1 hr 50 min	7 gal 1 qt ×6	5)12 wk 2 days

Summary

Measures have been devised by man to use in answering the question "How much?" as it relates to length, surface, volume, weight or mass, capacity, and value. In tracing the development of measures one is impressed with the wide variety of methods and instruments used by primitive man when answering his questions about quantity. The economic need for accuracy stimulated him to search for increasingly accurate standardized measures acceptable throughout the world. The transition from the use of parts of the body as an accepted standard to the use of parts of the universe itself as a standard has been relatively slow and is by no means complete.

All measuring is preceded by a question in the mind of some individual or individuals. The process of measuring consists of choosing an appropriate instrument to use in answering the question, of applying it to the quantity to be measured, and of recording the result of the measurement. The numbers used in recording the result of the measuring tell *how many* units of measure are used. The numbers are usually used in conjunction with the name of the measuring unit, and in conjunction with the name of the substance measured.

Measuring instruments sometimes have a shape corresponding to the characteristic shape of the object being measured. Thus the instrument used to measure length possesses the characteristic of length: i.e., an inch, foot, yard, and meter all have the common characteristic of length. Measuring units used to measure surface have the characteristic of surface: i.e., square inches, square feet, square yards. Measuring units used to measure solids may be solids of a specific shape: i.e., cubic inch, cubic foot.

Measuring instruments sometimes have a shape to which the substance being measured can conform. Thus the gallon, bushel, and liter are used to measure liquids or dry substances. The dry substances may be grain, apples, or potatoes. Sometimes the measuring instruments are used to measure change. To illustrate, a clock measures changes that result from the passage of time; a thermometer measures the change in a liquid, gas, or other substance that takes place as a result of heating or cooling. Time and temperature are intangibles that are not measured by the direct application of a measuring instrument to them. The technique of measuring intangibles must differ from the technique of measuring tangibles. In each case the instrument or unit has been devised for a specific purpose: i.e., to answer the question "How much?"

Formulas have been derived to be used in finding areas and volumes. These formulas are short-cut rules. The letter at the left of the equality sign can be thought of as asking a question, and the letters at the right can be thought of as telling what to do to answer the question. To illustrate, in $A = lw$, A asks, "What is the area?" To answer the question, multiply the length times the width as indicated by lw at the right of the equality sign. The formulas used in finding areas and volumes are used in working with English, United States, or metric units of measure.

When it is necessary to substitute equivalent smaller units of measure for a given number of larger units, *multiply*, using as a multiplicand the number of smaller units equal to one of the larger units. To substitute equivalent larger units for a given number of smaller units, *divide* using as a divisor the number of smaller units equal to one of the larger units.

The metric system is a decimal system with three basic units of measure which are: the meter used to measure length, the liter used to measure capacity, and the gram used to measure weight. All units are related to the meter and as long as the length of the meter is known, the other units can be reconstructed. Each unit in the metric system is ten times larger than the unit to its right. The prefixes deka, hecto, and kilo represent tens, hundreds, and thousands. The prefixes deci, centi, and milli represent tenths, hundredths, and thousandths. In the metric system substituting larger units for smaller units and smaller units for larger units is as simple as substituting tens for ones and ones for tens.

Regardless of the system of weights and measures used, all measurement is an approximation. Man's search for completely accurate means of answering the question, "How much?" is an unceasing search that will not end in the foreseeable future.

SUGGESTED QUESTIONS FOR STUDY

1. What reasons can you give for helping pupils in the elementary schools to discover, to understand, and to apply the essential meanings in practical measurement?

2. What methods does man use to record the results of his measuring?

3. How did primitive man solve the problems faced in measuring length? In measuring time? In measuring capacity?

4. What are the essential steps or procedures that pupils should observe when solving the problems faced in measuring quantity or quantities?

5. What is the need of world-wide standardization authority in regard to measures and what steps has man taken to meet these needs?

6. What is the relationship between practical measurement and consumer economics?

7. What are the psychological steps involved in substituting for smaller units an equivalent number of larger units of measure?

8. What are the psychological steps involved in substituting an equivalent number of larger for smaller units of measure?

9. Which of the English systems of measures is based on the binary number system? Which is based on the duodecimal number system?

10. Upon what number system is the metric system based?

11. What are the basic units of measure in the English system of measures? In the metric system of measures?

12. What is the relationship between the basic units of measures in the metric system?

13. What units of measure have been developed to assist man in atomic research?

SUGGESTED ACTIVITIES FOR TEACHERS

1. Prepare a list of practical meanings and skills that teachers should help pupils to develop regarding: (*a*) linear measure, (*b*) surface measure, (*c*) cubic volume, (*d*) time, (*e*) temperature, (*f*) weight, (*g*) money.

2. Prepare a list of meanings and skills that teachers should help pupils to discover and understand about the (*a*) English system, (*b*) the United States system, (*c*) the metric system.

3. Prepare a representative diagnostic test to determine a pupil's ability to compute with denominate numbers.

4. Preview a number of filmstrips or films and evaluate them in terms of how they might assist a pupil to learn about measures and their use.

5. Prepare a list of measuring instruments such as might be placed on an arithmetic table in a classroom. For each instrument prepare a question or questions that could be put on the board near the table for the purpose of stimulating children to answer them.

SUGGESTED ACTIVITIES FOR PUPILS

1. Discuss and demonstrate the evolution of units and devices used in measuring length.

2. List the measuring units and devices you have used during the week.

3. Look for the inspection stamp on scales and gasoline pumps.

4. Estimate, verify, and record the weights and heights of children.

5. Keep data for current prices on foods as found in various stores. Compare prices of comparable grades of merchandise bought in different stores.

6. Plan actual budgets.

7. Prepare to discuss government spending and income in regard to the amount of expenditure, purpose, benefit to citizens, to the country, etc.

8. Plan and make purchases for school events.

9. Read gas, electric, and water meters and compare readings at various intervals of time.

10. Determine the cost of sending communications by various mail services, telegraph, radiogram, cablegram.

11. Plan trips by rail and air considering distance, cost, time, time schedules, time zones, etc.

12. Use accurate measurements in making many things in the workshop, kitchen, sewing room, etc.

PRACTICE EXERCISES

1. 2 yr 3 mo = ______ yr   2 hr 40 min = ______ day

2. 3 yd 3 inches = ______ in.   4 gal 2 pt = ______ qt

3. 2 m 6 cm = ______ m   2 kg 50 g = ______ g

4. 1 sq ft = ______ sq in.   1 cu yd = ______ cu ft

5. 36 cu inches = ______ cu ft   3 hr 15 min = ______ min

Find the area of each of the following plane surfaces:

1. Rectangle: $b = 9$ ft, $h = 4$ ft. Parallelogram: $b = 4.6$ ft, $h = 4.2$ ft

2. Triangle: $b = 4\frac{1}{2}$ in, $h = 6\frac{1}{4}$ in.

3. Trapezoid: base $a = 5\frac{1}{4}$ ft, base $b = 8\frac{3}{4}$ ft, altitude $= 3\frac{1}{2}$ ft

4. Circle: circumference = 22 ft   Circle: radius = 7 mi

Find the volume of each of the following solids:

1. Rectangular solid: $l = 7$ in., $w = 5$ in., $h = 4$ in.

2. Pyramid: $l = 8$ ft, $w = 6$ ft, $h = 12$ ft

3. Cone: $d = 28$ in., $h = 16$ in.

4. Sphere: $r = 12$ in.

Find the answer to each example:

1.

3 ft 9 in. 4 ft 6 in +8 ft 5 in	15 min 30 sec −7 min 45 sec	8 yd 2 ft ×7	4)9 gal 2 qt

2. $\sqrt{196}$ $\sqrt{1940}$ $\sqrt{9216}$ $\sqrt{9896}$ $\sqrt{4250}$

SELECTED REFERENCES

1. Bendick, Jeanne, *How Much and How Many*. New York: McGraw-Hill Book Company, Inc., 1947.

2. Hogben, Lancelot, *The Wonderful World of Mathematics*. New York: Garden City Books, 1955.

3. Karpinski, L. C., *The History of Arithmetic*. Chicago: Rand McNally & Company, 1925.

4. National Society for the Study of Education, *The Measurement of Understanding* (Forty-Fifth Yearbook) Part 1. Chicago: University of Chicago Press, 1946.

5. Sanford, Vera, *A Short History of Mathematics*. Boston: Houghton Mifflin Company, 1930.

6. Smith, David Eugene, *History of Mathematics* (2 vols.). Boston: Ginn & Company, 1923–25.

7. Ulrich, Louis E., Sr., *Streamlining Arithmetic*. Chicago: Lyons & Carnahan, 1943.

11

Meaning and Function of Problem Solving

Introduction

One of the primary functions of elementary schools is to provide situations, materials, and instruction that will motivate and assist pupils in developing interest, attitudes, and mental abilities in solving problems. The values and skills that are productive in dealing with real and vicarious problems experienced in personal and community living are learned ways of thinking and acting. Competency in living and working in an age of applied science is dependent upon a person's understanding of and skills in using the scientific method and problem-solving methods in personal, social, and economic situations.

Teachers have the opportunity to help pupils to learn the value of the language and computational operations of arithmetic in finding solutions to various kinds of problems to be found in the school, in the home, and in the community. The mental processes that are essential in identifying problems and in determining appropriate solutions should be as important to the teacher and pupils as the correctness of answers. Improvement in problem-solving methods can be experienced by directing the attention of pupils to the "how" and "why" in the methods they use when seeking to solve problems. Teachers should place emphasis on such mental processes as: (1) discriminating observation, (2) reflective reading, (3) qualitative reasoning, (4) formulating hypotheses, (5) collecting pertinent information, (6) testing the accuracy of solutions, and (7) deriving efficient generalizations. The teacher's understanding of the psychological nature of the problem-solving process influences in many ways the psychological behavior of each pupil who is seeking to find solutions to real and personal problems.

Exploratory Questions

These questions are presented for teachers and prospective teachers who want to appraise their interpretation of problem solving as a psychological process. They may be useful in stimulating a critical evaluation of the ideas and suggestions given in this chapter for improving methods of teaching and methods of learning in the area of problem solving.

1. What is a problem? Who is a "problem solver"?

2. What are the psychological as well as mathematical meanings and principles involved in problem solving that should be understood by teachers?

3. How may textbook problems have different meaning and purpose for the teacher and for individual pupils?

4. Under what conditions may verbal or teacher-assigned problems become "real" or "accepted" problems for each pupil?

5. What are the important outcomes or learnings that the teacher should expect pupils to gain from their use of problem solving in arithmetic and other curriculum subjects?

6. What are some of the factors that affect the developmental progress of pupils in solving various kinds of problems?

7. How may teachers use verbal problems and exercises in the textbook to help pupils to develop interest and to improve mental processes in solving problems?

8. What different types of problem-solving situations may be used to enrich the classroom program?

9. How do you interpret the relationships between reading ability and success with problem solving.

10. How may the mental hygiene climate of the classroom influence the behavior of the teacher and pupils in problem solving?

11. Why is it normal that pupils reveal differences in learning and applying methods in solving problems?

12. What have research studies revealed to be more effective methods in teaching problem solving?

13. How may resource materials assembled from out-of-school environments be used in helping pupils to define problems and to prepare original problems?

14. What do research studies reveal concerning the effectiveness of teaching methods that require pupils to use formal patterns or formulas in finding the solution to problems?

15. How do you appraise the relationship between the methods of problem solving in arithmetic and methods used to determine the solution to problems in social studies and elementary science?

Interpretation of a Problem

"What is a problem?" is a fundamentally important question. A teacher's answer to this question will condition his objectives and methods in teaching problem solving. Some teachers and many pupils may restrict their interpretation of a problem to the verbal problems given in the textbook or written problems assigned by the teacher. Problems of this kind do present worthwhile learning situations. Yet a broader meaning of problems needs to be understood if teachers are to be successful in helping pupils to identify themselves with the practical and psychological nature of problems and problem solving.

A problem is a particular situation in which a person encounters a blocking of mental and/or physical action in reaching a desired goal. The degree of awareness of a goal and the tension resulting from blocking depend on the nature of each problem situation and quality of motivation felt by the person. Problems vary in complexity from a relatively easy question to situations that present the need for identification, analysis, and verified solution. Each of these problems presents a situation that is different in complexity:

1. John has 6 marbles. His father gave him 8 marbles. John asks himself, "How many marbles do I now have?"

2. Mary sold 3 boxes of Girl Scout cookies. The selling price for each box was 35c. Mary desires to answer the question, "How much money did I receive for the 3 boxes?"

3. Henry and his father traveled 900 miles on a trip. The car averaged 15.5 miles on a gallon of gasoline. Henry's father paid 31.5c per gallon each time he bought gasoline. Henry wants to know, "How much did my father spend for gasoline on the trip?"

4. A merchant bought 6 gross of pencils for $24. He sold the pencils for 5c each. How much profit did he make? What was the percent of profit?

5. Mary's father budgets his income so as to allow 25% for rent, 15% for clothing, 30% for food. The annual income is $5600. Mary desires the answer to these questions: "How much did my father budget for rent?" "How much was allowed for clothing?" "How much was budgeted for food?"

Problems may be experienced by individuals or by a group of persons. For example, pupils in a class decided they wanted to go on a picnic. Their goal was the pleasure of a picnic. Before reaching their goal they faced such blocking as: "Where to go?" "What food should they take?" "How much will the food cost?" "How can they earn the money to cover cost of food and transportation?" From the conception of the idea of a picnic they had to overcome certain barriers or blocks that involved discussion, planning, and decision making. Problem solving as experienced by the pupils was real and purposeful.

Verbal problems are descriptions of problem situations. They must be understood and accepted by the learner before they are identified as personal problems. Guidance and time are essential in assisting pupils to read and define verbal problems found in the textbook or prepared by the teacher so that they change the problems into real problem situations. Teachers need to examine carefully the important concept that any problem that is meaningful and purposeful to pupils must be understood and accepted as a personal problem. To become real, the problem must be identified and accepted in each pupil's "under-the-skin" behavior.

Step Problems

A problem where the solution calls for finding an answer to one question is a one-step problem. For example, John collected 26¢ on Monday from the sale of papers, 33¢ on Tuesday, and 30¢ on Wednesday. How much did he collect in all? One question is asked, and one computation, addition, is required to find the answer.

A problem introducing a direct question and also a "hidden" or second question is a "two-step-to-a-solution" problem. Attention and time must be given in finding the answer to the second or "hidden" question before finding the answer to the direct question. For example: Henry purchased 3 tops that cost 15¢ each and a bag of marbles that cost 18¢. He wanted to know, "How much money did I spend in all?" Before he could answer this question he had to find the amount spent for the tops and also the money spent for the marbles. He used multiplication to answer the indirect question and then used addition to find how much money he had spent. The mental process involved in identifying the situation, in analyzing the problem to determine the facts known and the questions, and the formulation and testing of probable solutions in "two-steps-to-a-solution" problems is more complex than in a "one-step-to-a-solution" problem. Generally more time is needed to complete the former problem than the latter.

A problem that contains a direct question and two indirect, yet related, questions is classified as a "three-step-to-a-solution" problem. Teachers should be familiar with the mathematical and thought complexity of such problems. For example: Bill went to the store with a $5 bill. He bought 4 pounds of meat at 79¢ a pound and 3 cans of orange juice at 47¢ a can. He desired to know, "How much change should I receive?" The solution depends on finding the answer to these questions: "How much did the meat cost?" "How much did the orange juice cost?" "How much change should I receive?" Problems that require a "three-step-in-a-solution" process are rather difficult for many elementary school pupils. If the problems are personal and real the complexity in thinking may be reduced by the strong desire to reach the solution or goal. When textbook problems are of this type, time should be given to develop motivation, to make one or more analyses, and to formulate and test the solution.

Pupils vary in their ability to solve one-step, two-step, and three-step problems. The outcomes reached by pupils will depend on the teacher's effort to select problems best suited to the performance level of each pupil or group of pupils. An awareness of desired purpose and a sense of achieving are powerful motivating factors influencing the progress of pupils in solving verbal and personal problems.

Who Is the Problem Solver?

Each pupil is his own problem solver. He may work independently or as a member of a group, yet the meaningfulness of his goal, identification of the situation, and methods used in seeking and verifying a solution are the result of his mental or "under-the-skin" thinking. When a pupil is confronted with a real or verbal problem and accepts a solution from another person he has not improved in his problem-solving ability. Each person becomes a problem solver when he interprets the problem as a real situation and desires to find his way to an acceptable solution. Teachers can obtain valuable information concerning the "under-the-skin" behavior of the problem solver by observing and appraising his overt behavior and communication.

Many factors may affect the psychological behavior of each problem solver, such as experiential background, self-motivation, understanding of the vocabulary and operations in arithmetic, reading ability, readiness to ask questions, emotional stability, sense of achievement, and feeling of status with the peer group or the teacher. A vital question to be appraised at all times by the teacher is, "Does the problem solver give evidence of working only to meet the demand of the teacher, to obtain a favorable mark or reward, or to achieve a self-accepted goal?" Teachers can improve problem solving only by providing guidance and activities that may arouse in the problem solver motivation to make improvement and by interpreting clearly how he may change his methods when dealing with problem situations. Problems and problem solving increase in difficulty when one or more psychological factors retard the problem solver's progress in interpreting the problem, creating a desired goal, analyzing the situation, and determining and verifying methods leading to a solution.

Pupils may better comprehend their role in problem solving when they have the opportunity to discuss frequently, under the teacher's guidance, one or more of these qustions: "Who is a problem solver?" "What are the characteristics of a good problem solver?" "What is a problem?" "What is the purpose of a textbook problem?" "What is the meaning of the process called problem solving?" "Why is more time needed to solve some problems than others?" "Why is it normal for pupils to differ in abilities to solve problems?" and "How can the teacher help pupils to become better problem solvers?" Pupils should be encouraged to focus attention on ways that they can help themselves and to assist each other in improving motivation and mental methods in all problem-solving situations.

Interpretation of the Problem-Solving Process

Problem solving is a personal way of thinking and acting in a situation where there is a blocking in reaching a desired objective. Since it is a complex way of behaving mentally in a given situation, adequate time and guidance are necessary in learning its meaning and the skills involved. Satisfactory progress in learning the methods that may be used in solving verbal and real problems is dependent on such learned abilities as: reflective reading, defining the situation, determining the facts and circumstances, relating the situation and facts to past experiences, locating the questions that are asked or are implied, formulating a solution or solutions that may lead to the solution, selecting the arithmetical operations that will aid in reaching an answer, experimenting to find the reasonableness of one or more hypotheses or probable solutions, testing or verifying the accuracy and reliability of the best solution, reconstructing and reapplying the mental processes used in thinking through the situation to the accepted solution. All meaningful learning situations are experiences in solving problems. How pupils learn and apply methods in solving various kinds of problems is as important, if not more so, than the answers obtained.

Different logical steps to be taken in reasoning or problem solving have been described by philosophers and mathematicians. One of the most frequently cited descriptions of logical or systematic thinking is found in the steps described by John Dewey in his book, *How We Think*. The five steps in problem solving may be stated briefly: (1) conscious awareness of a blocking in action, (2) a critical analysis of the difficulty and the situation, (3) formulating one or more hypotheses or probable solutions to initiate and guide the search for data needed, (4) thinking through the probable results of each selected hypothesis, and (5) testing the validity of the hypothesis or method of solution used. It may be helpful to teachers to study the philosophical and psychological concepts that are applied in Dewey's description of a constructive way to resolve a problem situation. Teachers may interpret these steps by suggesting to pupils that they devote attention to such mental steps as they may discover to be useful in seeking solutions to problems in arithmetic, social studies, elementary science, school affairs, and community situations:

1. Observe or read to find what is creating the problem situation.
2. Devote time to interpreting the situation. What is known about

the problem? What are the relationships of the factors that have created the problem?

3. Examine the situation to find out who is facing the problem. How important is the problem?

4. Think of ways that may be applied to find an appropriate solution. Also collect any information that may be useful in reaching a solution.

5. Think through the method or methods for solving the problem and examine the usefulness of each method and solution.

6. Select what you think to be the most useful method of solution and then apply it to appraise the correctness and reliability of the result.

Pupils will modify somewhat the method or methods they have learned when they are thinking through to solutions in new problem situations. They should be encouraged to seek to find several ways to solve any given problem. Tension and thwarting barriers may be escaped when pupils recognize that there is no one best method in problem solving, but that each pupil should do his own best reasoning and thinking when using one or more ways to solve a given verbal or personal problem.

Many problems may not be solved in a short period. When dealing with a complex situation, pupils should have the opportunity after preliminary analysis to postpone further action. A period for incubation may prove most helpful in many situations. Little reliable information is now available concerning the part that the subconscious mind may play in resolving difficult problems. Pupils may find it helpful to read, discuss, and analyze a few problems during one period and postpone applying and testing probable methods of solution until the following day. In fact, the teacher will find it profitable to introduce the idea of a certain concept perhaps two weeks or so before the class is planning to study it in detail. She will find that the actual learning and usage in problem solving becomes simpler as a result of the children's having had the chance to mull over the idea for some time ahead. For example, a bulletin board display that shows fraction concepts several weeks before the fraction is to be discussed is one way in which this could be done.

Preparation for Problem Solving

Effective thinking and reasoning are nourished by the pupil's awareness of self-identification with the setting of each problem. When problems present words, terms, information, or a background setting that are not familiar to individual pupils the application of problem solving should be postponed until the elements of newness or difficulty have been removed. Problems should be examined in advance by the teacher to locate words that may be unfamiliar, to determine how the setting of problems may be related to the experiential background of the pupils, and to discover if operational processes that are to be used in finding solutions have been learned by the pupils. Preparation in advance of the class period may provide the teacher with many ideas for helping pupils to develop a psychological readiness for the problem-solving experiences.

Preparation for solving problems may produce desirable changes in the mental behavior of pupils. They may be asked to give their interpretation of the meanings of terms presented by the teacher. They may be asked to read a problem to find if there are any unfamiliar words or if they are familiar with the description of the problem. They may be asked to make up problems in their own words. Children who attend school in an urban area may experience additional difficulty in solving problems related to rural life unless time is taken to become familiar with the somewhat new words and setting of the problems. In a similar way, pupils living in rural communities may benefit from preparation-discussion sessions before attempting to solve verbal problems related to urban life. When problems use arithmetical terms or require computations that may not be understood properly by pupils, much may be gained by them and the teacher when time is taken to recall previous learnings or to discuss the terms and operations they need to understand.

The kind and amount of preparation for solving problems will vary with the age of the pupils. Young children need more time and guidance in preparing themselves to solve problems. Pupils in the intermediate and upper grades may be expected to work more independently, yet there may be many pupils who will receive valuable help from time used in getting mentally ready to experience meaning and success in solving problems that are somewhat unrelated to their previous learnings and experiential background.

Mental Hygiene Climate

It is a reasonable assumption that there can be a high correlation between the mental hygiene climate of the classroom and the interest and progress of pupils in learning and refining the problem-solving process. Each pupil creates mentally his interpretation of the personality and methods of the teacher. A friendly, understanding, and helpful approach on the part of the teacher will evoke positive responses from pupils. The overt action of the teacher should arouse among the pupils a feeling of working together, should foster a spirit of mental inquiry, should encourage readiness to ask questions, to offer hypotheses, and should motivate willingness to receive assistance from the teacher or members of the class. When problems in the textbook are assigned without taking time to help pupils to appraise the "how" and "why" in solving them, the quality of the mental hygiene in the room may be lowered to the point where pupils easily encounter or create barriers to personal interest, purposeful inquiry, and a desire to make the problems real and acceptable to each problem solver.

The fact that pupils differ in maturity and problem-solving ability needs to be recalled. Teachers should accept the challenge to adapt the work to serve the abilities and needs of the normal achiever, the rapid achiever, and also the slow achiever. To do this well requires understanding, patience, careful preparation, and time. It is not the number of problems solved but the progress made in solving problems that needs to be emphasized. Emphasis on speed may seriously handicap some pupils. Rapid achievers may experience worthwhile learnings when invited to help other pupils who desire assistance, yet they should work with other pupils in ways to assist in thinking rather than doing the thinking for them. The classroom environment should, in so far as possible, motivate pupils at all times to experience interest, progress, and a sense of achieving in defining, analyzing, and solving both personal and group problems. In a classroom where pupils appear to have little interest in problem solving a careful analysis of the psychological factors that underlie the mental hygiene climate for teacher and pupils may secure many corrective approaches.

Time

Creative teaching takes time. Meaningful learning requires adequate time. Reasoning and thinking cannot be hurried. Some pupils require more time than others to define and think their way through a problem situation. Every effort should be made by the teacher to prevent pupils from feeling that they are being rushed. There is a difference in taking sufficient time to do one's best work in problem solving and using too much time. How much time is adequate for each learning period can be answered only by the teacher and the pupils.

The desire for speed in problem solving may be present sometimes to a harmful extent in the pupil even when not in the teacher. In an effort to complete a problem he will try to choose the one operation that will accomplish the entire job in a very little time instead of the two or three operations needed in the cases of two-step and three-step problems. This is particularly true of a child who has been a rapid achiever as far as computing is concerned and has a feeling within himself that he is not succeeding unless he can be as rapid in problem solving. There are several things that may improve this situation. The child can be given problems in which the analysis of the problem is as satisfying as finding the solution. Also, for this pupil an analysis of his mistakes in problem solving, discussing what his wrong solution means in relation to the given facts and how that meaning differs from the one being sought will be helpful.

Emphasis on the number of problems solved may introduce psychological conditions that retard a pupil's discovery of the importance of continued improvement in the mental "how" when solving verbal and nonverbal problems. Since problem solving is a mental process in applying and in revising learned ways in thinking through a given situation to a reasonable solution, pupils should be encouraged to give attention to "why," "how," and "what" they are thinking rather than the number of problems for which they hurriedly compute numerical answers. Assigning a large number of verbal problems to be solved in a class period may cause pupils to shift their attention from qualitative and quantitative thinking to a "trial and error" type of computation. Improvement in the quality of "how" pupils seek to solve problems should be accepted by pupils and the teacher as the desired objective rather than the mere quantity of problems worked. Sufficient time and purpose in fostering quality in thinking are prerequisites for meaningful and satisfactory improvement in mental problem solving.

One desired outcome in problem solving is the ability to judge how much time is needed to improve the quality of thinking in all problem-solving situations. The "psychological clock" is a more reliable measure of time in a classroom than a spring or electrical clock.

Identifying Problems

Some problems are relatively easy to identify. The mental process involved in defining certain kinds of problems is more complex and requires more time for deliberation. The first basic step in all problem solving is identifying or defining the problem. Until the problem solver understands the nature and significance of the verbal problem he has difficulty in accepting it as a challenging problem. Faulty habits can be learned when pupils think the first and most important step to be taken is to select the computational process that will lead to the answer.

Reading is an indispensable way to find the information needed to define mentally the meaning of a problem. Pupils may be asked to read a problem silently and then take time to reflect on what has been read. They then may be asked to give orally their definition or understanding of the problem. They may respond to such questions as: "What is the problem?" "What makes it a problem?" "Have we had a problem like this one before?" "Who is the problem solver in this problem?" Each pupil must identify himself with the problem situation if he is to recognize and accept it as a problem he desires to solve.

Making an Analysis

Ability to make an analysis of a problem situation is another important outcome in all problem-solving experiences in the classroom. Pupils, after they have defined the problem, may be asked to read the problem again to find answers to such questions as: "What information and/or facts are presented?" "What is the relationship of these items to each other?" "What questions are raised in the problem?" "How realistic are the data included in the problem?" After the second reading pupils may share in a discussion of their analysis. They may discover interest in hearing the different analyses that may be derived from one problem. Experience in mental analysis followed by oral communication may help pupils to discover ways to improve their individual methods of mental analysis. At other times, pupils may be asked to write the analysis each has made and then to exchange papers. Frequently pupils may welcome assistance by receiving an oral interpretation from the teacher about the method she uses in making an analysis of a verbal or real problem. Effective mental analysis is based on discerning, discriminating, examined reading and thinking.

Formulating a Hypothesis

A hypothesis is a mentally created interpretation of a probable way to solve a problem. Pupils may experience motivation and improvement in determining one or more ways to solve the problem by first reading silently the problem and after a period of reflective thinking, sharing orally the method or methods they would use in finding the answer. For example, pupils may read the problem: "John sold 3 basketball tickets at 35¢ each. Harry sold 5 basketball tickets at 35¢ each. How much money did they have in all?" One probable way to solve the problem is by addition. Another way to find the answer involves multiplication and addition. Pupils through sharing thought-out hypotheses may readily discover that some probable solutions may lead to a correct solution, yet are more difficult and require more time in solving than other hypotheses. One important purpose of a formulated hypothesis or hypotheses is to make it possible for the problem solver to think through to the solution by each method and then select the method that has been appraised to be the most reasonable and best suited to the problem solver. After each pupil has selected the appropriate hypothesis he is then ready to verify his selection by computing the answer and testing its accuracy. Many pupils may experience satisfactory improvement in problem solving when they are asked to state orally or in writing the method they have reasoned to be a desirable one. Frequent periods may be restricted to finding the hypothesis or hypotheses that may be used in resolving each problem.

Progress in defining, analyzing, and formulating probable methods of solution or solutions may be facilitated by teacher and pupils devoting many periods in which the emphasis is on reflective reading and critical reasoning in descriptive situations instead of computing answers on paper or on the blackboard. Since reasoning or problem solving is a unique mental process for each pupil, the use of pencil and paper should be recognized to be useful as aids to thinking in complex situations and a means to record computation and answers for verification or communication. In the intermediate grades and junior high school where problems may be more complex in setting and computation, paper and pencil may prove to be useful in keeping track of the mental process or in preparing diagrams as aids in meaningful and accurate reasoning. Teachers should seek to arouse an interest on the part of pupils in becoming independent and accurate in mental problem solving. In too many instances problems are worked to find computations and answers to be written on paper to be handed to the teacher for verification. One effective way to appraise a pupil's ability in formulating and verifying a hypothesis is to ask him to think and to express orally "what" and "how" he is reasoning his way through a problem to a hypothesis and a tested solution.

Estimating Answers

In many problem situations an estimated answer will serve an immediate purpose. In other situations an estimated answer may prove to be a useful procedure in selecting an appropriate method of solution and in appraising the soundness of an analysis and a selected method of solution. As pupils improve in their ability to round off numbers and to think with rounded off numbers they come to appreciate the value of estimating an answer as an aid in solving problems.

Teachers may set aside periods in which the purpose is to stimulate interest in improving ability to reason out estimated answers to assigned problems. They may present a prepared problem or select one in the textbook. A few minutes may be spent profitably in discussing with the pupils the "how" and "why" in estimating answers. The pupils may then be asked: to read carefully the problem, to define mentally the problem situation, to make a careful analysis of all the known and unknown factors, to arrive at a probable method of solution, and then to estimate what each problem solver thinks to be an estimated or approximate answer. After time has been given for mental deliberation, the pupils may be asked to express what they have decided is a reasonable estimate of the answer. The opportunity is provided for pupils to discover how individuals who read and analyze the same problem may reach a different estimate of the answer. One or two pupils may then do the computation required to find the correct answer so each pupil may appraise the closeness of his estimated answer to the computed answer.

For example, pupils may be asked to read and reach an estimated answer for each of these examples:

1. Judy bought 2 dozen apples at a price of 78¢ a dozen and 6 grapefruit at 19¢ each. What is the estimated cost? Pupils may round off 78¢ to 80¢ and think, "2×80 equals \$1.60." The price of the grapefruit is rounded off to 20¢, so the process is $6 \times .20 = \$1.20$. The total amount is now estimated by adding \$1.60 and \$1.20, which gives \$2.80. (The computed solution is, $2 \times .78 + 6 \times .19 = \$2.70$.)

2. Mr. Brown who is a salesman drove his car 3076.5 miles in January and 4237.2 in February. What is a reasonable estimate of the number of miles he drove in all? Pupils may round off 3076.5 to 3080, and 4237.2 to 4240. Adding 3080 to 4240 gives 7320 as the estimated answer. (The computed answer is 7313.7 miles.)

Pupils in the intermediate and junior high school may be encouraged to collect problems from newspapers and magazines about the adult population, the school population, taxes, and governmental expenditures to be used as meaningful practice in finding estimates to problems. Many useful problems may be obtained from their readings in social studies and elementary science. A member of a commercial or industrial firm may be invited to talk to the class about the value of estimating answers to problems in the business he represents.

Problems Without Numbers

Unless provision is made for pupils to analyze and solve problems that do not include numbers, they may form the generalization that problems without numbers do not require mental problem solving. In addition, many pupils may acquire such faulty methods of solution as: in problems where there is a large number and a small number, they should try to resolve the problem by multiplication or division, and in problems where there are several unequal numbers they should add. Pupils should interpret problem solving as a mental process to be applied in solving problems with or without numbers.

For example:

1. If the members of a football team knew how many games they won and how many games they lost in a season, how could they find the percent of games won? The percent lost?

2. If Mr. Jones kept a record of the number of automobiles he sold in one week and also knew the percent of commission he received, how could he find the amount he earned for the week?

3. If the pupils were planning to make a trip from school to the city art museum, how could they determine the best route to take to reach the museum in the school bus?

A majority of the problems encountered by pupils in out-of-school situations do not involve numerical computation in finding appropriate solutions. They do present the need for abilities in recognizing, interpreting, and analyzing problem situations. One purpose in devoting some periods in arithmetic in solving or in attempting to solve verbal problems without numbers is to provide experiences and motivation in learning and improving mental procedures that may prove to be useful in many kinds of problems encountered in personal and community life. Teachers may collect valuable resource material by asking pupils to look for "problems without numbers" in out-of-school environments and to bring a description of some of the more interesting of these situations to class to enrich their work in problem solving.

Finding Missing Facts

Many problems that need to be solved by pupils and adults may not include all the necessary data required in finding an adequate solution. Beginning in the primary grades and continuing through the junior high school, opportunities should be provided for determining what additional information is needed to arrive at a satisfactory solution to some problems. Situations of this kind may stimulate interest in developing abilities and in carrying on investigations and research.

For example, a relatively simple problem may be described in this manner:

1. John's father purchased 5 pounds of grass seed. How much did he pay for the grass seed?

2. The pupil's in grade four wanted to make some money to purchase some junior magazines. What magazines did they want to purchase? What was the total cost? How could they earn the money?

3. The pupils in grade three wanted to make Christmas decorations for their parents. They decided to buy 6 yards of ribbon at a cost of 15¢ a foot. What was the total cost of the ribbon?

4. The pupils in grade seven, with the consent of their parents, decided to make a trip to the state capital. They wanted to determine the cost of the trip for each pupil. What facts were needed to arrive at the answer?

Experience in solving problems with missing facts may help pupils to free themselves from the faulty habit of attempting to base their anaylsis and solution solely on the information included in problems.

Problem Solving as Game Theory

It should not be overlooked that for some pupils problem solving in mathematics offers greater pleasure than any other mental activity. To them any statement that can be translated into the language of numbers is a problem, meaning a situation for which they are motivated to find the solution. They will find problems of a mathematical nature in many situations where no one else in the room would recognize them. It is possible to recognize a child gifted in arithmetic at an early age because of the two general ways in which creativity exhibits itself in this area. A child who sees a problem in situations that would seem completely unproblematic to the other children exhibits one type of creativity in mental analysis. A child who works out different and more efficient solutions to given problems exhibits another kind of creativity. A teacher who recognizes these two types of creativity on the part of pupils can often start a child who is gifted in arithmetic in the right direction for making the best use of his potentialities.

Field Trips

Motivation and interest in improving abilities in problem solving may be experienced through excursions or planned visits to business places in the community, such as: a large grocery store, the post office, a commercial bank, a hardware store, a department store, a hospital, or a manufacturing plant. Before taking an excursion, teacher and pupils should consider such questions as: "What is the purpose of our trip?" "What information do we want to obtain?"

"What illustrations of problem solving will we look for?" and "What social manners should we observe?" Pupils in the primary grades may seek to find information concerning foods and products sold when they are working on economic questions. Much material can be assembled to be used in preparing and solving problems with and without numbers during some of the class periods.

Pupils in the intermediate grades and junior high school may seek information about the buying and selling price of food and products; cost of operation; kind of taxes paid; salaries to employees; the meaning of profit, discount, and loss; and principles of the American system of free enterprise in business and industry. This information may be used as resource material in preparing and solving economic problems related to the industrial and commercial life of the community and nation. This approach to problem solving provides the opportunity for pupils to experience the functional relationships among discriminating observation, purposeful questions, applied economics, social studies, meaningful arithmetic, language, and problem solving. Arrangements may be made for rapid achievers in arithmetic computation and problem solving to have small-group experiences, to extend their understanding of business economics, and to collect information that they may use in preparing problems and special reports.

Problem Solving in a Global World

The children now in elementary school depend on the schools to help them to become prepared to live as adults in an interdependent global world. The accelerated speed and scope in mobility of ideas, people, and materials give a definite advantage to individuals who are informed concerning the problems and opportunities in living on the part of people in other countries. Proficiency in arithmetic and problem solving may be of assistance to young adults in determining answers to such questions as: "What are the differences among the populations of various countries?" "What is the distance in flying hours between the United States and Brazil or Australia, between Paris and Hong Kong, and between other cities?" "What are the differences in the standards of productivity, income, and living among such countries as the United States of America, China, India, Denmark and Great Britain?" "How many people travel by airplane each year from the United States to other countries?" "What has been the increase in trade by various means of transportation between the United States and the countries in South America?" "What are some of the cultural, political, and economic barriers that retard improvement in human relations among the free countries of the world?"

The Problem Solver and Self-Evaluation

Each pupil is his own problem solver. His improvement in the abilities involved in solving problems may be accelerated when he accepts readiness and responsibility to appraise the mental methods he has learned from previous experience and applies them in new situations. Teachers may be of assistance when pupils are encouraged to discuss and to use such questions as the following when making self-evaluation of their progress in problem solving:

1. Am I solving problems for the teacher or for my own purpose?

2. Do I read carefully verbal problems to find what I know and do not know before attempting to find solutions?

3. Do I take time to find the meanings of words, terms, and mathematical questions that I do not understand when they are presented in the problem?

4. Do I seek to identify myself as the problem solver in each problem situation?

5. Do I read carefully each problem as the means to find: What is the problem? Why is it a problem? What is known? What is unknown? What is the question?

6. How successful am I in analyzing a problem and in creating a tentative, workable solution or solutions?

7. Am I willing to ask questions or seek assistance when I encounter difficulty in analyzing and solving a problem?

8. Am I trying to solve problems to find answers to my questions or am I trying to solve problems presented in class to earn a good mark or the teacher's approval?

9. In what ways do I think I am making improvement in my skills in solving problems?

10. What can I do as a problem solver to improve my methods in solving problems in arithmetic and in other subjects?

Summary

Competency in solving problems is an essential asset in personal living and occupational pursuits in modern society. Each pupil is his own problem solver and must learn his own methods for solving problems. Many factors may influence the mental behavior of the problem solver in each situation, such as experiential background, sense of achieving, interest, meaningful purpose, mental hygiene climate in the classroom, vocabulary, and understanding of the mathematical concepts and principles involved. Teachers have the professional opportunity: to seek to understand the problem solver, to enrich the curriculum, to provide resource materials, to offer motivating and helpful instruction, and to accept problem solving as a logical method in thinking and acting that can be applied in all areas of the curriculum.

Careful preparation on the part of the teacher and the pupils arouses motivation, stimulates critical thinking, and fosters meaningful learning in each problem-solving situation. The quality of the "how" in solving problems conditions the quality of the results. The abilities that teachers should strive to help pupils learn and refine in solving problems are: recognizing problems; identifying problems as personal goals; careful reading; thinking one's way through a problem; finding the known, the unknown, and the question; formulating a hypothesis or workable solution; estimating a reasonable answer; applying an appropriate method of computation; testing the correctness of the solution; and deriving social and economic generalizations from experiences in solving various problems. Since problem solving is a mental way of dealing with problems, success in teaching may be appraised by evidence of each problem solver's growing interest in problem solving, continuous improvement in meaningful skills, and readiness to make frequent self-evaluation of his needs and progress. The real test of the problem solver's learnings in problem solving is his readiness to use his learnings in dealing with problems in all personal situations and in all subjects of the classroom curriculum.

SELF-EVALUATION QUESTIONS

These questions may prove useful to teachers and prospective teachers who desire to appraise their understanding of the ideas presented in this chapter and also to determine the improvement they have made in their interpretation of the psychological nature and application of methods in problem solving. The questions may be used by teachers in meetings devoted to a discussion of ways to improve teaching and learning in problem solving in arithmetic and in other school subjects.

1. What changes in an interpretation of the psychological nature of problem solving have resulted from research related to learning?

2. In what ways is problem solving a learned way of behaving in various problem situations?

3. What contributions has each of these persons made to a better understanding of problem solving and the problem solver: (*a*) Dr. Brownell, (*b*) Dr. Thorndike, (*c*) Dr. Johnson, (*d*) Dr. Wertheimer, (*e*) Dr. Brueckner, (*f*) Dr. Henderson, (*g*) Dr. Thorpe, (*h*) Dr. Dewey?

4. What are the abilities in problem solving that teachers in the primary grades should seek to help pupils learn? In the intermediate grades? In the junior high school?

5. What has research revealed to be the salient psychological factors that affect a pupil's learning and use of problem solving?

6. What has research revealed to be some of the difficulties some pupils may experience in learning problem solving? What procedures may teachers apply to help pupils to overcome any of these difficulties?

7. How may teachers provide instruction and activities to serve the divergent abilities among pupils in a classroom?

8. What procedures may teachers use to enrich learning in problem solving and also to relate the curriculum to out-of-school situations?

9. What are some of the understandings in consumer and business economics that pupils in the elementary schools should be expected to learn from their work in problem solving?

10. What criteria may be prepared and applied by teachers in evaluating the needs and progress of the problem solvers in the primary grades? In the intermediate grades? In the junior high school?

11. What criteria may be prepared by pupils to use in making a self-evaluation of their interpretation of their skills and progress in solving problems in arithmetic? In other curriculum subjects?

12. What suggestions concerning activities, resource materials, and instructional procedures can you give for improving teaching and learning in problem solving in arithmetic and in other school subjects?

13. To what extent does the problem solver use his developing skills in problem solving in finding answers to questions or solutions to problems presented in other subjects in the curriculum and in out-of-school activities?

14. What application does the maturing problem solver make of analytical thinking when interacting with materials read or heard, certain types of advertising claims and sales talks, and propaganda speeches and articles?

PROBLEM EXERCISES

1. Mary bought 4 records at 56¢ each and a book for $1.98. How much did she spend?

2. John weighs 110 pounds, Henry weighs 97 pounds, Bill weighs 103 pounds, James weighs 94 pounds, and Robert weighs 108 pounds. What is their average weight?

3. Mr. Smith drove his car on a 640-mile trip. If the car averaged 17 miles to 1 gallon of gasoline and if the price of gasoline was 31.6¢ a gallon, how much did the gasoline for the trip cost?

4. What is the area of a triangle surface that has a base of 8 feet 6 inches and an altitude of 4 feet and 3 inches?

5. Mr. Jones sold an automobile for $2200 and a truck for $2475. His commission was 5%. How much commission should he have received?

6. A liter is equivalent to 1.06 quarts. How many quarts of milk are in a barrel that contains 3000 cubic centimeters of milk?

7. Mr. Williams works on a commission of 4% of his sales. How much should be the amount of his sales if he is to earn in one month $560?

8. A building and loan association pays 3% interest every 6 months on saving accounts. Mrs. McBride deposited $1460 in the association. How much interest should she receive on her account at the end of 1 year?

9. If it is 9:00 in the morning, standard time, in New York, what is the corresponding time in Honolulu? (standard time)

10. Mr. Sullivan owns a house that has been assigned an assessed value of $18,600. His tax bill for 1957 shows a tax rate of $1.43 per $100. What was the amount of the taxes he paid for 1957?

11. If there were 250,000 television sets in the United States in 1947 and 28,000,000 in 1953, what is the percent of increase in the number of television sets in 1953 as compared with 1947?

12. How many square pieces of floor covering 6 inches on a side will be needed to cover the floor of a porch that is 20 feet long and 16 feet wide?

13. How many liters of water are needed to fill a tank that is 4 feet long, 3 feet wide, and $1\frac{1}{2}$ feet deep?

14. Susan purchased a spool of ribbon that contained $6\frac{1}{2}$ yards. She wants to cut the ribbon into strips that measure $\frac{3}{4}$ yard each. How many strips can she obtain from the spool of ribbon?

15. John's father bought $8\frac{1}{2}$ feet of fence wire. He used $7\frac{3}{4}$ feet. How much was not used?

16. How many cards 2×8 inches can be cut from 100 sheets of card stock measuring $18\frac{1}{2} \times 22\frac{3}{4}$ inches?

17. What is the measurement of the volume capacity of a silo that has a diameter of 14 feet and a height of 25 feet?

18. A teacher received a 5% increase in salary, which amounted to $125. What was the amount of her new salary?

19. Mr. Wilson wanted to buy a car. The list price was $2450. The salesman offered him a 20% discount. He also told Mr. Wilson that he would give him another 5% discount if he paid cash for the car. If Mr. Wilson purchased the car and paid cash, how much did he pay for the car?

SELECTED REFERENCES

1. Brownell, William, and Hendrickson, Gordon, "How Children Learn Information, Concepts, and Generalizations," Chap. IV, *Learning and Instruction*, Forty-Ninth Yearbook, Part I. National Society for the Study of Education. Chicago: University of Chicago Press, 1950.

2. Boole, M. E., *The Preparation of the Child for Science*. London: Oxford University Press, 1904.

3. Brueckner, Leo J., and Grossnickle, Foster E., *How to Make Arithmetic Meaningful*. Philadelphia: John C. Winston Company, 1947.

4. Dewey, John, *How We Think*. Boston: D. C. Heath and Company, 1933.

5. Henderson, Kenneth, and Pingry, Robert E., "Problem-Solving in Mathematics," Chapter VIII, *The Learning of Mathematics. Its Theory and Practice*. Twenty-First Yearbook. Washington, D. C.: National Council of Teachers of Mathematics, 1953.

6. Johnson, Wendell, *People in Quandaries*. New York: Harper & Brothers, 1946.

7. Keyes, Kenneth S., *How to Develop Your Thinking Ability*. New York: McGraw-Hill Book Company, Inc., 1950, p. 246.

8. Polya, G., *How to Solve It*. Princeton, N. J.: Princeton University Press, 1945, p. 224.

9. Russell, David Harris, *Children's Thinking*. Boston: Ginn & Company, 1956.

10. Thorndike, Robert L., "How Children Learn the Principles and Techniques of Problem Solving," Chapter VIII, *Learning and Instruction*. Forty-Ninth Yearbook, Part I. National Society for the Study of Education. Chicago: University of Chicago Press, 1950.

11. Thorpe, Louis P., and Schmullen, Allen, *Contemporary Theories of Learning*. New York: The Ronald Press Company, 1954.

12. Wertheimer, Max, *Productive Thinking*. New York: Harper & Brothers, 1945.

13. Wheat, Harry Grove, *How to Teach Arithmetic*. Evanston, Ill.: Row, Peterson & Company, 1951.

14. Witty, Paul, *et al.*, *Mental Health in Modern Education*. Fifty-Fourth Yearbook, Part II. National Society for the Study of Education. Chicago: University of Chicago Press, 1955.

12

Evaluation in Arithmetic

Introduction

Evaluation may be interpreted as an appraisal of the results obtained from instruments and procedures used in evaluating the progress of pupils in developing meanings and psychological skills in arithmetic. Another interpretation places evaluation in the teaching and learning process. The desired outcome in evaluation is continuous improvement in learning, teaching, and the curriculum. Frequent use of evaluative instruments and procedures enables teachers to gain information about the needs and abilities of the pupils, which is useful in providing appropriate instruction, activities, and resource material. The teacher's philosophy of education, interpretation of the learning process, and understanding of the meanings in arithmetic affect their use of evaluation and evaluative instruments as means to improve learning through improved teaching.

Exploratory Questions

1. What is your interpretation of the nature and function of evaluation in the school?

2. What psychological and mental hygiene principles should underlie the use of evaluative instruments and procedures?

3. What do you think is the relationship and also difference between objective evaluation and subjective evaluation?

4. What is the role of the teacher when evaluating the responses of pupils during their work in arithmetic?

5. How may pupils be helped to recognize the value and function of self-evaluation when learning meanings and skills in arithmetic?

6. What may be the advantages in using the group approach when helping pupils in their appraisal of work in arithmetic?

7. What kinds of evaluative instruments and procedures may teachers use to obtain information about the needs and progress of the pupils?

8. Why are teacher-prepared diagnostic tests valuable instruments in appraising the pupils' understanding and use of the meanings, vocabulary, and mathematical principles in arithmetic?

9. In what way is a cumulative record for each pupil helpful to the teacher? To the pupils? To the parent? To the school system?

10. What are the important desired outcomes in arithmetic that should be appraised by teachers and pupils?

Purpose of Evaluation

Each elementary school is an agency of the public to design and to administer curriculum, instruction, and resource activities. These are utilized by teachers in helping pupils to discover and to develop foundational understandings and interests in the value of arithmetic in personal and community life. Evaluation is a professional method by which teachers obtain informational data useful in interpreting how well pupils have learned the desired outcomes. The primary functions of evaluation in the classroom are: (1) to make a continuous appraisal of the effectiveness of curriculum and instruction; (2) to use appropriate instruments and procedures in diagnosing the emerging attitudes, interests, meanings, and mental skills of pupils; (3) to provide corrective guidance and materials when needed; (4) to determine how well the pupils are learning the desired outcomes in arithmetic, and (5) to present periodically a report to parents about the achievement of pupils.

The selection and application of evaluative instruments and procedures should be the responsibility of classroom teachers. Each teacher is an educational diagnostician of pupil learnings. Specialists in testing and evaluative research function properly in the degree that their services assist teachers in diagnosing more accurately the changes in the psychological behavior of pupils and in selecting methods and materials to facilitate improvement in teaching and learning. The center of evaluation should be in the classroom.

Psychological Principles Related to Evaluation

Evaluation functions continuously in the process of teaching and in learning. There are important psychological principles that affect the mental behavior of teachers and pupils as related to evaluation. Some of the principles or concepts that teachers should understand as a foundation for their evaluative procedures are:

1. Each pupil is a unique individual continuously active in developing through accepted learnings a mind and personality. His interpretations of the teacher and arithmetic are created mentally as he appraises and accepts the learnings obtained from his interacting in the classroom environment.

2. Learning for each pupil is a mental process of discovering, examining, appraising, and applying meanings and skills in each curriculum situation.

3. Teaching is a professional process used by a teacher in motivating, guiding, appraising, and enriching the learning of desired outcomes by pupils during their work in arithmetic.

4. Each pupil's responses and progress in learning are influenced by his normal pattern and rate in mental maturing. Therefore, individual differences among pupils in a classroom reflect a normal situation.

5. There is a psychological and mathematical sequence in teaching arithmetic which, when observed by teachers, offers valuable assistance to pupils as they experience developmental sequence in discovering, interpreting, and organizing their interpretations and thought processes in arithmetic.

6. Greater mental effort is required on the part of teacher and pupils to correct faulty learnings than in learning properly in the beginning each mathematical meaning, term, and skill.

7. The teacher's competence and interest in arithmetic influence the degree in which pupils discover and learn the desired outcomes in arithmetic.

8. Pupils are aided in their development of psychological sequence in mathematical understandings and mental skills when teachers

have reached agreement regarding instructional methods, curriculum contents, and resource materials to be used in the different grades.

9. Pupils may discover and learn more readily the different meanings and terms in arithmetic when the initial approach presents concrete situations and materials. Stress on rote learning and abstract drill can cause many pupils to create psychological barriers to meaningful learning and thinking.

10. Professional use of evaluation produces best results for teacher and pupils in a classroom environment that motivates encouragement, a sense of achieving, the acceptance of teacher's and classmate's suggestions to aid in individual and class improvement in learning and in using the language and system of arithmetic.

The Teacher and Evaluation

Each teacher is, in a degree, a unique member of the school faculty. He makes his own interpretations of the school's curriculum and appropriate teaching methods. It is reasonable to assume that each teacher has accepted mentally the meanings, vocabulary, and computational operations of arithmetic, which he seeks to help pupils to learn. Also, each teacher has formulated mentally the desired outcomes and evaluative standards to be followed in appraising the mental and overt behavior of pupils. Evaluating is a thinking and appraising process used by each teacher when interacting with the communicative behavior of each pupil. This process of professional evaluating affects the teacher's communicative behavior and also the receptive evaluation of each pupil of his teacher and his work in arithmetic.

Teachers may improve their interpretation and use of professional evaluation by examining, frequently, the answers they may give in response to the following questions. (1) How familiar am I with the home environment of each pupil? (2) Do I accept teaching to be a process in guiding the self-education of pupils? (3) How well do I understand the arithmetical meanings, terms, and thought processes in computation that I want the pupils to discover and understand? (4) Do I place more emphasis on abstract rules and rote drills than on situations, questions, and materials to teach mathematical thinking and mental computation? (5) Do I encourage pupils to feel free to ask for help when they do not understand what is being taught?

(6) How often do I use evaluation to make a judgment of a pupil rather than as a process in diagnosing and guiding pupil behavior? (7) Do I recognize that each pupil creates mentally his own psychological interpretation of the meanings, terms, and computational skills in arithmetic? (8) How often do I use the group discussion method to motivate self-appraisal by pupils of their progress in arithmetic? (9) Do I depend too heavily on the textbook? (10) Do I ask pupils to collect materials from out-of-school environments to illustrate the social value of the classroom work in arithmetic? The meaning and use of evaluation on the part of each teacher are revealed in the quality of instructional methods, the enrichment of the curriculum, and the communicative interaction with pupils. Each teacher is a professional evaluator of teaching and learning in the classroom.

Pupil and Evaluation

Since each pupil is in some degree a unique individual, he creates and evaluates his mental interpretation of persons, symbols, materials, and situations with which he interacts. He learns in the degree to which he relates previous learnings to each new situation and appraises the meaning and functional value of new learnings. Mental evaluation is used in each act of learning. He creates and acts on his mental evaluation of the teacher's communication as well as on his interpretation of the learning materials in arithmetic. Guidance procedures should be used in the classroom to stimulate pupils to become interested in and responsible for high standards in group and self-evaluation rather than to become more dependent on the evaluative judgment of their teacher.

Improvement in the application of self-evaluation may be experienced when teachers assist pupils to prepare and use questions to stimulate thinking about their work and progress. Pupils may become interested in appraising their response to such questions as: (1) Am I discovering meanings from what I am studying? (2) Do I interpret arithmetic as a language and a number system, and also a way of thinking? (3) Am I able to illustrate with objects or drawings the meanings I have learned? (4) Am I willing to ask for guidance when I do not understand or do I remain silent or try to bluff? (5) Do I try to take time to do my best thinking when working an example or problem? (6) How often do I bring materials to school to illustrate the meanings or use in the work in the classroom? (7) What do I like and dislike about arithmetic? (8) Am I careful about penmanship and neatness of my written work? (9) Do I use my teacher and the textbook as aids to my learning in arithmetic? (10) Do I keep a record of the new meanings and words that I have learned? (11) Do I talk with my parents about what I have learned from my work in arithmetic? Encouragement and guidance in formulating work standards and processes for self-evaluation will help pupils to interpret properly the function of teacher evaluation and to develop skill and to accept responsibility for their own appraisal of their learnings and work-study skills in arithmetic.

Class Evaluation

Indirect guidance and evaluation can be as effective at times as direct teacher-pupil evaluation. Pupils can gain valuable assistance from their interpretation of their class discussion of work-study skills, strengths and weaknesses in learning, and the thought processes involved in computation and problem solving. Pupils should be encouraged to devote time once a week to interacting with questions designed to arouse individual and group thinking and evaluating. Some examples of questions to be discussed by the class group are: (1) What meanings and terms have we learned this week? (2) Why is all arithmetical computation really a thinking process? (3) How accurate have we been in our computation? (4) How can we improve in our work-study habits? (5) How careful have we been in reading mathematical examples or verbal problems? (6) What use have we observed in the community of the methods that we learned in arithmetic this week? (7) Can we illustrate with objects or drawings the meaning of what we have learned? (8) What do we tell our parents about our work in arithmetic at school? These class sessions in the group process in pupil evaluation provide experience in shared responsibility for meaningful learning and good work-study skills. In the degree that the group method is carried on in a climate of friendly mental hygiene, pupils have the opportunity to learn to give and to receive appraisal and to exchange helpful suggestions for improved work.

Desired Outcomes to Be Evaluated

There are important outcomes that should be expected of pupils in each grade. The outcomes should be determined by the teachers with proper recognition for sequence and new meanings to be taught from year to year. Evaluative instruments and procedures may then be selected that have been appraised to be most appropriate to measure pupil progress in learning these outcomes. A classification of outcomes accepted by all teachers may be:

1. *Arithmetical or mathematical meanings*

These meanings are an essential part of the language and content of the Hindu-Arabic number system. Each pupil through observing, experimenting, thinking, and proving discovers and refines his interpretation and use of each meaning. An illustration of a mathematical meaning may be gained from a few examples.

(*a*) A number is a mathematical symbol to express an idea of an amount of a quantity.

(*b*) Addition is both a mathematical and a mental process of combining objects or numbers and then of showing by the notated number the total amount or value.

(*c*) Subtraction is both a mathematical and mental process to find the difference between two numbers and then to write the number that shows the amount of difference.

(*d*) The center of the Hindu-Arabic number system is the ones place.

(*e*) A fraction is a number to show a fractional unit of an object, to show the relationship between one or more units of a given group of like units or objects and the entire group, to express the ratio relationship between two numbers.

(*f*) The denominator of a common fraction is a number that shows the number of even divisions of an object or group of objects. Teachers will find a listing of the meanings and terms to be learned in each grade a ready reference when evaluating pupil progress.

2. *Vocabulary or terms*

A functional knowledge of arithmetic includes a meaningful interpretation of arithmetical terms. When pupils have discovered the meaning of essential terms they experience no difficulty in using them correctly in thinking and in oral and/or written communication. The authors recommend that teachers refrain from substituting what they may think is a simpler word for what is interpreted to be an abstract term or a word with many letters. For example, the word "minuend" stands for a definite meaning. Pupils should not be permitted to call it, "the top number." The word "multiplier" represents a definite meaning in multiplication. Pupils may confuse its meaning if they are permitted to call it, "the bottom number." The correct word or term and meaning should be learned when pupils first encounter its mathematical use. Difficulty in spelling a term should not be considered a good reason to substitute another word. Young children may not be able to spell "airplane"; yet they may interpret properly its meaning and use. The requirement about correct spelling of some arithmetical terms should be adapted to the maturity of the pupils.

Questions and informal tests are effective means to evaluate understanding and correct application of the vocabulary of terms that have been developed in the different grades. From time to time, pupils may be given a list of terms and then asked to tell or write the correct meaning of each. A ditto sheet showing a number of examples with completed computation and a list of corresponding terms can be used to diagnose the ability to associate a specific part of the computation with the appropriate term. Pupils may find interest in preparing informal tests or exercises to appraise their classmates' understanding of the arithmetical vocabulary used in the grade.

3. *Computation skills*

Computation is a mental process and ability in using mathematical principles and facts to find the answer or solution to an example or verbal problem. Speed and accuracy in computation depend on a pupil's interpretation of and maturity level in addition, subtraction, multiplication, and division with integers, common fractions, decimal fractions, and denominate numbers. Writing figures on paper when computing should not be mistaken for mathematical thinking. All computation is a mental process. The result of thinking can be expressed by notating or writing numbers on paper. The example, 3×8 apples $=$? asks the pupil to think, "How many apples in all and what written number stands for all?" The product will be a number that shows the total amount. Teachers cannot appraise adequately the mental process in computation by considering a pupil's written answers to examples. Only when the pupil is asked to compute orally does the teacher have the opportunity to diagnose and to appraise the processes used in computation. Informal tests can be prepared that will give teachers important information about pupils' ability to compute correctly the answer to examples at different developmental levels. An appraisal of oral computation must be made before a teacher can say he has made a diagnostic evaluation of a pupil's competency in computation. A sample of a diagnostic test is given as an illustration.

Diagnostic Test—Addition

Directions: Compute the answer to each example in each row.

Row *A*

3	5	6	2
+4	+2	+3	+4

Row *B*

8	9	4	5	7
+7	+6	+6	+8	+4

Row *C*

12	13	14	11
+4	+5	+3	+7

Row *D*

18	14	15	16	19
+9	+6	+8	+5	+6

Row *E*

23	15	56	32	44
+55	+22	+33	+14	+23

Row *F*

47	19	24	35	29
+47	+26	+38	+18	+34

Row *G*

87	62	45	74	88
+45	+78	+55	+96	+99

The examples in Row *A* represent a sampling of addition, with a sum under ten. In Row *B*, the examples represent a sampling of the addition facts with a sum 10 or more. The process of substituting 1 ten for 10 ones is necessary. The examples in Row *C* involve higher decade addition without the thought process of substituting. The examples in Row *D* require the thought process of substituting 1 ten for 10 ones. The examples in Row *E* call for the adding of 2 two-place numbers. A knowledge of the addition facts with a sum under 10 can be used when adding the addends in the ones place and then the addends in the tens place. Computing the answers to examples in

Row *F* calls for the ability to substitute 1 ten for 10 ones. In Row *G*, an ability to use the thought process of substituting 1 ten for 10 ones, and then 1 hundred for 10 tens is required in computation. This diagnostic instrument may be extended to diagnose the ability of pupils to add examples of higher developmental levels, such as adding 2 three-place numbers or 2 four-place numbers with and without substitution. Examples in proper sequence may be used to diagnose ability in column addition. In a similar way, diagnostic instruments may be prepared for subtraction, multiplication, and division. Each test should be so constructed to diagnose the facts and principles that have been taught in the grade.

Problem Solving

One objective in learning arithmetical meanings, principles, terms, and mental computation is their functional value in solving examples and verbal problems related to home, school, and community life. Computing the solution to real or verbal problems can be a complex mental process. The answer written on paper reveals little information of the mental process used in finding the solution. Pupil progress in developing ability in problem solving is affected by the emphasis given in class to critical reading, locating data, estimating, and verification.

Scores made by pupils on a Standard Achievement Test in Problem Solving indicates the ability of a pupil to solve correctly a specific number of problems in an assigned period of time. Additional information should be obtained if a more reliable evaluation is desired with reference to the ability of the different pupils to solve verbal problems. Informal instruments may be prepared to appraise: (1) ability of comprehension in reading; (2) ability to define, after reading, the problem situation; (3) ability to locate significant data; (4) ability to determine the question or questions asked in the problem; (5) ability to select appropriate computation or computations to use; (6) ability to estimate a reasonable answer; (7) ability to compute; (8) ability to establish proof of reliability in thinking and computation. Diagnosis may be made by asking pupils at different periods to solve orally verbal problems in the textbook. Group evaluating may be done by the class to determine the need and method of improving their abilities in problem solving.

Evaluation and Applied Arithmetic

The expansion in technology, research, and business has increased the value of applied mathematics in modern society. Pupils should be encouraged to conduct informal surveys and interviews to appraise the social value of their work in school to success in employment and business. An exhibit and report of their findings may be made available to other pupils. An appraisal of the use of and requirements in arithmetic in modern society can be productive in helping pupils to understand the reasons for their learning arithmetic in school.

Instruments and Procedures

It is common practice for the administration and faculty in a school system to use four types of tests to obtain information on the abilities and progress of the pupils in arithmetic. These are: (1) standard achievement tests, (2) standard diagnostic tests, (3) local school achievement tests, and (4) informal diagnostic tests prepared by teachers.

A standard achievement test is an effective instrument when making a general survey of the school or a class. The contents of the test have been selected and arranged systematically by research specialists. Each form of the test has been prepared to measure pupil responses in vocabulary, computation, and problem solving in relation to an established progress scale. The manual gives standard directions to be observed in administering and scoring each form of the test. The reliability, validity, and grade norms have been determined statistically. One form of the standard test may be administered near the beginning of the school year and another near the end of the year. A comparison of each pupil's score with the grade and age norms will indicate the progress achieved during the year. Some of the standard tests that may be purchased are:

1. *California Achievement Tests*—California Test Bureau, Los Angeles
2. *Coordinated Scales of Attainment*—Educational Test Bureau, Minneapolis
3. *Iowa Every-Pupil Test of Basic Study Skills*—State University of Iowa, Iowa City

4. *Metropolitan Achievement Tests*—World Book Company
5. *Modern School Achievement Tests*—Bureau of Publications, Teachers College, Columbia University, New York

The bureaus of research in a few school systems have prepared standard achievement tests in arithmetic, which are designed to measure pupil progress in relation to the desired outcomes in arithmetic formulated by the teachers and administrative staff. The criteria and procedures observed in constructing a local school achievement test are similar to the ones applied in the preparation of General Survey Standard Tests.

Pupils differ in the psychological methods used in learning, in rate of learning, and in the outcomes of learning. It is important, therefore, for the teacher to construct informal tests for making frequent diagnosis of the unique psychological learnings and processes of each member of the class. Informal diagnostic tests can be prepared to measure the psychological responses of pupils to questions, directions, examples, or problems related to a specific part of curriculum in arithmetic. The responses of pupils on a diagnostic instrument provide information to be used by the teacher in making decisions concerning the amount of reteaching to be done, how much individual help should be given, and what enrichment activities and materials to provide. When no achievement marks are recorded on the tests, pupils readily accept diagnostic instruments as useful and interesting aids in improving their understanding and skills in arithmetic.

Illustrations of Informal Diagnostic Instruments

The authors have prepared a sample of a part of several diagnostic instruments to illustrate how they may be prepared by the classroom teacher. A complete diagnostic test may include more questions and directions but be adapted to a particular grade and curriculum area.

I. Meanings and the Number System

Directions: Read carefully each statement, question, or direction. Then write your answer where it should be placed.

1. Read the number 483. Draw a circle around the digit that is in the tens place.

2. Read the number 705. Draw a line under the symbol that shows that there are no units in one of the place-value positions.

3. Here are three digits, 3, 2, and 5. Use them to write the largest possible three-place-value number. ______

4. Write a three-place-value number that shows no digits or units in the tens place and the ones place. ______

5. Read the number 389. Draw a circle around the digit that is in the largest place-value position.

6. Fill in a number in each blank. 564 = ____ (100) + ____ (10) + ____ (1)

7. What is the smallest two-place-value number you can write without using the symbol for zero? ______

8. What number should be written to notate or show one hundred thirty-five books? ______

9. Read the number 678. In what place-value position is the digit 6? ______

10. What is the largest number of units you can show by writing a digit in any place-value position? ______

II—Diagnostic Instrument—Meanings Related to Common Fractions

Directions: Read carefully each question, statement or direction. Write the correct response for each.

1. A fraction is a ______________________________

2. What are the three meanings a fraction may show?

   (*a*) ______________________________

   (*b*) ______________________________

   (*c*) ______________________________

3. Read the fraction $\frac{3}{4}$ ft. Draw a circle around the number that shows how many fraction units are being considered.

4. Read the fractions $\frac{1}{4}$ ft, $\frac{1}{3}$ ft, $\frac{1}{2}$ ft, $\frac{1}{6}$ ft. Write the fraction that shows the largest measurement size fraction unit. ______

5. Read the fraction $\frac{5}{8}$ lb. Draw a circle around the denominator.

6. When $\frac{3}{4}$ has been substituted for $\frac{9}{12}$, the new fraction units will be how many times larger? ______

7. What fraction with higher terms can you substitute for $\frac{2}{3}$?

______

8. Notate the fraction, seven-eighths of a pound. ______

9. Only what kind of fractions can be added? ______

10. What fraction of the box is shaded?  ______

11. In subtraction, you find the difference between the ______ of the two like fractions.

12. Before you can divide unlike fractions, you must change to *what kind* of fractions? ______

13. What does the denominator of a fraction tell you? ______

14. When the multiplier is a fraction, what meaning of multiplication must be used? ______

15. When the dividend is a number smaller than the number that is the divisor, the quotient will show what meaning? ______

III. Vocabulary

A. Meaning of Terms

Directions: Read each term. Think what it tells. Then write what it tells on the blank line.

1. Sum______

2. Minuend______

3. Subtrahend______

4. Multiplicand______

5. Multiplier______

6. Partial Product ____________________

7. Product ____________________

8. Denominator ____________________

9. Numerator ____________________

10. Dividend ____________________

11. Divisor ____________________

12. Quotient ____________________

B. Matching Terms with Numbers in Computation

Directions: Read the terms. Then read the completed computation. Draw a line between the term and the number in the completed example.

1.

Difference	48
Subtrahend	−19
	——
Minuend	29

2.

Product	24
Multiplier	×8
	——
Multiplicand	32
Partial Products	16
	——
	192

3.

Quotient	36
Dividend	9)327
Divisor	27
	——
Remainder	57
	54
	——
	3

4.

Multiplier	$\frac{3}{4}$
Denominator	×5
	——
Fraction	$3\frac{3}{4}$
Numerator	
Product	

IV. Measurement and Measures

Directions: Read each partially completed statement. Think the word that is needed, then write it on the blank line.

1. Linear units of measure are used to measure ______ .

2. One foot is equal in length to ______ inches.

3. The area of a surface is found by using a ______ unit.

4. One gallon is equal in capacity to ______ quarts.

5. The formula that is used to find area is ______ .

6. The three basic units in the metric system are ______ , ______ , and ______ .

7. One pound is equal in weight to ______ ounces.

8. The formula that is used to find the area of a triangle is ______ .

9. One hour is equal to ______ minutes.

10. There are ______ standard time zones in the United States.

V. Multiplication—Integers

Directions: Read each example in each row and compute the answer.

Row *A*

2	4	5	3	2
×2	×2	×1	×3	×4
?	?	?	?	?

Row *B*

4	7	5	9	6
×6	×8	×6	×9	×3
?	?	?	?	?

Row *C*

22	31	12	11	44
×2	×3	×4	×6	×2
?	?	?	?	?

Row *D*

24	15	12	25	14
×4	×5	×6	×3	×7
?	?	?	?	?

Row *E*

34	65	87	36	25
×8	×4	×9	×7	×4
?	?	?	?	?

Row *F*

21	44	14	11	31
×31	×12	×22	×56	×23
?	?	?	?	?

Row *G*

24	40	72	87	54
×56	×28	×23	×96	×37
?	?	?	?	?

(*To the reader:* What understanding and computation ability is diagnosed by the examples in each row? What information may be obtained from a pupil's responses on this instrument?)

VI. Multiplication—Common Fractions

Directions: Read each question or example in each row. Compute the answer for each example.

Row *A* $2 \times \frac{1}{3} = ?$ $3 \times \frac{1}{8} = ?$ $2 \times \frac{2}{5} = ?$ $5 \times \frac{1}{6} = ?$ $7 \times \frac{1}{12} = ?$

Row *B* $2 \times \frac{2}{6} = ?$ $3 \times \frac{2}{3} = ?$ $5 \times \frac{3}{5} = ?$ $6 \times \frac{3}{4} = ?$ $8 \times \frac{3}{8} = ?$

Row *C* $3 \times 2\frac{2}{3} = ?$ $7 \times 3\frac{1}{8} = ?$ $6 \times 4\frac{1}{2} = ?$ $5 \times 4\frac{4}{5} = ?$ $12 \times 2\frac{1}{2} = ?$

Row *D* $\frac{1}{2} \times 6 = ?$ $\frac{2}{3} \times 24 = ?$ $\frac{3}{5} \times 27 = ?$ $\frac{5}{8} \times 40 = ?$ $\frac{3}{4} \times 36 = ?$

Row *E* $\frac{1}{3} \times \frac{1}{3} = ?$ $\frac{3}{4} \times \frac{1}{2} = ?$ $\frac{3}{8} \times \frac{2}{3} = ?$ $\frac{1}{2} \times \frac{5}{8} = ?$ $\frac{2}{3} \times \frac{3}{4} = ?$

Row *F*	$3\frac{1}{3}$	$12\frac{3}{4}$	$18\frac{1}{2}$	$26\frac{1}{4}$	$24\frac{2}{3}$
	$\times 4\frac{1}{2}$	$\times 8\frac{1}{3}$	$\times 7\frac{1}{2}$	$\times 6\frac{1}{2}$	$\times 10\frac{2}{3}$
	?	?	?	?	?

(*To the reader:* What understanding and computation ability is diagnosed by the examples in each row? What is the meaning of multiplication used in rows *A*, *B*, and *C?* What is the meaning of multiplication used in rows *D* and *E?* What two meanings of multiplication are used in row *F?*

VII. Diagnostic Test—Multiplication with Decimals

Directions: Read each example or question in each row. Compute the product for each example.

Row *A*	.2	.3	.04	.03	.122
	×4	×3	×2.	×3.	×4.
	?	?	?	?	?
Row *B*	.8	.5	.08	.13	.253
	×3	×8.	×9	×5.	×4
	?	?	?	?	?
Row *C*	2.4	14.3	36.2	14.04	12.8
	×4	×8	×9	×8.	×5
	?	?	?	?	?

Row *D*	3. ×.2	6. ×.4	4. ×.02	8. ×.05	10. .5
	?	?	?	?	?
Row *E*	2.4 ×.8	3.1 .9	7.04 ×.3	24.04 ×.5	50.8 .6
	?	?	?	?	?
Row *F*	3.6 ×2.4	5.1 ×1.5	2.15 ×3.3	50.4 ×6.5	72.5 ×3.2
	?	?	?	?	?

(*To the reader:* What meaning and computational ability is diagnosed in each row? What concept of multiplication is diagnosed in rows *D* and *E?* What meanings of multiplication are diagnosed in Row *F?*

Teachers in a school may cooperate in the preparation of informal diagnostic instruments. The mimeograph or ditto stencils may be filed in a master cabinet. In a few years the teachers will have prepared and will have available a valuable set of informal instruments that are related directly to the desired outcomes in arithmetic formulated for the school.

Follow-Up Action

The value of a classroom or school program in using instruments and procedures to obtain information about the pupils' interpretation of mathematical meanings, vocabulary, principles, and computation depends on the use teachers and pupils make of their findings. Evaluation is a teacher or pupil process used in changing behavior with reference to discovered strength, needs, and incorrect learnings. The findings of tests and informal instruments become meaningful and useful in the degree that: (1) teachers use the information to revise their subjective appraisal of pupils and strive to make such changes in teaching methods and materials as the findings indicate; (2) pupils accept the findings as useful and strive to make changes in their mental behavior that contribute to improvement in their understanding and application of arithmetic.

Teachers may find helpful the practice of making summaries of the information obtained from pupil responses on tests and in interviews. These may be revised as corrective teaching methods and new test data indicate desired changes in the mental behavior of pupils. Flexible grouping of pupils in the classroom may also be arranged with reference to specific needs and abilities. A frequent review of the follow-up action activities will indicate the constructive changes experienced by teachers and pupils for findings obtained from standard tests and informal diagnostic instruments in arithmetic.

REVIEW QUESTIONS

1. What are the major purposes of evaluation in a school system? In the classroom?
2. What psychological concepts and principles should be observed in planning and carrying on a program of evaluation by the administrators and teachers?
3. How may objective data be used by teachers to improve their subjective evaluation of the progress and needs of pupils in arithmetic?
4. What are the limitations of a standard achievement test as an instrument for diagnosing the understandings and mental processes or skills of the pupils in a classroom?
5. How may standard survey-achievement tests in arithmetic be used in a school system to improve instruction? To improve the curriculum? To appraise the abilities of pupils? To improve public relations?
6. What kinds of diagnostic instruments may teachers prepare to diagnose the learnings and psychological behavior of pupils in arithmetic?
7. What criteria and construction steps should be observed when preparing informal diagnostic instruments?
8. Why is the classroom teacher the key person in a school evaluation program?
9. How may a system of cumulative records serve teachers in appraising the progress, interests, attitudes, and specific difficulties of pupils during the year and from grade to grade?

10. In what ways may testing be related to but different from evaluating?

11. Why are a pupil's answers to examples and problems on an achievement test an inadequate indicator of the thought processes used in computing the answers?

12. What are the results to be derived by administrators and teachers from the practice of administering one form of a standard achievement-survey test in the fall and the spring of each school year?

Summary

The evaluation program should be based upon and consistent with the philosophy and objectives accepted for the school system. However, the primary function of evaluative instruments and procedures is to improve teaching and learning. Testing includes instruments and procedures that have been designed to produce data about the behavior of pupils. Evaluation, properly interpreted, is a professional process on the part of administrators and teachers to interpret the assembled data and to apply their interpretations when appraising and guiding the mental development of each pupil in elementary mathematics.

Important learnings in foundational mathematics to be appraised are: meanings, vocabulary, computational thinking, problem solving, and social usage. Standard tests are best suited to the purpose of making a general survey of pupil progress in a school system. Informal instruments and procedures, when prepared by classroom teachers, may be more effective in diagnosing understandings and mental skills of individual pupils. The content and structural sequence of diagnostic instruments should be selected in relation to what has been taught in each grade. The class or group process in appraisal of learnings and work-study skills is useful in motivating and helping pupils to interpret the functional value of self-appraisal in their work in arithmetic.

A system of cumulative records should serve to keep teachers informed of the developmental progress and needs of pupils in arithmetic and also other curriculum subjects. These records may be used when desired to communicate information on pupil and school progress to the parents and the public. The quality of teaching and evaluating is related to the quality of the pupils' learning and application of the desired outcomes in mental and social arithmetic.

SUGGESTED ACTIVITIES

1. Prepare a list of the desired outcomes in arithmetic for the primary grades. For grades four, five and six. For the junior high school.

2. Obtain and examine copies of the tests and manuals of several widely used standard tests in arithmetic.

3. Prepare a diagnostic test to be used in the primary, intermediate, or upper grades for: (*a*) mathematical meanings, (*b*) vocabulary, (*c*) computational skills, and (*d*) measurement.

4. Formulate a set of criteria to be used by pupils when using the class or group method in appraising their work in arithmetic.

5. Prepare a set of criteria you recommend to be applied by administrators and teachers when appraising the objectives, procedures, and outcomes of the school's evaluation program.

SUGGESTED REFERENCES

1. Brueckner, Leo J., and Grossnickle, Foster E., *Making Arithmetic Meaningful.* Philadelphia: John C. Winston Company, 1953, Chap. X.

2. Fernald, Grace M., *Remedial Techniques in the Basic School Subjects.* New York: McGraw-Hill Book Company, Inc., 1943.

3. *The Measurement of Understanding.* Forty-Fifth Yearbook, Part I, National Society for Study of Education. Chicago: University of Chicago Press, 1946.

4. *Learning and Instruction. Forty-Ninth Yearbook, Part I,* National Society for Study of Education. Chicago: University of Chicago Press, 1950.

5. Remmers, H. H., and Gage, N. L., *Educational Measurement and Evaluation,* rev. ed. New York: Harper & Brothers, 1955.

13

Curriculum Sequence in Arithmetic

Introduction

The superintendent, principals, and teachers in a school system have the professional responsibility to determine the objectives, content, and instructional sequence of the curriculum in arithmetic. The curriculum is the decision of the faculty concerning the underlying philosophy, the psychological concepts related to instructional and learning methods, the desired mathematical outcomes, the grade sequence, and the enabling activities and materials. The design of the curriculum effects purpose and understanding in learning. A teacher's manual or written curriculum is a valuable aid to teachers as they plan a classroom program consistent with the nature and structure of arithmetic and the psychological development of individual pupils. A carefully prepared curriculum helps teachers to interpret properly: (1) the mathematical meanings and mental processes that pupils are expected to learn, (2) the instructional methods and materials that facilitate learning as the result of questioning, observing, investigating, problem solving, and proof.

Exploratory Questions

The purpose of these questions is to encourage teachers and prospective teachers to re-examine their understanding of the interrelationship of the curriculum and teaching methods to differentiate between what is expected of pupils and the meanings and skills they really learn, and between what may be called the school or external curriculum and the pupils or internal curriculum.

1. How may the philosophy of education that is accepted by teachers and administrators influence the design of the curriculum?

2. How may the school curriculum affect the nature and outcomes of the learning process as experienced by pupils?

3. What are the salient characteristics of a curriculum that is based on a comprehensive interpretation of the theory of learning from experience?

4. What may be the advantages of a curriculum that reflects some agreement among the teachers concerning:

(*a*) The guiding purposes in teaching arithmetic?

(*b*) The mathematical meanings, mental processes, and vocabulary that pupils are expected to learn?

(*c*) A reasonable consistency in observing psychological principles in teaching?

(*d*) The selection and sequential organization of content and materials?

5. To what extent should the curriculum be adapted to sequence structure of the number system and the computational operations?

6. What reasons can you give to justify deferring the teaching of the more abstract meanings and computational processes until pupils have acquired an understanding of the foundational meanings and mental processes?

7. Should the allocation of various topics be based on a theory of grade placement or on a theory of psychological maturing?

8. What procedures may teachers use in determining differences in learning and performance abilities among pupils? What provisions may be made by teachers in serving these individual differences?

9. What may be the advantages to be derived from the practice of providing definite instructional periods at frequent intervals during the week?

10. How may a teacher's or curriculum guide serve as an effective instrument in improving the sequence and results in teaching and learning?

A Philosophy of Education Influences the Curriculum

One interpretation of a philosophy of education places great emphasis on teaching and learning subject matter. Classroom practices stress verbal telling, verbal explanation, rigid following of the textbook, mathematical rules, and drill exercises. Pupils are expected to hear, to understand, and to learn the topics as they are taught by the teacher. An inadequate amount of time and very few situations are provided as means to help pupils discover the meaning of topics they are taught. The curriculum consists primarily of abstract numbers, mechanical computations, and assigned exercises.

In a classroom where the teacher accepts the conviction that subject matter is of first importance, and that how pupils learn meanings and how they should learn to think are relatively insignificant, the topics in arithmetic are determined by the teacher and the textbook. Pupils learn primarily through repetition and memory, number symbols, computational rules, and frequent drill exercises. Pupils who are good in verbalizing numbers, in grasping mathematical rules, in finding the correct answers to assigned examples, in feeling security in being told what to do and how to do it, and in receiving approval from the teacher when instructions are properly carried out are successful on achievement tests that measure computational skills. Pupils who are less able to respond to such instructional methods soon find they are unable to meet the expectation of teachers, and thus begin to become mentally confused and discouraged. The concomitant learnings they experience soon begin to act as motivating deterrents in meaningful learning and satisfactory developmental progress in learning arithmetic. Many pupils who are appraised to be slow in arithmetic in the intermediate and upper grades may be the victims of a somewhat abstract curriculum, verbal instruction, confusion of rules, meaningless drill, evaluation based chiefly on standardized tests, and deterring concomitant learnings.

A more effective philosophy of education places a high value on meaningful subject matter and computational skills and an equally high value on accepted purpose, motivated exploration, productive thinking, and functional testing and applications of what has been learned. Topics are presented in relation to the sequence nature of the number system and the computational operations. Instructional methods and materials are selected to foster mental curiosity, to examine the why and how in each mathematical situation, to promote understanding of the mathematical meanings and computations, and to teach pupils to apply what has been learned to new learning experiences and social situations. Ample time is given to discovery periods in which pupils under professional guidance learn the meaning of mathematical terms, numbers, the number system, and the basic mental processes involved in mathematical computation. Satisfaction is derived as much from understanding the what and the why of the various topics studied in arithmetic as from the vocal approval of the teacher or scores made on tests. Teachers who recognize the values to be derived from the application of such a philosophy of education are cognizant of the uniqueness of each learner, the role of self-respect in learning, the worthy membership in group endeavor, the need for a feeling of achieving, readiness on the part of pupils to find answers to mathematical questions, and the relationship between the mathematical sequence in the number system and a corresponding sequence in learning and using the number system, numbers, and the computational operations.

The Curriculum

There are divergent interpretations of the nature and use of the curriculum in arithmetic. It is important that teachers and administrators in a school system take time to define the meaning they apply to the terms used in the curriculum. In the degree that there is lack of understanding and agreement, the results to teachers and pupils may become serious.

The school curriculum may be defined as the program that has been planned and developed cooperatively by all members of the school faculty. It presents the educational objectives, the topics teachers are expected to present in the classroom, the learnings pupils are expected to discover and refine, information concerning the sequence of topics, suggestions for improving instructional methods, the use of resource activities and materials, criteria for appraising pupil progress and needs, and a statement of the mathematical meanings to be presented in the elementary and junior high grades. The school curriculum in arithmetic is a teacher's guide to what is to be taught and what and how pupils are expected to learn. It is a valuable guide to teachers in safeguarding appropriate sequence in topics and teaching methods.

The pupil, or "under-the-skin" curriculum, represents the cumulative learnings he accepts from day to day. This emerging curriculum is the product of self-education as experienced in school under professional guidance. The meaning, organization, and psychological sequence of the pupil's curriculum are influenced by the quality of the learner's interaction with the school or teacher curriculum.

The curriculum plan for the presentation of topics in arithmetic is partly dictated by the sequence of the number systems and research findings in the field of child development. Pupils need to learn the vocabulary of counting before they can count with mathematical understanding. They need to learn to visualize individual objects as a group before they can properly comprehend the meaning and use of a number symbol to represent a quantitative concept or idea of a given group. Pupils need to learn the meaning and mental process of counting before they can begin to interpret the meaning and use of adding and the sequence levels in addition. Before pupils are able to understand the correct mathematical meaning of subtraction they should understand addition and also the component numbers of a given number. The mental process involved in subtraction with numbers is more complex than the physical act of removing a part from an object or a group of objects. Pupils must learn how to add equal groups before they can interpret meaningfully the mathematical processes of multiplication of numbers and division of numbers. The psychological sequence in learning mathematical concepts and mental processes should be consistent with the developmental sequence in the number system. What is done in the presenting and in the learning of the topics in arithmetic is conditioned by the way the teacher understands the sequential pattern in arithmetic, by the teacher's philosophy of education, and by the way the teacher understands and feels about children.

It is the considered judgment of the authors that the democratic philosophy when applied in the classroom insures optimum results in creative teaching and meaningful thinking and learning in arithmetic. One of the guiding theses in the preparation of this book has been the psychological concept that the ideas expressed by numbers, symbols, and words must be developed in the mind of each learner before pupils are able to think quantitatively and to use mathematical numbers and symbols to interpret and to relate ideas of quantity and relationship of quantities. There is a cumulative sequence in the mental behavior of each pupil from previous learnings to the discovery of new ideas; to the identification of new ideas with previous learnings; and to the testing and acceptance of expanded ideas and skills. The amount of time and guidance needed to discover meanings, to reorganize previous learnings, and to develop psychological sequence in mathematical thinking varies according to the learning rate and maturing progress of individual pupils. It is normal for pupils to differ as to quality and amount of progress in learning mathematical meanings, principles, and computational skills.

Teachers who understand the values and principles of a democratic philosophy of education will utilize various means to adapt curriculum content and outcomes to the "under-the-skin" abilities, needs, and maturing progress of individual pupils. It is a reasonable assumption that teachers will have provided situations, instruction, and materials that will have enabled all pupils before completing the elementary school to have developed a functional understanding of the various topics included in the school curriculum. Variation in mental abilities will have helped many pupils to have achieved understandings and skills to perform at a higher level in abstract thinking, problem solving, and creative experimentation.

Desired Outcomes

The school curriculum presents the outcomes that all pupils are expected to have achieved. Since learning is a unique mental process, the desired outcomes must be understood and be accepted by each learner as desired goals to attain. Some of the essential outcomes that teachers should strive to help pupils accept as reasonable, personal goals in arithmetic are:

1. To experience satisfactions that come to individuals who possess an understanding of the meanings and operations in foundational mathematics.

2. To comprehend and appreciate the important contribution of arithmetic to modern society and personal living.

3. To possess a meaningful mastery of the basic facts in addition, subtraction, multiplication, and division.

4. To understand the relationship and also numerical difference between integers, common fractions, decimal fractions, and denominate numbers.

5. To possess abilities and interest in observing, defining, analyzing, and solving various kinds of problems.

6. To develop ability to estimate and verify answers to mathematical examples and problems.

7. To possess ability in comparing and making judgment values concerning consumer goods.

8. To be able to read and interpret graphs and tables that present information and facts in the field of consumer economics.

9. To understand different kinds of units of measure and to be able to select and apply with precision appropriate units of measure in various situations.

10. To possess an understanding of the meanings, vocabulary, and operations involved in foundational mathematics.

11. To have developed abilities, values, and interests to motivate continued study of mathematics in the secondary school.

12. To possess abilities in understanding the value and application of foundational mathematics in personal and business economics.

13. To understand the important role of mathematical meanings and operations in scientific and technological research and progress.

14. To understand the need for learned competency in using the language and science of arithmetic in responsible citizenship.

The Arithmetic Lesson

Each lesson or instructional period is an important unit in a sequentially presented curriculum in arithmetic. The period should be planned and devoted with reference to previous lessons and should serve as a connected experience between what has been learned and what is expected to be learned. Attention needs to be given by teachers to the psychological principle that the degree of awareness accepted by the pupils concerning purpose and expected outcomes affects the quality of each learner's thinking about the topic or topics presented during the class period. There is a greater probability, however, that pupils will experience continued improvement from their work when they are encouraged to strive for progress in achieving one or more of these outcomes:

1. To develop increasingly mature ideas about the nature and sequential structure of the decimal number system.

2. To improve their understanding of the mathematical relationship between the computational operations (e.g., the relationship between multiplication and division).

3. To refine their interpretation of the correct meaning and use of mathematical terms and symbols.

4. To improve their mental abilities in applying previous learnings to new situations with the purpose of revising previous learnings and discovering and organizing new meanings.

5. To define more clearly the situations presented and the questions asked by addition, subtraction, multiplication, and division examples and to gain increasing facility in quickly determining correct answers.

6. To develop increasingly mature skills in recognizing, analyzing, and solving problems, with or without numbers.

7. To interpret more clearly the relationship of their classroom work to the use of arithmetic in out-of-school situations.

8. To accept responsibility in meeting higher standards in mathematical thinking and mental computation.

Near the end of each class session pupils should be encouraged to spend a few minutes in reflecting on what they started out to do and what was accomplished.

Planning the Curriculum

The curriculum used in a school system is more productive in outcomes when it is planned and prepared through cooperative study and discussion on the part of teachers, principals, supervisors, and the superintendent. All members of the faculty should share in some degree in reaching decisions on matters such as the underlying philosophy of education, the sustaining psychological concepts, outcomes to be expected, selection and sequential organization of topics, teaching methods, utilization of audiovisual learning aids, adaptation of requirements to serve individual differences, criteria to be used in appraising pupil progress, and the application of arithmetic to important learnings in consumer economics.

Frequent teacher in-service meetings may be effective means in motivating and assisting members of the faculty in reaching some agreement concerning desired outcomes, instructional methods, sequence in presentation of topics, the sequential structure of the number system, standards of pupil evaluation, the curriculum, and the adopted textbook. Teachers are the persons who translate the school curriculum into classroom experiences. The opportunity for pupils to develop with mathematical sequence their mental system of arithmetic is provided when teachers practice some agreement in teaching arithmetic. Psychological and mathematical sequence in teaching and learning the meanings and operations in arithmetic may be safeguarded when a statement such as, "Do you agree?" is prepared by the teachers. A statement or report of this nature may be prepared for primary teachers, for intermediate grade teachers, and for teachers in the junior high school. A representative statement for the intermediate grade teachers is given as an illustration.

Do Intermediate Grade Teachers Agree

A. Addition—Integers **Do You Agree:**

1. That the adding of examples is a mental process; the notated or written numbers reveal the result of mental addition?

2. That pupils, before adding an example, should identify the question?

3. That pupils should be asked when adding to add from the top addend to the bottom addend?

4. That pupils be encouraged to determine the accuracy of their answer by adding from the bottom to the top in column addition?

5. That pupils be asked frequently to give orally the thought process used in finding the answer in addition?

6. That pupils be expected to understand the mathematical process of substituting one unit in the next higher place-value position when the sum of the digits in a given value position is ten or more?

7. That teachers should prepare and administer diagnostic tests to determine the pupils' computational level in addition?

B. Substraction—Integers **Do You Agree:**

1. That pupils interpret all notated subtraction examples as asking the question, "What is the difference between the minuend and the subtrahend?"

2. That the difference between two numbers in any place value position can be determined by comparing the numbers to find the difference between the minuend and the subtrahend?

3. That pupils be expected to use the substitution rather than the borrowing method when a digit in the minuend in a given place-value position is smaller than the digit in the corresponding place-value position in the subtrahend?

4. That pupils be expected to understand the mathematical process of rewriting the minuend when substituting ten units in the next lower place-value position for one unit in a given place-value position?

5. That pupils be expected to verify the accuracy of the answer by adding the subtrahend to the answer to determine if the sum equals the number that is the minuend?

6. That pupils be asked, frequently, to give orally the thought process used in finding the answer in subtraction?

7. That teachers should prepare and administer diagnostic tests to determine the pupils' computational level in subtraction?

C. *Multiplication—Integers* **Do You Agree:**

1. That pupils occasionally be asked to state the question asked by the multiplication example before beginning computation?

2. That pupils interpret the multiplicand to be one of the like-size numbers and the multiplier to tell the number of like-size numbers to be grouped and the amount notated with one number?

3. That pupils be taught to recognize the difference in the question asked in a multiplication example when the multiplicand and multiplier are reversed?

4. That pupils be asked frequently to give their interpretation of the quantitative meaning of the product?

5. That pupils when computing the product of an example where the multiplier is a two-place-value number be expected to think and understand: ones times ones give ones, ones times tens give tens, ones times hundreds give hundreds, tens times ones give tens, tens times tens give hundreds, and so forth?

6. That pupils be taught the meaning and use of *substitution* in multiplying rather than *carrying* when the product in any given place-value position is ten or more?

7. That pupils understand when verifying the accuracy of the product by reversing the multiplicand and multiplier they are applying a theoretical principle, but have changed the nature of the question asked in the original example?

8. That pupils be asked, frequently, to give orally the thought process used in finding the answer in multiplication?

9. That teachers should prepare and administer diagnostic tests to determine the pupils' computational level in multiplication?

D. Division—Integers **Do You Agree:**

1. That pupils be able to identify the three kinds of quantitative situations that involve division in determining the solution?

2. That pupils understand that in computing the quotient in all written examples in division they are finding the ratio between the dividend and the divisor?

3. That pupils not be expected to think of the divisor as being divided into the dividend when computing the quotient?

4. That pupils be expected to think, "When the dividend is changed into numbers the size of the divisor, there will be how many numbers?"

5. That pupils be expected to use the long-division method when computing the quotient until they understand and are able to notate correctly the short-division method?

6. That pupils use their meanings and skills in multiplication when working division examples, rather than subtraction?

7. That when pupils desire to verify the accuracy of division they multiply a number that is the divisor by the number that is the quotient (and add the remainder, if the division is uneven)?

8. That pupils be asked, frequently, to state orally the thought process used in formulating the question asked and in finding the quotient?

9. That pupils be given time and practice in finding the quotient to examples in division where the divisor is a one-place number before they do division involving a two-place number?

10. That teachers should prepare and use frequently diagnostic tests to determine the operational level of the pupils in division?

E. Common Fraction—Addition **Do You Agree:**

1. That pupils should learn to think and use a fraction as a number?

2. That pupils should learn that in adding common fractions they add only the fraction number which is the numerator?

3. That pupils should understand the meaning of changing a fraction to lower terms or higher terms before they solve many exercises in addition of common fractions?

4. That pupils be expected to use the vertical method rather than the horizontal method when adding common fractions?

5. That pupils understand that they can add only like-size fraction numbers (i.e., $\frac{3}{4} + \frac{7}{4} = \frac{10}{4}$ or $2\frac{1}{2}$) ($\frac{2}{3} + \frac{1}{4} = \frac{8}{12} + \frac{3}{12} = \frac{11}{12}$)?

6. That teachers should ask pupils frequently to state orally the thought process they used in finding the sum when adding common fractions?

7. That teachers prepare and administer, at given intervals, diagnostic tests to determine the understanding and computational level of pupils in adding common fractions?

F. *Subtraction—Common Fractions* **Do You Agree:**

1. That pupils be expected to interpret the mathematical relationship between the subtraction of integers and the subtraction of common fractions?

2. That pupils understand that when subtracting notated or written common fractions they should answer the question, "What is the numerical difference between the minuend and the subtrahend?"

3. That pupils understand that they can compare or find the difference between numbers (the numerators) that represent like-size fractions?

4. That pupils understand and be able to use the mathematical process of substitution or rewriting the minuend when the subtrahend is smaller than the minuend (i.e., $3\frac{1}{2} - \frac{3}{4} = \frac{7}{2} - \frac{3}{4} = \frac{14}{4} - \frac{3}{4} = \frac{11}{4} = 2\frac{3}{4}$)?

5. That pupils be expected to use the vertical rather than the horizontal method when computing the answer in subtraction?

6. That teachers should prepare and administer at given intervals diagnostic instruments to determine the understanding and ability of pupils in subtraction involving common fractions or mixed numbers?

7. That pupils be asked, from time to time, to state orally the mental process they used in finding the difference between two fraction numbers or mixed numbers?

G. *Multiplication—Common Fractions* Do You Agree:

1. That pupils be asked to read and think the meaning of the question presented in the example before beginning to multiply?

2. That pupils be expected to apply their learnings about multiplication of integers when computing the product for examples involving fractions?

3. That examples in multiplication of common fractions be limited to a multiplier that is an integer until pupils have gained understanding and competency in this type of multiplication of fractions?

4. That pupils understand that a different mathematical question is asked when the multiplier is a fraction (a number less than one)?

5. That pupils do not learn the habit of multiplying the denominator of the multiplier by the denominator of the multiplicand when both the multiplier and multiplicand are fractions? ($\frac{3}{4} \times \frac{2}{3} = ?$ Pupils should think, $\frac{3}{4} \times \frac{1}{3} = \frac{3}{12}$ and $2 \times \frac{3}{12} = \frac{6}{12}$.)

6. That pupils, when multiplying examples where the multiplicand and multiplier are mixed numbers, be expected to use the vertical method?

7. That pupils be asked, from time to time, to state orally the thought process they used when multiplying an example where:

(*a*) the multiplicand is a fraction and the multiplier is an integer,
(*b*) the multiplicand is an integer and the multiplier is a fraction,and
(*c*) the multiplicand and multiplier are fractions or mixed numbers?

8. That teachers prepare and administer diagnostic tests to determine the understanding and computational abilities of pupils in multiplication involving fractions or mixed numbers?

H. *Division—Common Fractions* Do You Agree:

1. That pupils be expected to read and to identify the mathematical question asked before beginning to compute the answer?

2. That pupils be expected to understand the mathematical relationship between division with integers and division with fractions and to apply their learnings for division with integers in their division with fractions?

3. That the presentation and work in division with fractions follow this sequence:

(*a*) Dividend is an integer and divisor is a fraction?

(*b*) Dividend is a fraction and divisor is a fraction (like-size fractions)?

(*c*) Dividend is a fraction and divisor is a fraction (unlike size fractions)?

(*d*) Dividend is a mixed number and divisor is a fraction?

(*e*) Dividend is a mixed number and divisor is a mixed number?

4. That pupils be expected to learn and use with proficiency the like-fraction method in division before teachers present the inversion method?

5. That the cancellation in division be postponed until pupils have understood the meaning and use of division of fractions or mixed numbers by the *like-fraction method?*

6. That all examples in division of integers, fractions, and mixed numbers be limited to reasonable-size numbers until pupils have attained a thorough understanding of the mathematical process and are able to compute with accuracy?

7. That pupils understand that in division examples where the dividend is a number smaller than the divisor a different concept of division is involved? (The concept if stated mathematically is "The dividend is what fractional part of a number like the divisor?")

8. That pupils in the elementary grades not be given examples in division where the dividend is a number smaller than the divisor?

9. That pupils be asked to state orally, from time to time, the thought process they used in computing the quotient to division examples involving fractions or mixed numbers?

10. That teachers prepare and administer at given intervals diagnostic instruments to determine the understanding and computational level of pupils in division with fractions or mixed numbers?

I. Decimals—Addition **Do You Agree:**

1. That pupils understand a decimal to be a number?

2. That pupils apply their learnings about integers and common fractions when adding decimal fractions or mixed decimals?

3. That pupils interpret the decimal point as a symbol to indicate a change in thinking from ones to units of less than one.

4. That the classroom work follow a sequence such as:

(*a*) Addition of tenths?

(*b*) Addition of hundredths; addition of tenths and hundredths?

(*c*) Addition of mixed decimal numbers?

5. That pupils understand the meaning and use of mathematical substitution when the sum of the units notated in any given place-value position is ten or larger?

J. Subtraction—Decimals **Do You Agree:**

1. That pupils should learn that many of the mathematical meanings they have learned about subtraction of integers and common fractions can be applied in subtracting decimal fractions and mixed numbers?

2. That the mathematical concept of substitution involved in subtracting integers and common fractions applies to subtraction with decimal fractions or mixed numbers?

K. Multiplication—Decimal Fractions and Mixed Numbers
Do You Agree:

1. That pupils should learn that many of the mathematical meanings and principles that they learned about multiplication with integers and mixed numbers can apply to multiplication with decimal fractions and mixed numbers?

2. That pupils be expected to keep the decimal point in the partial products under the decimal point in the multiplicand until they have developed a meaningful understanding of the process of multiplication?

4. That the presentation of the topics and work with decimals follow a sequence consistent with the mathematical levels, such as:

(*a*) Multiplicand is an integer; multiplier is an integer?

(*b*) Multiplicand is a decimal fraction; multiplier is an integer?

(*c*) Multiplicand is a mixed decimal; multiplier is an integer?

(*d*) Multiplicand is an integer; multiplier is a decimal fraction?

(*e*) Multiplicand is a mixed number; multiplier is a decimal fraction?

(*f*) Multiplicand is a mixed number; multiplier is a mixed number?

5. That teachers prepare and administer diagnostic tests at frequent intervals to determine the understanding and computational abilities of pupils in division with decimal fractions and mixed numbers?

L. Division—Decimal Fractions and Mixed Numbers
Do You Agree:

1. That more time be used in working with concrete materials and practical situations to help pupils in discovering the basic meanings and operations involved in division with decimals?

2. That pupils understand the relationship of mathematical questions and processes involved in division with integers and common fractions to division with decimal fractions and mixed numbers?

3. That the curriculum in division with decimals follow a sequence consistent with the number system, such as:

(*a*) Dividend is tenths; divisor is tenths?

(*b*) Dividend is hundredths; divisor is hundredths?

(*c*) Dividend is an integer; divisor is tenths, hundredths, or tenths and hundredths?

(*d*) Dividend is a mixed number; divisor is tenths or hundredths, or tenths and hundredths?

(*e*) Dividend is a mixed number and divisor is a mixed number?

4. That pupils learn to work examples without applying the abstract rule that a decimal fraction or mixed number in the divisor may be changed to an integer by multiplying the divisor and dividend by the same multiple of ten? (The ratio remains the same but the numerical question is changed.)

5. That pupils be asked, from time to time, to state orally the mental process they used in determining the quotient in examples involving division with integers, decimal fractions, and mixed numbers?

6. That teachers prepare and use frequently diagnostic tests to determine the understanding and computational abilities of pupils in division with integers, decimal fractions, and mixed decimals?

M. Percent **Do You Agree:**

1. That pupils should learn that percent is a business application of decimal fractions with a numerical value of hundredths?

2. That pupils should learn that 1 is equivalent to 100 percent or 100%; .01 is equivalent to 1 percent or 1%; and .005 is equivalent to .5 percent or .5%?

3. That percent and percentage should be presented as a business application of decimal fractions?

4. That the three questions answered by the application of percent are:

(*a*) What is a given percent of a given number?

(*b*) A given number is what percent of a given number?

(*c*) What is the number when the percent and percentage are known?

5. That pupils should be encouraged to bring illustrations found in magazines, newspapers, and from business firms with reference to their work in the classroom with percent?

6. That teachers should prepare and administer diagnostic tests to determine the pupils' understanding of the meaning and business use of percents and percentage?

N. *Measures—Denominate Numbers* Do You Agree:

1. That pupils should understand that denominate numbers are used to express approximate measurement of a quantity or quantities?

2. That pupils should learn that in measurement the three important steps to take are:

(*a*) Select an appropriate unit of measure?

(*b*) Apply the unit of measure to the given quantity to determine the size?

(*c*) Determine the accuracy and precision of the measurement?

3. That pupils should be expected to develop a meaningful understanding and use of the metric system of measures and measurement?

4. That pupils should not be expected to memorize the different tables of measures but rather to comprehend their application?

O. *Problem Solving* Do You Agree:

1. That each pupil is his own problem solver?

2. That school and textbook problems should be interpreted and accepted as real problems if they are to motivate the best thinking on the part of pupils?

3. That the major outcomes desired in problem solving are:

(*a*) Increasing ability to observe or to read problems?

(*b*) Increasing ability to define and analyze the related factors in each problem situation?

(*c*) Increasing ability to formulate a workable solution or solutions and verify the accuracy of the solutions?

(*d*) Increasing ability to derive economic generalization from the solution to personal and social problems?

P. A "Must" List for Citizens [1]

1. COMPUTATION. Can you add, subtract, multiply, and divide effectively with whole numbers, common fractions, and decimals?

2. PERCENTS. Can you use percents understandingly and accurately?

3. RATIO. Do you have a clear understanding of ratio?

4. ESTIMATING. Before you perform a computation, do you estimate the result for the purpose of checking your answer?

5. ROUNDING NUMBERS. Do you know the meaning of significant figures? Can you round numbers properly?

6. TABLES. Can you find correct values in tables, e.g., interest and income tax?

7. GRAPHS. Can you read ordinary graphs; bar, line, and circle graphs? The graph of a formula?

8. STATISTICS. Do you know the main guides that one should follow in collecting and interpreting data; can you use averages (mean, median, mode); can you draw and interpret a graph?

9. THE NATURE OF A MEASUREMENT. Do you know the meaning of a measurement, of a standard unit, of the largest permissible error, of tolerance, and of the statement that "a measurement is an approximation"?

10. USE OF MEASURING DEVICES. Can you use certain measuring devices, such as an ordinary ruler, other rulers (graduated to thirty-seconds, to tenths of an inch, and to millimeters), protractor, graph paper, tape, caliper micrometer, and thermometer?

11. SQUARE ROOT. Can you find the square root of a number by table, or by division?

12. ANGLES. Can you estimate, read, and construct an angle?

13. GEOMETRIC CONCEPTS. Do you have an understanding of point, line, angle, parallel lines, perpendicular lines, triangle (right,

---

[1] Prepared by the National Council of Teachers of Mathematics, Washington, D. C.

scalene, isosceles, and equilateral), parallelogram (including square and rectangle), trapezoid, circle, regular polygon, prism, cylinder, cone, and sphere?

14. THE 3-4-5 RELATION. Can you use the Pythagorean relationship in a right angle?

15. CONSTRUCTIONS. Can you with ruler and compasses construct a circle, a square, and a rectangle, transfer a line segment and an angle, bisect a line segment and an angle, copy a triangle, divide a line segment into more than two equal parts, draw a tangent to a circle, and draw a geometric figure to scale?

16. DRAWINGS. Can you read and interpret reasonably well, maps, floor plans, mechanical drawings, and blueprints? Can you find the distance between two points on a map?

17. VECTORS. Do you understand the meaning of vector, and can you find the resultant of two forces?

18. METRIC SYSTEM. Do you know how to use the most important metric units (meter, centimeter, millimeter, kilometer, gram, kilogram)?

19. CONVERSION. In measuring length, area, volume, weight, time, temperature, angle, and speed can you shift from one commonly used standard unit to another widely used standard unit; e.g., do you know the relation between yard and foot, inch and centimeter, etc.?

20. ALGEBRAIC SYMBOLISM. Can you use letters to represent numbers; i.e., do you know the meaning of exponent and coefficient?

21. FORMULAS. Do you know the meaning of a formula—can you, for example, write an arithmetic rule as a formula, and can you substitute given values in order to find the value for a required unknown?

22. SIGNED NUMBERS. Do you understand signed numbers and can you use them?

23. USING THE AXIOMS. Do you understand what you are doing when you use the axioms to change the form of a formula, or when you find the value of an unknown in a simple equation?

24. PRACTICAL FORMULAS. Do you know from memory certain widely used formulas relating to areas, volumes, and interest, and to distance, rate, and time?

25. SIMILAR TRIANGLES AND PROPORTION. Do you understand the meaning of similar triangles, and do you know how to use the fact that in similar triangles the ratios of corresponding sides are equal? Can you manage a proportion?

26. TRIGONOMETRY. Do you know the meaning of tangent, sine, cosine? Can you develop their meanings by means of scale drawings?

27. FIRST STEPS IN BUSINESS ARITHMETIC. Are you mathematically conditioned for satisfactory adjustment to a first job in business; e.g., have you a start in understanding the keeping of a simple account, making change, and the arithmetic that illustrates the most common problems of communication and everyday affairs?

28. STRETCHING THE DOLLAR. Do you have a basis for dealing intelligently with the main problems of the consumer, e.g., the cost of borrowing money, insurance to secure adequate protection against the numerous hazards of life, the wise management of money, and buying with a given income so as to get good values as regards both quantity and quality?

29. PROCEEDING FROM HYPOTHESIS TO CONCLUSION. Can you analyze a statement in a newspaper and determine what is assumed, and whether the suggested conclusions really follow from the given facts or assumptions?

Illustrative Curriculum Sequence

No single curriculum sequence will meet the needs of all school systems. The faculty of each school system faces the responsibility to design a curriculum sequence of topics that is best suited to the accepted philosophy of education and the objectives and desired outcomes in arithmetic. The illustrative curriculum sequence here outlined has been based on the authors' view of research and several curriculums and is presented as an aid to teachers in planning a curriculum sequence for the school and for a specific grade. A careful reading of the outline may reveal a relationship between the mathematical sequence in arithmetic and the steps involved in developing a similar mathematical sequence in a mental system of arithmetic.

Curriculum Sequence for Grade One

1. A one-to-one relationship between objects, name of objects, and amount of objects and numbers that stand for the conceptual ideas.

2. Number system—recognizing amount of groups smaller than 9; cardinal meaning of numbers 1 to 9, meaning of *10* as a base value unit and ordinal numbers to fifths.

3. Counting and writing to 50, and beyond if needed.

4. Addition—meaning of basic facts with a sum less than 10, column addition of three addends with a sum less than 10, use of zero in column addition, meaning of the signs + and =.

5. Subtraction—meaning of the physical act of removing or comparing, subtraction (addition facts) facts that do not involve substitution.

6. Multiplication—counting by 2's to 8, 3's to 9.

7. Division—separating 4, 6, 8, 9 into equal-size groups or numbers.

8. Common fractions—meaning and use of $\frac{1}{2}$ and $\frac{1}{4}$ in practical situations.

9. Money—value of cents, nickels, and dimes; making change from a nickel, from a dime.

10. Measures—quantitative concepts such as big, bigger, biggest, long, longer, longest, tall, taller, tallest; meaning of a foot and a yard; reading the hands on a clock; recognizing days in the week, names of the days and months.

11. Shapes—recognizing a circle, a square, a triangle.

12. Problem solving—learning what is a simple problem and solving simple oral word problems.

Curriculum Sequence for Grade Two

1. Understanding the one-to-one relationship between objects, groups of objects, ideas of amount, and words or numbers to express quantitative ideas.

2. Counting—by 1's, 2's, and 5's to 100, and beyond if needed.

3. Number system—cardinal value of numbers to 500, ordinal meaning of numbers to tenths, use of 10 and 100 as basic units.

4. Reading and writing numbers to 500 and beyond, if needed.

5. Addition—basic facts with a sum under 10 and, if desired, basic facts with a sum over 10; adding column addition with three addends; adding two-place-value numbers, if desired.

6. Subtraction—basic facts (and related addition facts) with a difference under 10, and over 10 if desired; meaning of minuend, subtrahend, difference.

7. Multiplication—counting by 5's and 10's to 100 and basic facts with product under 10.

8. Division—dividing groups as large as 18 into equal groups.

9. Common fractions—using $\frac{1}{2}$, $\frac{1}{3}$, $\frac{1}{4}$ in meaningful situations.

10. Money—value of cents, nickels, dimes, quarters, half-dollar and dollar; making change from a dime, quarter, and half dollar.

11. Measures—meaning of dozen, half-dozen, inch, foot, pound, half-pound, cup, quart, pint, gallon; telling time by reading hands of the clock; names of days of the week and months of the year; beginning the reading of a thermometer.

12. Problem solving—solving simple oral and written problems involving the mathematical meanings that have been learned; awareness and definition of a problem; ability to read and solve an easy verbal problem.

Curriculum Sequence for Grade Three

1. Number system—the meaning of zero and place value as used in three-place numbers, reading and writing numbers to 1000, Roman numerals through XII.

2. Addition—addition facts, adding three addends with as many as three places, with or without substitution.

3. Subtraction—basic facts, subtracting numbers with as many as three places, with or without substitution.

4. Multiplication—basic facts, multiplying two- and three-place-value numbers with a one-place multiplier, without substitution.

5. Division—facts corresponding to multiplication facts. Readiness for uneven division.

6. Common fractions—meaning and use of $\frac{1}{2}$, $\frac{1}{3}$, $\frac{1}{4}$ in functional situations.

7. Decimals (money)—writing money numbers using the decimal point; adding, subtracting, multiplying, dividing money numbers.

8. Measures—inches, feet, yards; pints, quarts, gallons; minutes, hours, days, weeks, months, years; ounces, pounds; dozen; thermometer.

9. Shapes—recognition of circle, square, rectangle.

10. Problems—analyzing one-step problems, deciding the process, finding the answer, checking the computation.

Curriculum Sequence for Grade Four

1. Number system—meaning of numbers, reading and writing numbers with as many as six places, Roman numerals through L.

2. Addition—column addition of four addends with as many as five places.

3. Subtraction—subtracting numbers with as many as five places.

4. Multiplication—all basic facts, multiplying four-place numbers by a one-place multiplier; multiplying a two-place number by a two-place multiplier.

5. Division—all the basic facts, dividing four-place numbers by a one-place divisor.

6. Common fractions—meanings, fractional parts of whole numbers, fractions in measures.

7. Money (decimals)—four fundamental operations involving small amounts of money.

8. Measures—fractional parts of inches, gallons, pounds; dry measure including pints, quarts, pecks, bushels; time including A.M., P.M., and seconds.

9. Shapes, perimeter, area—triangle, perimeter and area of square and rectangle.

10. Problems—oral and written, simple two-step related to home, school and community situations.

Curriculum Sequence for Grade Five

1. Number system—meaning of numbers from hundredths to hundred millions, reading and writing numbers with as many as nine places, Roman numerals through M.

2. Addition—column addition of five addends with as many as five places.

3. Subtraction—subtracting numbers with as many as five places.

4. Multiplication—multiplying four-place numbers by two-place numbers, multiplying three-place numbers by three-place numbers.

5. Division—dividing five-place numbers by two-place numbers.

6. Common fractions—meanings, denominator, numerator, proper, improper, mixed numbers, reducing, least common denominator.

7. Addition of fractions—mixed numbers, unlike denominators.

8. Subtraction of fractions—mixed numbers, unlike denominators.

9. Decimal fractions—meanings, reading and writing through hundredths.

10. Addition of decimal fractions—mixed decimals including tenths and hundredths.

11. Subtraction of decimal fractions—mixed decimals including tenths and hundredths.

12. Measures—fractional parts of feet, yards, quarts, bushels; dry measure including cups; weight including hundredweight, ton; square measure including square inches, square feet, square yards; gross.

13. Shapes, perimeter, area—continuation of work with triangle, perimeter and area of square and rectangle.

14. Problems—oral and written including two-step.

Curriculum Sequence for Grade Six

1. Number system—meaning of numbers to billions, reading and writing numbers through billions, rounding large whole numbers.

2. Addition—columns of large numbers.

3. Subtraction—subtraction of large numbers.

4. Multiplication—multiplying four-place numbers by three-place numbers.

5. Division—dividing six-place numbers by three-place numbers.

6. Meaning of fractions—substituting fractions for whole numbers, cancellation.

7. Addition of fractions—mixed numbers, unlike denominators.

8. Subtraction of fractions—mixed numbers, unlike denominators.

9. Multiplication of fractions—multiplying a mixed number by a mixed number.

10. Division of fractions—division method and inversion method, dividing mixed numbers with unlike fractions.

11. Meaning of decimals—decimal fraction equivalents, decimal fractions as quotients, rounding of decimal fractions.

12. Addition of decimal fractions—mixed decimals through thousandths.

13. Subtraction of decimal fractions—mixed decimals through thousandths.

14. Multiplication of decimal fractions—mixed decimals with multiplier and multiplicand expressed to nearest hundredth.

15. Division of decimal fractions—mixed decimals with divisor and dividend expressed to nearest hundredth.

16. Measures—rod; time including decade, century, 24-hour clock; square measure; equivalents of an acre expressed in square feet, square yards, square miles; metric units of length; equivalent measures; graphs.

17. Shapes, perimeter, area—continuation of work with triangle, perimeter, and area of square and rectangle.

18. Problems—problems with unnecessary facts, using round numbers.

Curriculum Sequence for Grade Seven

1. Number system—meanings, using very large numbers and very small numbers.

2. Whole numbers—fundamental operations.

3. Common fractions—meanings, fundamental operations.

4. Decimal fractions—meanings, fundamental operations.

5. Percentage—meanings, adding and subtracting, fractions and decimal equivalents, three cases of percent used in elementary business practice, percent of increase and percent of decrease.

6. Measures—teaspoons, tablespoons; tons; equivalent square measures including square yards in a square rod, square rods in an acre; metric measures of length and capacity; nautical measures.

7. Shapes, perimeter, area, volume—perimeter of triangles; area of triangle, parallelogram, trapezoid, circle; diameter, radius, and circumference of a circle; volume of rectangular solids; angles and degrees.

8. Problems—practical applications in social-economic situations.

Suggested Curriculum Sequence for Grade Eight

1. Number system—meanings, reading, writing numbers through trillions.

2. Whole numbers—fundamental operations.

3. Common fractions—meanings, fundamental operations.

4. Decimal fractions—meanings, fundamental operations, multiplying and dividing by 10, 100, and 1000.

5. Percentage—meanings, applications, less than 1 percent.

6. Measures—metric measures including measures of area, volume, weight; units of cubic measure; units of circular measure; longitude and time; board feet.

7. Shapes, perimeter, area, volume—volume of a cylinder, capacity, metric units (see Measures).

8. Problems—formulas and equations, ratio, proportion.

Meeting Individual Differences

Many studies show the range of mental ages in any classroom. Children in a typical fifth grade may differ in arithmetic abilities by as much as five years.[2] Furthermore the variation tends to get greater as the pupils progress into the higher grades. The school is faced with the problem of organizing an arithmetic program fitted to the needs of the slow, normal, and rapid achievers. This program may consist of:

1. Providing a special program within the framework of the regular class.

2. Promoting children to a higher grade level, or in the case of low achievers, failure.

3. Organizing special classes or interest groups fitted to fast or slow achievers.

4. Combining one or more of the above three plans.

There is considerable danger of hurting children if they are fitted into a slow, average, or rapid achiever category too soon. At least in early grades, it is wisest to recognize the fact that there are great differences in children's backgrounds, interests, and attitudes, which affect achievement. For some children number ideas develop slowly, but once they develop the children progress rapidly. In the case of children possessing superior reading ability, teachers may expect them to be rapid achievers in arithmetic. Unfortunately superior readers are not necessarily superior in arithmetic. In most cases it is better for teachers to withhold judgment too long rather than to apply a label too soon.

---

[2] Vincent J. Glennon and C. W. Hunnicutt, *What Does Research Say About Arithmetic?* Washington, D. C.: Association for Supervision and Curriculum Development, 1952, p. 28.

Identifying the Superior Child

An excellent means of identifying the child who needs help because of superior learning ability in arithmetic is by observing the child's behavior in a number of situations. To insure the greatest possible objectivity in using observational procedures, four basic procedures are recommended.[3]

"1. Give each child equal consideration on each behavior characteristic.

"2. Observe each child in a variety of situations.

"3. Compare each child with the rest of the group.

"4. Be aware of your own biases."

The *Handbook*[4] also suggests, ". . . the use of cumulative records, the use of standardized tests, and the use of informal tests."

When observing the child for evidences of behavior that may indicate special aptitude in arithmetic, it is imperative to know some of the identifying characteristics of mathematicians. Following are representative questions a teacher might ask while observing individual children.

1. Does he appear to have a good memory, especially for relationships?
2. Does he seem to understand mathematical reasoning when it is explained?
3. Can he repeat a mathematical demonstration and explain in clear concise language the procedure used?
4. Can he recognize mathematical principles and apply them in new situations?
5. Does he seem to understand the relationship of elements to the whole?
6. Is he able to estimate answers to problems and then verify them by computation?
7. Can he determine original and satisfactory methods of solving problems?
8. Does he seem to be able to "see" answers to mathematical questions without resorting to trial-and-error methods?

---

[3] Jack Kough and Robert F. DeHaan, *Teacher's Guidance Handbook, Part I*, "Identifying Children Who Need Help." Chicago: Science Research Associates, Inc.

[4] *Ibid.*, p. 12.

9. Does he show superiority in arithmetical reasoning and computation?

A second means of identifying the child with superior ability is one of carefully studying the child's past record. The data recorded on cumulative records can be an invaluable aid. The pupils in the upper 20 percent of any class usually have the potential to learn arithmetic more readily than their classmates and may be in need of special attention.

A third means of identifying children in need of a special program is by administering intelligence tests, interest tests, and achievement tests. These are all helpful instruments providing teachers take time to analyze pupil responses to questions designed to determine quantitative reasoning, verbal comprehension, and ability to interpret relationships among diagrammatic materials.[5]

Providing a Special Program in the Regular Class

Most teachers are confronted with the task of meeting individual differences in the regular class since the skipping of grades or the segregation of children into special classes for the gifted are extreme measures usually determined by school administrators. Teachers report the use of at least six principal methods of providing for the needs of bright children in the regular classes.[6]

1. Group work within the class.
2. Letting a child work at his own level or speed.
3. Special assignments.
4. Projects.
5. Free choice on completion of regular work.
6. Individual work with the teacher on completion of regular work.

Ability Grouping Within a Class

A well-known method of meeting the varying needs of children in the regular classroom is ability grouping. Most teachers use this method in teaching reading. A child's placement in a group may be

[5] Earl M. McWilliams, and Kenneth E. Brown, *The Superior Pupil in Junior High School Mathematics*. Washington, D. C.: U. S. Department of Health, Education and Welfare.

[6] Norma E. Cutts, and Nicholas Moseley, *Bright Children*. New York: G. P Putnam's Sons, 1955, pp. 76–79.

determined by his ability to read material at a certain level of difficulty, by his interest in a particular story or topic under consideration by the group, or because of a particular kind of difficulty with a specific skill. While there is considerable flexibility in the grouping, the membership in some groups may not change for an entire school year.

Grouping as practiced in the teaching of reading cannot easily be applied to grouping children for the teaching of arithmetic. In reading, children in the various groups are assigned a reading book matched to their achievement in using reading skills. Several texts at varying difficulty levels may be in use by the teacher at any given time. If this plan were to be followed in the arithmetic class, the teacher might have three or more arithmetic groups, each with its own text. The problem of making lesson plans for a number of texts and of finding time to teach separate arithmetic lessons would be almost insurmountable.

A workable plan of grouping children for the teaching of arithmetic must be one in which all children use the same basic text. This is possible in classrooms where teachers use least abstract work on a page for the slow achiever, use the more abstract work for faster achievers, and expect gifted pupils to apply principles in numerous situations.

Appropriate Activities for Fast Achievers

The fast achiever needs the opportunity to go beyond the rest of the class in finding out the "how" and the "why" of the mathematical principles he is learning, as well as their applications in a variety of situations. No attempt has been made to provide a specific list of activities at the various grade levels. Many modern teachers' manuals give specific instructions for meeting individual differences. Representative activities are suggested for consideration and possible use in the classroom.

1. Preparing to give oral and written reports on the history of mathematics as it relates to a topic under consideration.

2. Constructing learning aids for the arithmetic center.

3. Making models illustrating topics such as finding volumes, finding areas, etc.

4. Constructing charts or murals to present ideas learned in studying an arithmetic topic.

5. Solving additional or different but more difficult and thought-provoking problems.

6. Studying a more advanced treatment of a topic that may be given in a different text.

7. Making vocabulary booklets in which mathematics words are defined.

8. Taking field trips to banks, the post office, stores, or factories to discover uses of arithmetic.

9. Reading and reporting upon books relating to mathematics.[7, 8]

10. Viewing films and filmstrips relating to mathematics. (See *Chicago Schools Supplement*, footnote 8.)

11. Using commercially prepared enrichment materials containing number tricks, puzzles, riddles, magic squares, brain teasers, etc. (See *Enrichment Program for Arithmetic*, Row, Peterson & Company.)

12. Developing original arithmetic games, puzzles, brain teasers, etc.

13. Developing short cuts for finding answers.

14. Composing original arithmetic problems relating to social studies or science.

15. Exploring the uses of mathematics in building skyscrapers, bridges, railroads; in agriculture; in astronomy; etc.

16. Making a collection of advertisements of small-loan companies, banks, and stores, which offer money or articles subject to repayments to be made over a period of several months. Comparing the financial obligations assumed by the borrower.

17. Using timetables to plan trips to distant points.

18. Deciding upon a sensible use of a personal allowance.

19. Deciding upon what to buy on a trip.

20. Finding information about other number systems.

21. Computing with number systems having a base other than 10.

---

[7] Ruth Hutcheson, Edna Mantor, and Marjorie Homburg, *The Elementary School Mathematics Library*. Washington, D. C.: National Council of Teachers of Mathematics, 1956.

[8] Joseph J. Urbancek, *Mathematical Teaching Aids*. Chicago School Journal Supplement, Vol. XXV, Nos. 3–6, 1954.

22. Using mental arithmetic.

23. Finding original methods of solving problems.

24. Making booklets of original problems.

25. Taking responsibility for school banks, stores, party activities, and so forth.

Evaluating Instruction and Curriculum

The quality of instruction is dependent upon the philosophy and objectives of the teacher, school, and community; upon teacher preparation, skill, and willingness and ability to use the finest instructional procedures; upon the curriculum; upon the school facilities; and upon human relations that exist between teachers and pupils, pupils and pupils, teachers and other adults in school and community, and pupils and other adults in school and community. The proof of the success of the arithmetic program must be observed in the behavior of the children. When the program is successful, children show by their behavior that they:

1. Understand the meanings of arithmetic.
2. Compute accurately.
3. Appreciate the usefulness of arithmetic.
4. Enjoy arithmetic.
5. Desire to learn new and increasingly abstract arithmetic procedures.

Evaluating Philosophy and Objectives

In appraising the philosophy and objectives of the teacher, school, and community it will be profitable to consider questions such as those that follow:

1. Do we have a fixed philosophy or is it subject to constant re-evaluation?

2. Do we make the greatest possible use of what we know about the ways in which children learn, grow, and develop?

3. Do we plan our program to meet the needs of groups as well as of individuals within the groups?

4. Do we give the children, teachers, and administrators an opportunity to use their intelligence in making group decisions appropriate to their needs and responsibilities?

5. Do we encourage mutual respect among all concerned in the teaching-learning situation?

6. Do we believe that teachers have the responsibility of becoming increasingly expert in subject matter?

7. Do we believe that teachers must actively guide the learning process?

8. Do we base instructional procedures upon the latest findings of research?

9. Do we believe that every child has the right and obligation to use his intelligence in learning arithmetic?

10. Do we expect every child to do increasingly mature work as he progresses through the school?

Evaluating the Teacher and Teaching Methods

In appraising a teacher's preparation for being a teacher of arithmetic and the methods used, it may be profitable to consider questions such as those that follow:

1. How recently has the teacher had a professional course in arithmetic?

2. Did the course emphasize computation, methods, or a combination of both?

3. How successful was the teacher in meeting the requirements of the course?

4. How recently has the teacher participated in an in-service education activity designed to increase competency in teaching arithmetic?

5. Of what professional organizations is the teacher a member?

6. What professional literature on the subject of arithmetic has been read by the teacher within the past month? Within the past year?

7. How well does the teacher like arithmetic?

8. Does the teacher take time to ensure readiness for a topic before formally introducing it?

9. Does the teacher seem to feel secure when guiding children in their discovery of mathematical principles?

10. What use does the teacher make of multisensory materials?

11. Does the teacher encourage children to think their way through arithmetical situations by asking pertinent questions to guide their thinking?

12. How dependent is the teacher upon the textbook or workbook?

13. Does the teacher encourage the children to ask questions and does she take time to help them clarify their thinking?

14. Does the teacher take time to evaluate the learning process?

15. Does the teacher make provisions for individual differences?

16. Does the teacher help children see socioeconomic applications of ideas learned?

17. Are teacher-made tests designed to determine the level of pupil thinking or to merely determine skill in computation?

Evaluating the Curriculum

The curriculum is the school's plan for creating a living-learning environment in which children have the opportunity to learn arithmetic. In appraising the plan (curriculum), it may be profitable to consider questions such as those that follow:

1. Is there a written arithmetic curriculum indicating both scope and sequence of the arithmetic program?

2. Is the written curriculum available to all administrators and teachers?

3. How were agreements reached before they were embodied in the written curriculum?

4. Are the teachers generally agreed on the merits of the curriculum plan and do they follow it in their day-to-day teaching?

5. Are the mathematical ideas presented in the curriculum in the correct sequence as determined by the number system; i.e., counting, addition, subtraction, multiplication, and then division?

6. Is the pupil load at each grade level kept within reasonable limits commensurate with the pupils' ability to learn?

7. Is the plan so organized that pupils are given an opportunity to extend their knowledge of each topic as they progress through the grades?

8. Are the more abstract topics deferred to later grades?

9. Are provisions made for the teaching of both the mathematical and social aspects of arithmetic.

10. Is the framework of the curriculum sufficiently broad to allow the teacher to provide experiences that meet the particular needs of the children in her class?

11. Is there a testing program?

12. Are the results of the tests used in planning to meet the needs of individual pupils?

13. What records are kept of pupil progress?

14. What plan has been evolved to inform subsequent teachers of a pupil's success in meeting the demands of the curriculum?

Evaluating School Facilities

Since the learning environment is a determining factor in the quality of learning, it too should be evaluated. Class size, lighting facilities, seating, and similar matters cannot be governed directly by the classroom teacher. The questions that follow relate to aspects of the physical environment more directly under the teacher's control.

1. Is there an arithmetic center that includes multisensory materials?

2. Are books and other reference materials available to the pupils?

3. How closely do the materials in the arithmetic center relate to the topics being taught?

4. How recently has the material in the arithmetic center been changed?

5. How much opportunity are pupils given to use multisensory materials?

6. Are there evidences of the teaching of the social aspects of arithmetic; i.e., a room store, post office, or bank?

7. Is the chalkboard large enough and is it being used to best advantage?

8. Are some of the bulletin board displays an outgrowth of the study of arithmetic?

9. How recently was the material displayed on the bulletin board?

10. Are the children seated so that they can see and hear easily?

11. Are the children encouraged to keep their work space orderly?

Information derived from answering the above and similar questions will prove helpful in determining the facilities of the school and the way in which they are used. When the information is available, it can be used in making desirable changes.

Summary

The curriculum sequence in arithmetic must fit the pattern determined by the number system. Thus it is necessary to begin by teaching number meanings, to proceed to teaching the use of numbers in counting, to teach the use of the number system in writing numbers, and to then teach in sequence the following topics: addition, subtraction, multiplication, and division. The number system also can be a determining factor for curriculum planners who must decide upon the sequence to follow in teaching addition, subtraction, multiplication, and division. The examples in each of the four fundamental operations can be arranged in series from simple to complex. This arrangement, determined by the number system, indicates the order in which examples should be presented.

But the curriculum in arithmetic must also fit the needs of the learners and of the society in which they live. Children in primary grades need to know how to use the four fundamental operations if they are to cope successfully with their day-to-day problems, which can usually be solved by using the simpler examples in each of the fundamental operations. As the children become more mature they will need to use the more complex examples. They may never have occasion to use the most complex examples in solving day-to-day problems, but they need to learn the complex examples to be able to master problems that may confront them in later years.

The general topics presented at each grade level are substantially the same. But at each succeedingly higher grade level, increasingly more complex material is presented.

Teachers are urged to reach agreements as to the mathematics vocabulary they will use when working with the pupils. They are also urged to agree upon the wording of the mathematical questions asked by the various examples and to be consistent in the instructional procedures used in various classes.

There are numerous methods of meeting individual differences. All children can be expected to learn to use effectively the simpler examples and to solve the simpler problems that develop out of each of the various topics. Teachers must accept the responsibility of challenging the rapid achievers to do increasingly mature and abstract thinking.

Evaluation of the curriculum, of instruction, of school facilities and the use made of them, and of other aspects of the arithmetic program should be a continuous process. The entire staff can use the results of the evaluation when working together to improve the program of the school.

SUGGESTED QUESTIONS FOR STUDY

1. What are the arguments for and against a planned arithmetic curriculum?

2. What reasons can you give to explain why a subject such as fractions might be introduced to children in the lower grades?

3. What are some reasons for deferring complex arithmetic examples and processes until later grades?

4. What are some advantages and disadvantages of deferring the teaching of percentage until the seventh grade?

5. What reasons can you give to explain the failure of arithmetic programs designed to teach arithmetic solely through incidental number experiences?

6. How would you help children develop a suitable arithmetic vocabulary?

7. What steps might be taken to determine the mathematical and experiential background of the children?

8. What steps might be taken to meet the needs of the slow learner? of the average learner? of the rapid learner?

9. What steps can teachers take to insure the teaching of minimal essentials in each topic at each grade level?

10. What are some effective ways to measure pupil growth in arithmetic?

11. What can be done to help children develop responsibility for self-evaluation in arithmetic?

SUGGESTED ACTIVITIES

1. Secure arithmetic sequence charts available from the publishers of widely used arithmetic series. Select various topics and compare the charts to find:

(*a*) The grade level where the topic is introduced.

(*b*) How much new material is introduced at succeeding grade levels.

(*c*) The grade level at which the pupil is assumed to have mastered the topic.

2. Compare a modern arithmetic series with a series published prior to 1940 to find the grade level in each at which:

(*a*) Division is introduced.

(*b*) Children are expected to know the division facts.

(*c*) Multiplication of fractions is taught.

(*d*) Division of fractions is taught.

(*e*) Percentage is introduced.

3. Compare the modern and older series of texts to find which gives greater emphasis to topics such as: (*a*) square root, (*b*) metric system, (*c*) drill exercises.

4. Prepare a list of arithmetic projects appropriate for fast achievers in a fifth grade class.

5. Prepare a list of diagnostic techniques appropriate to use with sixth grade pupils.

SELECTED REFERENCES

1. Brueckner, Leo J., and Grossnickle, Foster E., *How to Make Arithmetic Meaningful.* Philadelphia: John C. Winston Company, 1947, p. 513.

2. ______, *Making Arithmetic Meaningful.* Philadelphia: John C. Winston Company, 1953.

3. Buckingham, Burdette R., *Elementary Arithmetic: Its Meaning and Practice.* Boston: Ginn & Company, 1947.

4. Cutts, Norma E., and Moseley, Nicholas, *Bright Children.* New York: G. P. Putnam's Sons, 1955.

5. Dyer, Henry S., Kalin, Robert, and Lord, Frederic M., *Problems in Mathematical Education.* Princeton, N. J.: Educational Testing Service, 1956.

6. Glennon, Vincent J., and Hunnicutt, C. W., *What Does Research Say About Arithmetic?* Washington, D. C.: Association for Supervision and Curriculum Development, 1952.

7. Hutcheson, Ruth, Mantor, Edna, and Homburg, Marjorie, *The Elementary School Mathematics Library.* Washington, D. C.: National Council of Teachers of Mathematics, 1956.

8. Kough, Jack, and DeHaan, Robert F., *Teacher's Guidance Handbook, Part 1,* Identifying Children Who Need Help. Chicago: Science Research Associates, Inc., 1955.

9. Lindsey, Margaret, Beery, Althea, Deans, Edwina, and Martin, Frances K., *The Three R's in the Elementary School.* Washington, D. C.: Association for Superivision and Curriculum Development, 1952.

10. McWilliams, Earl M., and Brown, Kenneth E., *The Superior Pupil in Junior High School Mathematics.* Washington, D. C.: U. S. Department of Health, Education and Welfare.

11. Morton, R. L., *What Research Says to the Teacher, Teaching Arithmetic.* Washington, D. C.: National Education Association, 1953.

12. Scheifele, Marian, *The Gifted Child in the Regular Classroom.* New York: Bureau of Publications, Teachers College, Columbia University, 1953.

13. Shane, Harold G., and McSwain, E. T., *Evaluation and the Elementary Curriculum.* New York: Henry Holt and Company, Inc., 1951.

14. Spitzer, Herbert F., *The Teaching of Arithmetic,* 2d ed. Boston: Houghton Mifflin Company, 1954.

15. Ulrich, Louis E., Sr., *Streamlining Arithmetic.* Chicago: Lyons & Carnahan, 1943.

16. Urbancek, Joseph J., *Mathematical Teaching Aids.* Chicago School Journal Supplement, Vol. XXV, Nos. 3–6, 1954.

14

Basic Vocabulary Mathematical Meanings and Principles

Introduction

The language and system of arithmetic consist of words or names in addition to numbers and computation symbols. Correct interpretation of the basic words contributes to meaning and accuracy in thinking, problem solving, and computation. A specific meaning has been adopted for each word or term in arithmetic.

Teachers are cognizant of the importance of a meaningful vocabulary in reading and communication. Equally significant is the learning of a meaningful vocabulary in arithmetic. For example, when pupils have learned the mental process used in addition, they should have learned the names and correct meanings of the terms "addend," "sum," "partial sums," and "substitution."

Teachers should introduce concrete situations and materials to help pupils discover and learn the correct meaning of each word or term when it is first encountered. Pupils will experience little difficulty in naming the word or term and in learning the meaning when they have the means to discover its proper meaning.

Pupils should be motivated to keep a record of the words and terms previously learned and record new words as they use them and have discovered their mathematical meaning. At appropriate periods pupils should review to strengthen their understanding of words and terms previously learned. The correct spelling of terms with many letters should be adapted to the maturity level and academic ability of each pupil. In situations where pupils need to write a word and have not yet learned how to spell it correctly, they should apply the practice of referring to their cumulative vocabulary list.

Interest in and acceptance of responsibility for correct interpretation and use of the vocabulary in arithmetic may be fostered by: (1) frequent class discussion of words and terms that have been learned, (2) individual interviews when the teacher asks the pupil to express orally his interpretation of the meaning of certain words and terms, (3) collecting out-of-school material to illustrate the practical use of words and terms, (4) class periods in which pupils construct drawings to show their interpretation of words and terms they have learned from their work in arithmetic. It is reasonable to assume that all pupils on completion of the elementary school should have learned and should be able to use correctly the meaning of the words in the basic vocabulary as prepared by the authors of this book.

Basic Vocabulary in Arithmetic

Word	*Meaning*
1. *Abacus*	An instrument used in counting. It consists of beads or balls that move on a rod or wire set in a frame. Each rod or wire represents a specific place value; each bead or ball represents one unit.
2. *Abstract Number*	A number that expresses a specific amount without reference to any objects or quantity of things.
3. *Add*	A mathematical and mental process used to group two or more numbers and to express the total amount with one number.

4. *Addend*	A number to be added to another number. Each number in a set of numbers to be added is an addend.
5. *Addition*	A mathematical and mental process used to find without counting the total value or amount of two or more addends.
6. *Addition Facts*	The 81 primary combinations in addition that show the sum of 2 one-place numbers, i.e., $3 + 4 = 7$, $8 + 5 = 13$. There are 36 addition facts with a sum under 10, and 45 addition facts with a sum of 10 or more.
7. *Altitude*	A perpendicular line drawn from the vertex of the angle that is opposite the base of a triangle to the base.
8. *Amount*	The total of two or more objects. The total or sum of two or more numbers. The total of a given quantity.
9. *Angle*	A geometric figure formed by two lines that meet at a point.
10. *Arabic Numerals*	The nine digits or figures used in the Hindu-Arabic number system. 1, 2, 3, 4, 5, 6, 7, 8, 9. The symbol, 0, or zero is used to express the absence of a digit in a place-value position.
11. *Are*	A metric measure that equals 100 square meters. It is equivalent to 119.6 square yards.
12. *Area*	The amount of a surface when measured by a selected square unit of measure. It is found by multiplying the number of square units in the base line by the number of rows expressed by the height or width.
13. *Binary System*	A number system with place-value positions based on two and multiples of two. The system uses the digit 1 and the symbol 0.

14. *Cardinal Number*	A number that answers the question, "How many in all?" It expresses the total amount of units in a given group.
15. *Centimeter*	A unit of measure in the metric system that equals in length $\frac{1}{100}$ (.01) meter.
16. *Circle*	A closed curved line; every point on the line is equally distant from a point within that is called the center.
17. *Circumference*	A line that goes around or encloses a circular surface. It may be thought of as the perimeter of a circular area.
18. *Commission*	The rate or percent given to a person for a sale or service. Also the amount received by an agent for selling something or a service.
19. *Common Denominator*	A denominator that is the same for two or more fractions. It expresses a common size for the fractional units.
20. *Common Fraction*	A mathematical symbol or number to express one or more equal fractional units of a quantity, or one or more units of a given group of like units.
21. *Computation*	A mathematical and mental process used to find the answer to a given example or question.
22. *Concrete Number*	A number that represents a unit or units of specific objects or quantity.
23. *Cost*	The amount paid for an object or a service a person desires to obtain.
24. *Cube*	A rectangular solid bound by six equal squares or square surfaces.
25. *Decade Combination*	A combination of a two place-value number and a one place-value number.
26. *Decimal Fraction*	A fraction with a denominator of 10 or a power of 10.
27. *Decimal Number System*	A number system with place-value positions based on 10 and powers of 10. It employs the use of 9 digits and the symbol for zero.

28. *Decimal Point* — A symbol used to separate the place value one from the place value one-tenth. It does not identify the value of a decimal fraction or a mixed decimal.

29. *Decimeter* — A unit of measure in the metric system that is equal in length to $\frac{1}{10}$ (.1) meter.

30. *Degree* — A unit for measuring an angle or temperature.

31. *Denominate Number* — A number that expresses a unit or units of measure.

32. *Denominator* — A number that is written below the numerator of a common fraction to show the number of equal divisions made of one or any object or quantity. It names the fraction. In a decimal fraction, the denominator is shown by the use of one or more place-value positions.

33. *Diameter* — A straight line connecting two points on a circle, which passes through the center and divides the circle in half.

34. *Digit* — Any one of the numerals used in the Hindu-Arabic number systems, 1, 2, 3, 4, 5, 6, 7, 8, 9.

35. *Divide* — To change into two or more equal pieces or parts.

36. *Dividend* — A number that is to be regrouped into numbers equal to the number that is the divisor. It is similar to the product in multiplication.

37. *Division* — A mathematical and mental process used to change the dividend into numbers like the divisor. Also a process to find one of two factors when their product and one of the factors are known.

38. *Division Combinations or Facts* — A division combination is an example where the dividend is either a one- or two-place-value number and the divisor is a one-place-value number. There are 81 division facts or combinations.

39. *Divisor*	A number that shows the size of the numbers desired when the dividend is regrouped. It may be used to show the number of equal groups into which the dividend is to be divided so as to find the amount or size of each equal group. It is similar to the multiplicand in multiplication.
40. *Duodecimal Number System*	A number system based on place-value positions of 12 or powers of 12. The digits are 1, 2, 3, 4, 5, 6, 7, 8, 9, *T*, *E*. The symbol 0 is used to show absence of a digit in any place-value position.
41. *Equation*	A mathematical statement to show that two quantitative or numerical expressions are equal.
42. *Exact Number*	A number that represents the true amount or value of a given quantity; or shows the exact amount of units in a given group.
43. *Exponent*	An index number written above a number to show the power of the number. It is a number that is attached to a given factor to show how many times it is repeated.
44. *Face Value of a Number*	The collective meaning of the digits in a number as written in one or more place-value positions.
45. *Foot*	A unit of measure that is equivalent in length to 12 inches.
46. *Formula*	A short way to write a mathematical rule or a statement of a problem.
47. *Fraction*	A mathematical symbol to show the number of fractional units and their size in relation to any given base (object, group, or number).
48. *Fractional Unit*	A unit of quantity derived from a base that has been divided into a given number of even divisions.

49. *Frequency*	An expression of the number of units shown by a digit in any given place-value position.
50. *Gram*	A unit of measure in the metric system equal to the weight of 1 cubic centimeter of pure water.
51. *Improper Fraction*	A number with a numerical value equal to or greater than one.
52. *Inch*	A unit of linear measure that is equal in length to $\frac{1}{12}$ foot.
53. *Integer*	A counting number, a whole number, or a natural number.
54. *Interest*	The money paid on money borrowed or the money earned on money invested.
55. *Kilogram*	A unit of measure in the metric system that is equal in weight to 1000 grams.
56. *Kiloliter*	A unit of measure in the metric system that is equal in capacity or volume to 1000 liters.
57. *Kilometer*	A unit of measure in the metric system that is equal in length to 1000 meters.
58. *Least Common Denominator*	A number that is the same or common for two or more fractions and expresses the smallest size common to each fraction.
59. *Like Fractions*	Fractions that have a like or the same denominator.
60. *Liter*	A unit of measure in the metric system that is equal in capacity to 1000 cubic centimeters.
61. *Measurement*	A system of measures. Also the measured size, capacity, or amount of a given quantity.
62. *Meter*	A unit of measure in the metric system to measure length. The base unit in the metric system.
63. *Metric System*	A scientific system of measurement with a decimal scale. The primary units are meter, liter, gram.

64. *Mixed Number* — A number that contains an integer and a fraction. The sum of an integer and a fraction.

65. *Multiplicand* — One of a given number of like numbers to be grouped and the product notated by one number.

66. *Multiplication* — A mathematical and mental process of rapid addition of a given number of like numbers.

67. *Multiplier* — A number that shows how many like numbers are to be grouped or added and the product notated by one number.

68. *Multiply* — A mathematical and mental process to find the product of a given number of like numbers and to notate the sum with one number.

69. *Notation* — A way to express the amount of a given quantity by written number symbols.

70. *Number* — A mathematical symbol or symbols to show the idea of total amount of a quantity or total units in a group. It possesses place value and face value.

71. *Numeration* — A way to express the amount of a given quantity in number words. It is also a way of reading numbers.

72. *Numerator* — The number of a fraction that expresses the number of fractional units being considered.

73. *Obtuse Angle* — An angle that is larger than a right angle but smaller than a straight angle.

74. *Ordinal Number* — A number used to show the position of an object or a number in an established series.

75. *Ounce* — A unit of measure equal to 1/16 pound in common weight.

76. *Percent* — A word and a sign, %, to express hundredths. It is derived from the Latin words, *per centum.*

77. *Perimeter*	The sum of the length of the sides of a surface plane. The outer boundary of a plane.
78. *Pi* π	A Greek word and symbol to express the constant relationship between the diameter and circumference of a circle.
79. *Pint*	A unit of measure of capacity equal to $\frac{1}{8}$ gallon.
80. *Place Holder*	A mathematical symbol to show the absence of a digit in a place-value position.
81. *Place Value*	An ordered position in the number system with a numerical value determined by the radix of the system.
82. *Pound*	A unit of measure in the United States system equal to 16 ounces.
83. *Product*	The total amount of a given number of equal addends.
84. *Proper Fraction*	A fraction when the denominator is a number larger than the numerator.
85. *Proportion*	A mathematical statement expressing the equality between two ratios.
86. *Pure Decimal Fraction*	A decimal fraction that has a numerical value of less than one.
87. *Quart*	A unit of measure in the United States system of measures equal in capacity to $\frac{1}{4}$ gallon or 2 pints.
88. *Quinary Number System*	A number system with a radix or place-value position of 5 and powers of 5. The digits are 1, 2, 3, 4, and the symbol, 0.
89. *Quotient*	The number of equal groups or numbers when the dividend is divided into numbers equal to the number that is the divisor.
90. *Radix*	The base or place-value scale used in a number system. The radix of the decimal system is 10.

91. *Ratio*	A mathematical expression of the relationship between quantities or numbers. Also the quotient of one number divided by another number.
92. *Reciprocal*	The reciprocal of any number is 1 divided by the number.
93. *Rectangle*	A surface plane bounded by four straight lines, the opposite sides of equal length and parallel, and each angle is a right angle.
94. *Remainder*	A quantity or number when a given part has been removed. Also the number left in uneven division.
95. *Right Angle*	An angle formed by two lines that are perpendicular to each other. A right angle is 90 degrees.
96. *Right Triangle*	A triangle that contains a right angle.
97. *Roman Numerals*	The numerals used in writing numbers in the Roman system of notation.
98. *Rounded Off Number*	A large number expressed by two or three significant digits. The rounded number is less exact; it is an approximate number.
99. *Significant Digits*	The digits in a number that show the accuracy of the number. Also the digits that remain in rounding off a number.
100. *Square*	A flat surface that has four equal sides and four right angles. Also the product of a number multiplied by itself.
101. *Square Foot*	The area of a square that has four sides, each equal in length to 1 foot. A unit to measure surface area.
102. *Square Inch*	The area of a square with each of the four sides equal to 1 inch. A unit to measure surface area.
103. *Square Root*	A number that is one of the two equal factors of a number.

104. *Square Yard* — The area of a square that has four sides, each equal in length to 1 yard. A unit to measure surface area.

105. *Substitution* — In addition and multiplication, substitution is the mental process used to substitute one unit in the next higher place-value position for ten units in a given place-value position, i.e., $8 \times 7 = 5$ tens and 6 ones—$7 + 7 = 1$ ten and 4 ones. In subtraction and division, substitution is the mental process used to substitute ten units in the next lower place-value position for one unit in a given place-value position, i.e., $34 - 17 = 2$ tens $+ 14$ ones —1 ten and 7 ones.

$8\overline{)176} = 8\overline{)16 \text{ tens} + 16 \text{ ones}}.$

In reduction of fractions it is a process used to substitute higher terms for lower terms or lower terms for higher terms $\left(\frac{3}{4} \text{ or } \frac{6}{8} \quad \frac{6}{9} \text{ or } \frac{2}{3}\right)$.

106. *Subtraction* — A mathematical and mental process used to find the difference between two numbers or to find the remaining number when a component number is known.

107. *Subtrahend* — A number in subtraction that identifies one of the given component numbers of a given number.

108. *Sum* — An amount of a given quantity of like objects or like quantities. A number that expresses the total amount of given numbers when added.

109. *Take-Away* — A method in a physical situation to remove a part from a given quantity. Correctly used, the take-away process applies only to physical quantities.

110. *Time* — Continuous movement. Also a system of measures to express the relation between the movement of the earth and the sun.

111. *Ton*	A unit of weight in the United States that is equal to 2000 pounds.
112. *Total*	The whole or entire amount of a quantity or quantities. The number that expresses the sum of any given number of addends.
113. *Trial Divisor*	The digit in the divisor that is in the place-value position of greatest value. Dividing by a trial divisor is the same as dividing by a one-place divisor.
114. *Triangle*	A surface figure or plane that has three sides and three angles. The sum of the three angles is always 180 degrees.
115. *Unit of Measure*	Any one of the standard units used in determining the measure or amount of a given quantity or magnitude.
116. *Unlike Fractions*	Fractions that do not have a common or like denominator; fractions of unequal fractional units.
117. *Volume*	The measure of the space of a solid. The number of units of volume in the space of a solid. Volume is measured by cubic units of measure.
118. *Weight*	The amount of heaviness of an object or quantity. Also the measurement of the force with which a body is attracted toward the earth.
119. *Whole Number*	A counting or natural number. A number having a specific number property. Whole numbers are also called integers.
120. *Yard*	A unit of measure in the English and United States systems used to measure length. It is equal in length to 3 feet or to 36 inches.
121. *Zero*	A mathematical symbol, 0, used in notation to show the absence of a digit in any place-value positions.

A Summary of Mathematical Meanings and Principles

Introduction

Pupils who have learned the meaning of numbers, place-value system, and the computational processes should be provided guidance and exercises that will enable them to learn important principles and rules by which to extend their ability in abstract computation. On completion of the elementary school, the majority of the pupils should be expected to understand and to be able to apply with accuracy these mathematical principles and rules. The talented pupils in arithmetic may be encouraged to discover the meanings and interrelationships of these mathematical principles, to find more mature applications, and to share their discoveries with other pupils.

The summary of important mathematical principles and rules may be used by teachers to appraise their understanding of each principle or rule. Teachers may find the summary a useful guide when planning the curriculum to meet the different progress levels among the pupils in the class. Pupils should be expected to learn these principles and rules through meaningful interpretation rather than by rote memory. From time to time, teachers should appraise each pupil's understanding by asking the pupil to give an oral explanation of the principle or rule which has been applied during the computation.

In the summary, Part I presents four statements concerning a general interpretation of arithmetic. In Part II, five psychological concepts have been presented, which teachers should understand and apply when planning and sharing instruction in arithmetic. Parts III, IV, V, VI, VII, and VIII include the basic meanings pupils should be expected to discover and learn about the Hindu-Arabic number system; counting; mental computation in addition, subtraction, multiplication, and division; percent and percentage; problem solving; and measurement. Each meaning has been expressed in language that should be easily interpreted by pupils after their interaction with concrete situation and materials.

PART I—An Interpretation of Arithmetic

1. Arithmetic is a man-made language and number system based on mathematical meanings, principles, computational processes, and

terms that are used to think and communicate ideas of quantity and relationship of specific quantities.

2. The Hindu-Arabic system of notation and computation is universally adopted. The system is an ordered series of place-value positions of 1, 10, and powers of 10 and place-value positions to the right of 1 of $\frac{1}{10}$ and multiples of $\frac{1}{10}$.

3. Applied arithmetic is, at all times, for each individual, a mental process involving ideas of quantity, numerical numbers, place-value positions, and computation with numbers.

4. Arithmetic as a languge and numerical system is the quantitative foundation of all mathematics.

PART II—Psychological Concepts Related to Elementary Mathematics

1. There is a one-to-one relationship between concrete quantity and the pupil's mental perception or numerical idea of amount, the number name, and the written or notated number.

2. Each pupil through his interpretation and understanding in elementary mathematics creates and develops his own mental system of arithmetic. The arithmetical system that the pupil develops mentally must be consistent with the decimal number system if he is to experience accuracy and competence in arithmetical thinking and communication.

3. Pupils are aided in discovering and organizing a sequential system of mental arithmetic by working with concrete materials and physical situations under the guidance of teachers. Learning the language and numerical system is a mental process in deriving mathematical concepts from meaningful situations.

4. If pupils are to develop a functional understanding of the mathematical meanings and operations they should have the opportunity to follow a curriculum based on the sequential structure of the number system.

5. Emphasis on rote learning of vocabulary, computation, and abstract rules may prevent pupils from discovering and developing meaningful understandings and skills in arithmetic.

PART III—Important Meanings Related to the Hindu-Arabic or Decimal Number System

A. Integers

1. There is a one-to-one relationship between concrete objects or quantity and numerical ideas and numbers. The mental process is from observed quantity to mental perception, then number names and arithmetical symbols.

2. Any quantity that exists in the environments of pupils and adults can be described as having size, form, and amount.

3. The digits, 1, 2, 3, 4, 5, 6, 7, 8, and 9, are language symbols used to show or notate the number of units in each place-value position of a number 437 or 4 (100) + 3 (10) + 7 (1).

4. The decimal number is a sequence order of value positions or place-values of one, ten, and powers of ten.

Th	*H*	*T*	*O*	
4	4	4	4	= 4444

5. The symbol 0, called zero, is a language symbol used to show, or to notate, the absence of units in any place-value position (507).

6. A notated number in the decimal system represents a numerical organization by which a few digits may be used to show or to notate the idea of a large number of units.

(a) The number 100 shows only one unit with the numerical value of one hundred. One hundred ones cannot be written in the decimal system.

(b) The largest frequency of units that can be expressed in any place-value position is nine. The smallest frequency of units that can be expressed in any place-value position is one.

7. A number may show the amount of a group of objects of like quantity. This is the *cardinal* meaning of a number (15 marbles).

8. A number may show a position in a number series. Thus 24 is the unit position between 23 and 25. This is the *ordinal* meaning of a number. It is notated, 24th.

9. A mental interpretation of amounts of quantity precedes notated or written numbers.

B. Common Fractions

1. Both terms of a common fraction may be multiplied by the same number without changing the value of the fraction.

$\frac{3}{4} = \frac{3 \times 3}{3 \times 4} = \frac{9}{12}$ (Instead of three units there are nine units and each is one-third as large as each of the 3 one-fourths.)

2. Both terms of a common fraction may be divided by the same number without changing the value of the fraction $\left(\frac{8}{16} = \frac{8 \div 8}{16 \div 8} = \frac{1}{2}\right)$. (Instead of eight fractional units there now is one fractional unit, but it is eight times the size of the 8 one-sixteenths.)

3. To substitute a mixed number for an improper fraction, divide the numerator by the denominator ($\frac{21}{5} = 4\frac{1}{5}$).

4. To substitute an improper fraction for a mixed number, multiply the integer by the denominator of the fraction and add the numerator of the fraction; write the sum over the denominator of the fraction.

$$5\frac{2}{3} = \frac{(3 \times 5) + 2}{3} = \frac{17}{3}$$

5. To substitute a decimal fraction for a common fraction, express the numerator in hundredths and divide by the denominator of the common fraction.

$$\frac{1}{4} = \frac{1.00}{4} = .25 \quad \frac{3}{5} = \frac{3(1.00)}{5} = .60 \quad \frac{7}{8} = \frac{7(1.00)}{8} = .87\frac{1}{2}$$

C. Decimal Fractions

1. A decimal fraction is a fraction with a denominator that is one-tenth of one or powers of one-tenth of one (0.4 0.25 0.125 0.0025).

2. The decimal point is a mathematical symbol that is used to separate integers from decimal fractions (7.4 12.25).

3. A mixed decimal is a number that contains an integer and a decimal fraction (8.5 25.75 275.50).

4. To substitute a common fraction for a decimal fraction, write the decimal fraction in the form of a common fraction. Write the numerator of the decimal fraction over the decimal value of the fraction.

$.25 = \frac{25}{100}$ or $\frac{1}{4}$. $.80 = \frac{80}{100}$ or $\frac{4}{5}$. $1.25 = \frac{125}{100} = \frac{5}{4}$

5. Adding a zero or zeros to the right of a decimal fraction or a mixed decimal does not change its value. Only the terms are changed (.25 or .250 8.65 or 8.650).

PART IV—Mental Meanings and Processes Involved in Counting

1. Counting is a mental process of grouping units of quantity by 1's, 2's, 5's, and so forth.

2. The mental process involves $1 + 1 = 2$; and $2 + 1 = 3$; and $3 + 1 = 4$; and $4 + 1 = 5$; and so forth.

3. In counting, the last number expressed stands for all previous units in one group.

4. The greatest frequency of units that can be recorded in any value position is nine. When counting to ten and beyond, 1 ten must be substituted for each 10 ones, 1 hundred must be substituted for each 10 tens, and so on, since no more than nine units can be recorded in each value position in the decimal system.

5. Substitution when counting is a thought process of substituting 1 ten for 10 ones, 1 hundred for 10 tens, 1 thousand for 10 hundreds, and so forth.

PART V—Mathematical Meanings and Thought Processes Involved in Mental Computation

A. Addition—Finding the Sum of Integers

1. Addition is a mental and arithmetical process used to find the sum or total of any given units or addends.

2. Only numbers that represent like things or abstract numbers can be added ($36 \text{ ft} + 48 \text{ ft} = 84 \text{ ft} \quad 75 + 16 = 91$).

3. Addition of integers involves combining the digits in each place-value position and using substitution when the sum of the digits in any place-value position is 10 or more.

4. The addends may be added in any order; however, the sum will be the same ($8 + 4 + 9 + 6 = (4 + 6) + (8 + 9) = 10 + 17 = 27$).

5. To verify the accuracy of the sum, add in the opposite direction.

B. Addition—Finding the Sum of Fractions or Mixed Numbers

1. Only like fractions (fractions with a common denominator) can be added.

2. To add like fractions, add the numerators and write the sum over the like or common denominator ($\frac{2}{3} + \frac{5}{3} = \frac{7}{3} = 2\frac{1}{3}$).

3. To add unlike fractions, or fractions with unlike denominators, first change all fractions to like fractions or fractions with a common denominator; second, add the numerators and write the sum over the common denominator (reduce if desired).

$$\frac{1}{2} + \frac{3}{4} + \frac{2}{3} = \frac{6}{12} + \frac{9}{12} + \frac{8}{12} = \frac{23}{12} \text{ or } 1\frac{11}{12}$$

4. To add mixed numbers: first find the sum of the fractions; second find the sum of the integers; then add the two partial sums.

$$8\frac{3}{4} + 5\frac{1}{2} = 8\frac{3}{4} + 5\frac{2}{4} = (\frac{3}{4} + \frac{2}{4}) + (8 + 5) = \frac{5}{4} + 13 =$$
$$1\frac{1}{4} + 13 = 14\frac{1}{4}.$$

5. To verify the accuracy of the sum, add in the opposite direction.

C. *Addition—Finding the Sum of Decimal Fractions or Mixed Decimals*

1. Only digits in like decimal place-value positions can be added.

.42	84.050	94.055
+.756	+10.207	+18.295
1.176	94.257	112.350

2. To find the sum of two or more decimal fractions or two or more mixed decimals, add the digits in each place-value position. Use substitution when required.

.375	4.002	300.470
.942	7.125	472.384
+.28	+3.5	+146.285
1.597	14.627	919.139

ILLUSTRATIONS

	Integers	*Common Fractions*	*Decimal Fractions*	*Denominate Numbers*
(*a*)	4	$\frac{4}{8}$	.4	4 ft
	+3	$+\frac{3}{8}$	+.3	+3 ft
	?	?	?	?
(*b*)	348	$8\frac{3}{4}$	.348	3 yd 4 ft 8 in.
	+746	$+6\frac{2}{3}$	+.746	+7 yd 4 ft 6 in.
	?	?	?	?

3. To verify the accuracy of the sum add in the opposite direction.

D. Subtraction—Finding the Difference between Integers

1. In any physical or concrete situation subtraction may ask:

(*a*) What is left when a part is removed?

(*b*) How much larger is one quantity than another quantity?

2. In written or notated subtraction, the question is, "What number shows the numerical difference between the subtrahend and the minuend?" To find the answer compare the two numbers to find how much the minuend exceeds the subtrahend.

3. Only numbers that represent like things or abstract numbers can be subtracted (52 lb $-$ 24 lb $=$ 28 lb 400 $-$ 175 $=$ 225).

4. Only the digits in the same place-value position of two numbers can be subtracted. Use substitution when required. In the example 742 $-$ 311 $=$ 431, think, "The difference between 1 one and 2 ones is 1 one. The difference between 1 ten and 4 tens is 3 tens. The difference between 3 hundreds and 7 hundreds is 4 hundreds.

5. The difference between numbers can be computed by thinking a number which, when added to the number that is the subtrahend, will equal the number that is the minuend.

72 $-$ 26 $=$? ? ones and ? tens added to 6 ones and 2 tens $=$ 7 tens and 2 ones.

$$46 + 26 = 72, \qquad 72 - 26 = 46.$$

6. To verify accuracy, add the difference and the subtrahend. The sum should equal the minuend.

E. Subtraction—Finding the Difference Between Fractions

1. Only like fractions, i.e., fractions with identical denominators, can be subtracted ($\frac{7}{8} - \frac{4}{8} = \frac{3}{8}$).

2. To subtract unlike fractions, first substitute for the fractions in the example fractions with like denominators; second, find the difference between the numerators. ($\frac{3}{4} - \frac{3}{8} = \frac{6}{8} - \frac{3}{8} = \frac{3}{8}$).

3. To subtract mixed numbers with unlike denominators: first substitute for them fractions with like denominators; second, find the difference between the numerators. Then find the difference between the integers. ($24\frac{5}{8} - 11\frac{3}{4} = 24\frac{5}{8} - 11\frac{6}{8} = 23\frac{13}{8} - 11\frac{6}{8} = ?\ \frac{13}{8} - \frac{6}{8} = \frac{7}{8}$. $23 - 11 = 12$). Then the difference between $24\frac{5}{8}$ and $11\frac{3}{4}$ is $12\frac{7}{8}$.

4. To verify accuracy in computation, add the subtrahend and the difference. The sum should equal the minuend.

F. Subtraction—Finding the Difference Between Decimal Fractions or Mixed Decimals

1. Only digits in like decimal place-value positions can be subtracted.

2. To find the difference between two decimal fractions or between a mixed decimal and a decimal fraction, or between two mixed decimals, find the difference between the digits in each place-value position.

.75	.80	24.05	9.25
−.34	−.37	−8.96	−.87
.41	.43	15.09	8.38

3. To verify accuracy in computation, add the difference and the subtrahend. The sum should equal the minuend.

ILLUSTRATIONS

	Integers	*Common Fractions*	*Decimal Fractions*	*Denominate Numbers*
(*a*)	8	$\frac{8}{12}$	.8	8 in.
	−6	$-\frac{6}{12}$	−.6	−6 in.
	?	?	?	?
(*b*)	71	$72\frac{2}{3}$	.71	7 ft 1 in.
	−36	$-36\frac{3}{4}$	−.36	−3 ft 6 in.
	?	?	?	?

G. Multiplication—Finding the Product or Total of Integers

1. Multiplication is a rapid process of adding a given number of like value numbers.

2. Only numbers that represent like things or abstract numbers can be multiplied (9 × 7 in. = 63 in. 24 × 15 = 360).

3. The multiplicand shows the numerical value of one of the given numbers. (4 × *8* = 32).

4. The multiplier shows the number of like-value numbers to be combined and the total notated by one number (*7* × 9 = 63).

5. The mental process of multiplying requires the finding of the total or product of the digits in each place-value position.

6. The numbers of the multiplier and the multiplicand can be interchanged without changing the product. The question of the example is changed ($8 \times 7 = 56$ and $7 \times 8 = 56$ 8 sevens = 56 and 7 eights = 56).

7. To multiply a number that is a two-place-value number or larger by a two-place-value or large multiplier, multiply the digits in each place-value position and add the partial products (34×56 = 4 ones × 6 ones = 2 tens and 4 ones; 4 ones × 5 tens = 20 tens + 2 tens = 22 tens or 2 hundreds and 2 tens; 3 tens × 6 ones = 18 tens or 1 hundred and 8 tens; 3 tens × 5 tens = 15 hundreds + 1 hundred = 16 hundreds or 1 thousand and 6 hundreds; $(2H + 2T + 4 \text{ ones}) + (1Th. + 7H + 8T) = 2004$).

8. To multiply an integer by 10, move the decimal point in the multiplicand one place to the right ($10 \times 76 = 760$).

9. To multiply an integer by 100, move the decimal point in the multiplicand two places to the right ($100 \times 84 = 8400$).

10. To multiply an integer by 1000, move the decimal point in the multiplicand three places to the right ($1000 \times 75 = 75{,}000$).

11. To multiply an integer by 50, move the decimal point in the multiplicand two places to the right and then divide by 2($50 \times 486 = \frac{48600}{2} = 24300$).

12. To multiply an integer by 25, move the decimal point in the multiplicand two places to the right and then divide by 4 ($25 \times 385 = \frac{38500}{4} = 9625$).

13. To verify accuracy of the product repeat the multiplication. Another method is to change the position of the multiplier and multiplicand and multiply. The two products should be the same ($24 \times 36 = 864$ $36 \times 24 = 864$).

H. *Multiplication—Finding the Product or Total of Common Fractions or Mixed Numbers*

1. To multiply a fraction by an integer, multiply the numerator of the fraction by the integer and write the product over the denominator of the fraction ($4 \times \frac{3}{8} = \frac{4 \times 3}{8} = \frac{12}{8} = 1\frac{4}{8}$ or $1\frac{1}{2}$).

2. To multiply an integer by a fraction, first change the integer to an improper fraction; second find the product of the denominators; and third, find the product of the numerators. Then write the product over the denominator ($\frac{5}{8} \times 6 = \frac{30}{8} = 3\frac{6}{8}$ or $3\frac{3}{4}$).

3. To multiply a mixed number by a mixed number; first, multiply the fraction in the multiplicand by the fraction in the multiplier; second, multiply the integer in the multiplicand by the fraction in the multiplier; third, multiply the fraction in the multiplicand by the integer in the multiplier; fourth, multiply the integers. Then write the sum of the partial products.

$$2\tfrac{1}{2} \times 8\tfrac{3}{4} = (\tfrac{1}{2} \times \tfrac{3}{4}) + (\tfrac{1}{2} \times 8) + (2 \times \tfrac{3}{4} + (2 \times 8) = 21\tfrac{7}{8}$$

4. To verify the accuracy of the product, repeat the process. Another method is to divide the product by one of the factors. The quotient should be the other factor.

I. Multiplication—Finding a Part of an Integer or a Fraction

This is a different meaning and use of multiplication when the multiplier is a number less than one.

2. The multiplicand may be an integer or a fraction representing a given quantity.

3. The multiplier is a fraction used to ask, "What is a given fraction of an integer or fraction?"

4. The product will be less in value size than the multiplicand.

5. While cancellation is a short cut, it involves a complex abstract process of thinking.

ILLUSTRATIONS

	Integers	*Common Fractions*	*Decimal Fractions*	*Denominate Numbers*
(*a*)	4 ×3 ?	$\frac{4}{5}$ ×3 ?	.4 ×3 ?	.4 inches ×3 ?
(*b*)	75 ×36 ?	$\frac{3}{4}$ ×3 ?	.4 ×3. ?	4 inches ×3 ?
(*c*)	12 ×$\frac{3}{4}$?	$\frac{3}{4}$ ×$\frac{3}{4}$?	.12 ×.75 ?	13 ft ×$\frac{3}{4}$?

J. Division—Finding the Ratio of Integers When the Dividend is Larger Than the Divisor

1. Division in a physical or concrete situtation involves either dividing a quantity into a given number of equal size units (16 ft $\div$ 2) or dividing a quantity into an unknown number of units of known size (16 ft $\div$ 2 ft).

2. Abstract division is the computational process used to find the ratio between the number that is the dividend and the number that is the divisor ($24 \div 8 = 3$; the ratio is 3 to 1).

3. The dividend shows the numerical value of all the equal groups.

4. The divisor shows how many equal groups or how many in each like number.

5. The quotient shows how many numbers of the value size of the divisor are equivalent to the number that is the dividend.

6. Only numbers that represent like things or are abstract numbers can be divided (48 ft $\div$ 8 ft $= 6$; $96 \div 12 = 8$).

7. The dividend is equal to the product of the divisor and the quotient, plus the remainder when the ratio is uneven.

$$28 \div 9 = 3 \text{ and } R1 \qquad 3 \times 9 + R1 = 28$$
$$54 \div 6 = 9 \qquad 9 \times 6 = 54$$

8. To divide a number by 10, move the decimal point one place to the left ($345 \div 10 = 34.5$).

9. To divide a number by 100, move the decimal point two places to the left ($845 \div 100 = 8.45$).

10. To divide a number by 1000 move the decimal point three places to the left ($4697 \div 1000 = 4.697$).

11. To divide a number by 50, move the decimal point two places to the left and multiply by 2 ($464 \div 50 = 2 \times 4.64 = 9.28$).

12. To divide a number by 25, move the decimal point two places to the left and then divide by 4 ($855 \div 25 = 4 \times 8.55 = 34.20$ or 34.2).

13. When the dividend and the divisor are multiplied by the same number, the quotient or ratio will remain the same.

$$(12 \div 4 = 3 \quad (4 \times 12) \div (4 \times 4) = 48 \div 16 = 3$$

14. A number is divisible evenly by 2 when the number ends in 0 or an even digit ($324 \div 2 = 162 \quad 520 \div 2 = 260$).

15. A number is divisible evenly by 3 when the sum of the digits of the number is divisible by 3 ($1452 \div 3 = 484 \quad 12 \div 3 = 4$).

16. A number is divisible evenly by 4, when the digit in the tens place and the digit in the ones place make a number that can be divided by 4 ($3712 \div 4 = 928 \quad 12 \div 4 = 3$).

17. A number is divisible evenly by 5, when the number ends in 0 or 5 ($420 \div 5 = 84 \quad 345 \div 5 = 69$).

18. A number is divisible evenly by 6, when the number is even and the sum of the digits is a number that can be divided by 3 ($1944 \div 6 = 324 \quad 18 \div 3 = 6$).

19. A number is divisible evenly by 8, when the number made by the digits in the hundreds place, tens place, and ones place can be divided by 8 ($82768 \div 8 = 7846 \quad 768 \div 8 = 96$).

20. A number is divisible evenly by 9, when the sum of the digits is a number that can be divided by 9 ($4095 \div 9 = 455 \quad 4 + 9 + 5 = 18 \div 9 = 2$).

21. A number is divisible evenly by 10, when the number ends in 0 ($450 \div 10 = 45$).

22. The average or arithmetic mean of a given number of numbers or addends is computed by finding the sum of the given numbers and then dividing the sum by the total number of addends or numbers.

$$48 + 96 + 95 + 35 = 274. \text{ Arithmetic mean } = \frac{274}{4} = 68\tfrac{1}{2}$$

23. Division may be interpreted as the reverse process of multiplication. Therefore any product is divisible by either of the two factors.

$$9 \times 7 = 63 \qquad 63 \div 7 = 9 \qquad 63 \div 9 = 7$$

24. To verify accuracy in computation, repeat the operation. Another method is to multiply the divisor by the quotient and add any remainder. The product should equal the dividend.

K. Division—Finding the Ratio of Integers When the Dividend is a Number Smaller Than the Divisor

1. A different meaning of division is involved when the dividend is a number smaller than the divisor.

2. The question asked by an example in which the dividend is smaller than the divisor is, "What part of the divisor is equivalent to the dividend?"

3. When the dividend is smaller than the divisor, the quotient will always be less than one.

L. Division—Finding the Ratio of Common Fractions

1. Only like fractions or fractions with a common denominator can be divided ($\frac{7}{8} \div \frac{3}{8} = 7 \div 3 = 2\frac{1}{3}$).

2. To divide two like fractions, find the ratio or quotient between the numerator of the dividend and the numerator of the divisor ($\frac{5}{6} \div \frac{2}{6} = 5\ (\frac{1}{6}) \div 2\ (\frac{1}{6}) = 2\frac{1}{2}$).

3. To divide two unlike fractions, first substitute for the fractions in the example fractions with a like or common denominator. Then divide the numerator of the fraction that is the dividend by the numerator of the fraction that is the divisor.

4. To divide an integer or a mixed number by a fraction: first, change the dividend to an improper fraction; second, change the fractions to like fractions; third, divide the numerator of the dividend by the numerator of the divisor.

5. To divide a mixed number by a mixed number: first, change the two mixed numbers to improper fractions; second, change the fractions to like fractions; third, find the ratio or quotient between the numerator of the fraction that is the dividend and the numerator of the fraction that is the divisor.

6. *Inversion method.* To divide an integer by a fraction, multiply the dividend by the reciprocal of the divisor ($8 \div \frac{3}{4} = 8 \times \frac{4}{3} = \frac{32}{3} = 10\frac{2}{3}$).

7. *Inversion method.* To divide a fraction by a fraction, multiply the dividend by the reciprocal of the divisor ($\frac{7}{8} \div \frac{3}{4} = \frac{7}{8} \times \frac{4}{3} = \frac{28}{24} = 1\frac{4}{24}$ or $1\frac{1}{6}$).

8. *Inversion method.* To divide a fraction, or an integer, or a mixed number by a fraction, multiply the dividend by the reciprocal of the divisor.

$$\frac{3}{4} \div \frac{2}{3} = \frac{3}{4} \times \frac{3}{2} = \frac{9}{8} \text{ or } 1\frac{1}{8}$$
$$8\frac{1}{2} \div \frac{5}{6} = \frac{17}{2} \times \frac{6}{5} = \frac{102}{10} = 10\frac{1}{5}$$

9. To verify accuracy in computation, repeat the process. Another method is to multiply the divisor by the quotient and add the remainder. The product should equal the dividend.

M. Division—Finding the Ratio of Decimal Fractions and Mixed Decimals

1. To divide a decimal fraction or a mixed decimal by an integer, place the decimal point in the quotient directly above the decimal point in the dividend. Then divide as with integers.

$$\begin{array}{r} .22 \\ 8\overline{)1.76} \end{array} \qquad \begin{array}{r} 23.49 \\ 36\overline{)845.64} \end{array}$$

2. To divide a decimal fraction or a mixed decimal by a decimal fraction, multiply both divisor and dividend by a power of 10 that changes the divisor to an integer; then divide as with integers.

$$\begin{array}{r} 5 \\ .5\overline{)2.5} \end{array} \qquad \begin{array}{r} 3\ 25.2 \\ .24\overline{)78.04\ 0} \end{array} \qquad \begin{array}{r} 5.9 \\ .8\overline{)4.7\ 2} \end{array}$$

3. In division of decimal fractions when the divisor is larger than the dividend, the quotient will always be a decimal fraction. The quotient will show what decimal part of the divisor equals the dividend.

$$\begin{array}{r} .5 \\ .4\overline{).2} \end{array} \qquad \begin{array}{r} .5 \\ 2.4\overline{)1.2} \end{array} \qquad \begin{array}{r} .08 \\ 125\overline{)10.00} \end{array}$$

4. To verify accuracy in computation with division repeat the mental process. Another method is to multiply the divisor by the quotient and add the remainder. The product should be a number equal to the dividend.

ILLUSTRATIONS

	Integers	*Common Fractions*	*Decimal Fractions*	*Denominate Numbers*
(*a*)	$\begin{array}{r} ? \\ 49\overline{)98} \end{array}$	$2\frac{2}{3} \div \frac{1}{2} = ?$	$\begin{array}{r} ? \\ .5\overline{)2.75} \end{array}$	2 ft 9 in. ÷ 6 in.
(*b*)	$\begin{array}{r} ? \\ 24\overline{)18.} \end{array}$	$1\frac{1}{2} \div 3\frac{3}{4} = ?$	$\begin{array}{r} ? \\ 6\overline{).3} \end{array}$	9 in. ÷ 36 in. = ?

PART VI—Percent and Percentage

1. Percent serves an important mathematical function in business and industry as well as other fields.

2. Percent is derived from the Latin, *per centum*, which means by hundredths.

3. Percent has the numerical value of 1 one-hundredth of one.

4. The percent sign, %, is a business symbol used to show or notate hundredths.

5. 1 is equivalent to 100%. 4 is equivalent to 400%. .125 is equivalent to 12 $\frac{1}{2}$% or 12.5%. .75 is equivalent to 75%.

6. The business questions answered by the application of percent are:

(*a*) What is a given percent of a number? (8% × 72 = ?)

(*b*) A given number is what percent of another given number? (4 is what % of 16?)

(*c*) A given percentage is a given percent of what number? (8 is 25% of what number?)

PART VII—Problem Solving

1. The most commonly experienced kinds of problems are:

(*a*) Real or life problems.

(*b*) Vicarious or verbal problems.

(*c*) Teacher- and pupil-prepared problems.

2. The abilities required to solve verbal problems are:

(*a*) Reflective reading of the problem properly to interpret the problem situation.

(*b*) Careful examination of the problem situation to find:

(1) What is known.

(2) What question or questions are asked.

(*c*) Selecting an appropriate computational process to find the answer.

(*d*) Estimating a reasonable answer.

(*e*) Computing to find the correct answer.

(*f*) Proving the accuracy of the results of computation.

PART VIII—Measures and Measurement

1. Any quantity may be measured.

2. The measurement of any given quantity is found by selecting an appropriate unit of measure and then applying it to the given quantity.

3. Measures are denominate numbers. They represent approximate numbers.

4. Linear units of measure are used to find amount of length.

5. Square units of measure are used to find the amount of area of a surface.

6. Cubic units of measure are used to find the amount of volume.

7. The metric system of measure is a scientific decimal system.

8. In the metric system the three basic units of measure are meter, liter, and gram.

9. The prefixes used with the three basic units are as follows:

Greek Prefix		*Latin Prefix*	
kilo	1000	deci	.1
hecto	100	centi	.01
deca	10	milli	.001

10. The prefixes are used with the three basic units as indicated in the table below.

Km	Hm	Dm	meter	dm	cm	mm
Kl	Hl	Dl	liter	dl	cl	ml
Kg	Hg	Dg	gram	dg	cg	mg

11. Some common equivalents are given below.

Meter	= 39.37 inches
Centimeter	= 0.3937 inch
Inch	= 2.54 centimeters
Yard	= 0.9144 meter
Mile	= 1.6093 kilometers
Liquid quart	= 0.946 liter
Liter	= 1.0567 liquid quarts
Kilogram	= 2.2046 pounds
Foot	= 0.3048 meter
Kilometer	= 0.62137 mile

Summary

The language of arithmetic when well taught and properly learned permits accurate communication of ideas of quantity because each word or term has a precise mathematical meaning. Special emphasis needs to be placed upon vocabulary development whenever a new process is introduced. Pupils have little difficulty in learning to use the correct words provided they are taught in situations that make sense to them. In the early stages of learning, being able to recognize the words when heard or when seen on the printed page is of far more importance than being able to spell them correctly.

The mathematical principles and rules of computation are relatively few in number. They serve as guides to pupils when deciding what computation to use and how to use it. The principles and rules are best learned in situations that have meaning to the learner.

Teachers who know and understand the mathematical principles, meanings, and thought processes will use them as a guide in planning the curriculum to meet the needs of the pupils. The sequential nature of arithmetic dictates the sequence in which the new arithmetic skills should be taught. When the correct sequence is followed, pupils are able to apply to each new topic those principles and meanings previously learned.

SUGGESTED QUESTIONS FOR TEACHER SELF-EVALUATION

1. Why must teachers agree upon the meanings of arithmetic words that they plan to teach to pupils?

2. How can pupils be helped to develop a meaningful vocabulary in arithmetic?

3. What meaning do you attach to each of these words: addend, sum, partial sum, substitution, subtrahend, multiplicand, divisor?

4. What is the relationship among the sum in addition, the minuend in subtraction, the product in multiplication, and the dividend in division?

5. Why is it correct to call artithmetic a "mental process"?

6. What are the digits?

7. What is the significance of the symbol 0?

8. Why is it impossible to write 100 ones in the decimal system?

9. What ideas of quantity are expressed by a proper fraction? By an improper fraction?

10. What steps are involved in substituting an improper fraction for a mixed number.

11. What steps are involved in substituting a decimal fraction for a common fraction?

12. In counting, what does the last number expressed really represent?

13. What principles learned in the addition of integers can be applied to the addition of common fractions? Of decimal fractions?

14. In what ways does the subtraction of integers differ from the subtraction of common fractions?

15. Why is it correct to say that the subtraction of notated integers, common fractions, or decimal fractions involves finding the difference?

16. What principles learned in the multiplication of integers can be applied to multiplying a common fraction or decimal fraction by an integer?

17. When the multiplier is a fraction, what thought processes are used in the multiplication of an integer? of a common fraction?

18. What does the dividend represent?

19. What two different ideas may be represented by the divisor?

20. What principles learned in the division of integers can be applied to the division of fractions when the like fraction method is used?

21. What ideas are used in dividing fractions when the inversion method is used?

22. What abilities are used in problem solving?

23. What are advantages of the metric system of measures?

SUGGESTED ACTIVITIES

1. Make illustrations to show your interpretation of these words: altitude, angle, arc, obtuse angle, right triangle, radius.

2. Prepare a list of mathematical principles applicable to both addition and multiplication.

3. Prepare a list of mathematical principles applicable to both addition and subtraction of integers.

4. Prepare a list of mathematical principles applicable to both multiplication and division of integers.

5. Interview several pupils (or fellow students) to find their interpretation of the meaning of each of the following: counting, addition, subtraction, multiplication, division, fractions. If their interpretation is faulty, prepare questions to ask them to help them clarify their thinking.

SELECTED REFERENCES

1. Brumfiel, Charles, "Definitions in Arithmetic," *The Arithmetic Teacher*, Vol. III, No. 5 (November, 1956): 192–196.

2. Brune, Irvin H., "Language in Mathematics," *The Learning of Mathematics. Its Theory and Practice*, Twenty-First Yearbook of the National Council of Teachers of Mathematics. Washington, D. C.: The National Council of Teachers of Mathematics, 1953, pp. 156–191.

3. Buckingham, B. R., *Elementary Arithmetic, Its Meaning and Practice.* Boston: Ginn & Company, 1947.

4. Dantzig, T. *Number: The Language of Science.* (3d ed.) New York: The Macmillan Company, 1939.

Bibliography

Books

Allen, Frederick, *The Big Change*. New York: Harper Brothers, 1952. Pp. 308.

Bell, E. T., *The Development of Mathematics*. New York: McGraw-Hill Book Company, Inc., 1945.

Bendick, Jeanne, *How Much and How Many*. New York: McGraw-Hill Book Company, Inc., 1947. Pp. 182.

Boole, M. E. *Preparation of the Child for Science*. Oxford University Press, New York, 1904.

Boyer, L. E., *Introduction to Mathematics for Teachers*. New York: Henry Holt and Company, Inc., 1945. Pp. 478.

Brownell, William A., *The Development of Children's Number Ideas in the Primary Grades*. Chicago: University of Chicago Press, 1928.

Buckingham, Burdette R., *Elementary Arithmetic: Its Meaning and Practice*. Boston: Ginn & Company, 1947. Pp. 744.

Brueckner, Leo J., and Guy L. Bond, *The Diagnosis and Treatment of Learning Difficulties*. New York: Appleton-Century-Crofts, Inc., 1955. Pp. 424.

Brueckner, Leo J., and Foster E. Grossnickle, *Making Arithmetic Meaningful*. Philadelphia: John C. Winston Company, 1953. Pp. 570.

Clark, J. R., and L. K. Eads, *Guiding Arithmetic Learnings*. Yonkers, N. Y.: World Book Company, 1954.

Conant, L. L., *The Number Concept*. New York: The Macmillan Company, 1923.

Dantzig, Tobias, *Number: The Language of Science* (3rd ed.). New York: The Macmillan Company, 1939.

Dewey, John, *How We Think*. Boston: D. C. Heath and Company, 1933.

Drucker, Peter F., *America's Next Twenty Years*. New York: Harper & Brothers, 1957.

Educational Policies Commission. *Manpower and Education*. Washington, D. C.: National Education Association, 1956.

Friend, Newton, *Numbers: Fun and Fact*. New York: Charles Scribner's Sons, 1954. Pp. 208.

Glennon, V. J., and C. W. Hunnicutt, *What Does Research Say About Arithmetic?* Washington, D. C.: Association for Supervision and Curriculum Development, N.E.A., 1952. Pp. 45.

Harding, Lowry W., *Arithmetic for Child Development.* Dubuque, Iowa: Wm. C. Brown Company, 1957. Pp. 196.

Hayakawa, S. I., *Language in Action.* New York: Harcourt, Brace and Company, Inc., 1941. Pp. 341.

Hickerson, J. Allen, *Guiding Children's Arithmetic Experiences.* Englewood Cliffs, N. J.: Prentice-Hall, Inc., 1952.

Hogben, Lancelot, *The Wonderful World of Mathematics.* New York: Garden City Books, 1955. Pp. 69.

Hooper, Alfred, *The River Mathematics.* New York: Henry Holt and Company, Inc., 1945. Pp. 401.

Johnson, Wendell, *People in Quandaries.* New York: Harper & Brothers, 1946.

Karpinski, L. C., *The History of Arithmetic.* Chicago: Rand-McNally & Company, 1925.

Larsen, Harold D., *Arithmetic for Colleges.* New York: The Macmillan Company, 1950. Pp. 275.

Leaf, Munro, *Arithmetic Can Be Fun.* Philadelphia: J. B. Lippincott Company, 1949.

Lee, Irving J., *Language Habits in Human Affairs.* New York: Harper & Brothers, 1941. Pp. 278.

Lieber, Hugh G., and Lillian Lieber, *The Education of T. C. Mitts.* New York: W. W. Norton & Company, Inc., 1944. Pp. 229.

Logsdon, Mayme T., *A Mathematician Explains.* Chicago: University of Chicago Press, 1935.

Morton, Robert Lee, *Teaching Children Arithmetic.* Morristown, N. J.: Silver Burdett Company, 1953. Pp. 556.

Mueller, Francis J., *Arithmetic: Its Structure and Concepts.* Englewood Cliffs, N. J.: Prentice-Hall, Inc., 1956. Pp. 280.

National Council of Teachers of Mathematics, *Arithmetic in General Education.* (Sixteenth Yearbook). Washington, D. C.: National Council of Teachers of Mathematics. Pp. 348.

National Council of Teachers of Mathematics, *The Metric System of Weight and Measures* (Twentieth Yearbook). Washington, D. C.: National Council of Teachers of Mathematics, 1948.

Keyes, Kenneth S., *How to Develop Your Thinking Ability.* New York: McGraw-Hill Book Company, Inc., 1950. Pp. 246.

National Council of Teachers of Mathematics, *Multi-Sensory Aids in the Teaching of Mathematics* (Eighteenth Yearbook). Washington, D. C.: National Council of Teachers of Mathematics, 1945. Pp. 455.

National Council of Teachers of Mathematics, *The Learning of Mathematics.* Its Theory and Practice (Twenty-First Yearbook). Washington, D. C.: The National Council of Teachers of Mathematics, 1953. Pp. 355.

National Council of Teachers of Mathematics, *The Teaching of Arithmetic* (Tenth Yearbook). New York: Bureau of Publications, Teachers College, Columbia University, 1935. Pp. 289.

National Society for the Study of Education, *Learning and Instruction* (Forty-Ninth Yearbook), Part I. Chicago: The University of Chicago Press, 1950. Pp. 352.

National Society for the Study of Education, *The Measurement of Understanding* (Forty-Fifth Yearbook), Part I. Chicago: The University of Chicago Press, 1946. Pp. 338.

National Society for the Study of Education, *Mental Health in Modern Education* (Fifty-Fourth Yearbook), Part II. Chicago: The University of Chicago Press, 1955. Pp. 389.

Newman, James R., *The World of Mathematics* (4 vols.). New York: Simon and Schuster, Inc., 1956.

Piaget, Jean, *Judgment and Reasoning in the Child.* New York: Harcourt, Brace and Company, Inc., 1928.

Polya, G., *How to Solve It.* Princeton, N. J.: Princeton University Press, 1945. Pp. 224.

Rosenquist, Lucy, *Young Children Learn to Use Arithmetic.* Boston: Ginn & Company, 1949. Pp. 175.

Sanford, V. A., *A Short History of Mathematics.* Boston: Houghton Mifflin Company, 1930. Pp. 402.

Sarnoff, David, *et al.*, *The Fabulous Future.* New York: E. P. Dutton & Co., Inc., 1956. Pp. 206.

Smith, David Eugene, *History of Mathematics* (2 vols.). Boston: Ginn & Company, 1923–25.

Smith, David Eugene, *The Teaching of Elementary Mathematics.* New York: The Macmillan Company, 1902.

Spencer, Peter L., and Marguerite Brydegaard, *Building Mathematical Concepts in the Elementary School.* New York: Henry Holt and Company, Inc., 1952. Pp. 375.

Spitzer, Herbert F., *The Teaching of Arithmetic.* (2nd ed.). Boston: Houghton Mifflin Company, 1954. Pp. 397.

Stern, Catherine, *Children Discover Arithmetic.* New York: Harper & Brothers, 1949.

Stokes, C. Newton, *Teaching the Meanings of Arithmetic.* New York: Appleton-Century-Crofts, Inc., 1951. Pp. 523.

Thorndike, E. L., *Psychology of Arithmetic.* New York: The Macmillan Company, 1922. Pp. 140.

Ulrich, Louis E., Sr., *Streamlining Arithmetic.* Chicago: Lyons & Carnahan, 1943.

Urbancek, Joseph J., *Mathematical Teaching Aids,* Supplement, Chicago Schools Journal Nos. 3–6. Chicago: Chicago Teachers College, 1954. Pp. 80.

Urbancek, Joseph J., J. T. Johnson, and Don C. Rogers, *Arithmetic Teaching Techniques.* Chicago: Chicago Board of Education, 1949. Pp. 348.

Van Engen, Henry, and E. Glenadine Gibb, *General Mental Functions Associated with Division.* Cedar Falls, Iowa: Iowa State Teachers College, 1956.

Wertheimer, Max, *Productive Thinking.* New York: Harper & Brothers, 1945.

Wheat, Harry Grove, *How to Teach Arithmetic.* Evanston, Ill.: Row, Peterson & Company, 1951. Pp. 438.

Wilson, G. M. and *et al., Teaching the New Arithmetic.* New York: McGraw-Hill Book Company, Inc., 1951. Pp. 484.

Articles

Aftreth, Orville B., "Shall We Expose Our Pupils to Errors?" *The Arithmetic Teacher,* IV (April, 1957), 129–131.

Albrecht, Mary E., "A Teacher Plans Her Day." *The Arithmetic Teacher,* III (October, 1956), 151–156.

Ambrosius, Dorothy S., "Division for First Graders?" *The Arithmetic Teacher,* III (February, 1956), 27–28.

Armstrong, Elizabeth, "Keep Score on the Abacus." *The Arithmetic Teacher,* IV (April, 1957), 111.

Arnold, Frank C., "The Decimal Is More than a Dot." *The Arithmetic Teacher,* II (October, 1955), 80–82.

Bakst, Aaron, "Mathematical Recreations." *The Mathematics Teacher,* XLIV (January, 1951), 41–42.

Bane, Robert C., "How Are Your Nines?" *The Arithmetic Teacher,* III (March, 1956), 77–79.

Beeman, William E., "Originality in Arithmetic." *The Mathematics Teacher*, XLVIII (November, 1955), 495–496.

Bell, Clifford, "Addition, Subtraction, and the Number Base." *The Arithmetic Teacher*, II (April, 1955), 57–59.

Benz, Harry E., "Two-Digit Divisors Ending in 4, 5, or 6." *The Arithmetic Teacher*, III (November, 1956), 187–191.

Bernstein, Allen, "A Study of Remedial Arithmetic Conducted with Ninth Grade Students." *School Science and Mathematics*, LV (January, 1955), 25–31: (June, 1955), 429–437.

Blom, E. C., "Developing Understanding Through Counting." *The Arithmetic Teacher*, II (October, 1955), 83-85.

Boyce, Loretta, "Arithmetic for Kindergarteners." *The Mathematics Teacher*, XLIV (November, 1951), 458–462.

Boyer, Lee Emerson, "=, Equal, or Equals?" *The Arithmetic Teacher*, II (October, 1955), 91–92.

Brandes, Louis Grant, "Constructing the Common Cross-Number Puzzle." *School Science and Mathematics*, LVII (February, 1957), 89–97.

Brandes, Louis Grant, "Using Recreational Mathematics Material in the Classroom." *The Mathematics Teacher*, XLVI (May, 1953), 326–329.

Brewer, Shirley Stillinger, "The Scientific Method of Problem Solving." *The Arithmetic Teacher*, III (April, 1956), 117–118.

Brickman, Benjamin, "More Rationalizing Division of Fractions." *The Arithmetic Teacher*, II (February, 1955), 25–26.

Brown, Francis R., "Arithmetic—Friend or Foe?" *The Arithmetic Teacher*, IV (February, 1957), 1–9.

Brown, Gerald, "An Area of Neglect in the Study of Arithmetic—Mental Arithmetic." *The Mathematics Teacher*, L (February, 1957). 166–169.

Brownell, William A., "Meaning and Skill—Maintaining the Balance." *The Arithmetic Teacher*, III (October, 1956), 129–136.

Brownell, William A., "The Revolution in Arithmetic." *The Arithmetic Teacher*, I (February, 1954), 1–5.

Brumfiel, Charles, "Definitions in Arithmetic." *The Arithmetic Teacher*, III (November, 1956), 192–196.

Brumfiel, Charles, "Enlarging Number Systems," *The Arithmetic Teacher*, III (April, 1956), 109–112.

Brune, Irvin, "Arithmetic via Television—A Course for Teachers and Parents." *The Arithmetic Teacher*, III (October, 1956), 165–167.

Brydegaard, Marguerite, "Creative Teaching Points the Way to Help the Brighter Child in Mathematics." *The Arithmetic Teacher*, I (February, 1954), 21–24.

Buckingham, B. R., "Perspective in the Field of Arithmetic." *The Arithmetic Teacher*, II (February, 1955), 1–5.

Buckland, G. T., "Can 2 + 2 = 11?" *The Arithmetic Teacher*, II (November, 1955), 126–127.

Carr, Alice R., "Using a 'Calculator' to Develop Basic Understandings and Meanings in Arithmetic." *The Mathematics Teacher*, XLIII (May, 1950), 195–196.

Christofferson, H. C., "Meanings in Division." *The Arithmetic Teacher*, IV (February, 1957), 21–23.

Clark, John R., "The Intangibles of Arithmetic Learning." *The Arithmetic Teacher*, III (March, 1956), 56–58.

Clark, John R., "The Use of Crutches in Teaching Arithmetic." *The Arithmetic Teacher*, I (October, 1954), 6–10.

Coburn, Maude, "Flexibility in the Arithmetic Program to Promote Maximum Pupil Growth." *The Arithmetic Teacher*, II (April, 1955), 48–54.

Cook, Ruth, "Number Concepts for the Slow Learner," *The Arithmetic Teacher*, I (April, 1954), 11–14.

Davis, O. L., Jr., "Arithmetic at the School Camp." *The Arithmetic Teacher*, III (October, 1956), 157–161.

Dawson, Dan T., and Arden K. Ruddell, "An Experimental Approach to the Division Idea." *The Arithmetic Teacher*, II (February, 1955), 6–9.

DeVault, M. Vere, "The Abacus and Multiplication." *The Arithmetic Teacher*, III (March, 1956), 65.

Dubins, M. Ira, "Integration of Arithmetic with Science Through the Study of Weather in the Elementary School." *School Science and Mathematics*, LVII (February, 1957), 121–130.

Duker, Sam, "Rationalizing Division of Fractions." *The Arithmetic Teacher*, I (December, 1954), 20–23.

Duncan, E. R., "Arithmetic in New Zealand." *The Arithmetic Teacher*, III (October, 1956), 137–142.

Dwight, Leslie A., "Inconsistencies in the Teaching of Arithmetic in the Elementary Grades." *The Arithmetic Teacher*, III (March, 1956), 79–80.

Dwight, Leslie A., "Inconsistencies in the Teaching of Arithmetic—II." *The Arithmetic Teacher*, III (April, 1956), 98–103.

Eads, Laura K., "Arithmetic on the March." *The Arithmetic Teacher*, I (October, 1954), 10–14.

Eads, Laura K., "Ten Years of Meaningful Arithmetic in New York City." *The Arithmetic Teacher*, II (December, 1955), 142–147.

Eagle, Edwin, "Don't Let That Inverted Divisor Become Mysterious." *The Arithmetic Teacher*, I (October, 1954), 15–17.

Ernst, Richard, "Introducing Mr. '0' and Mr. 'Decimal Point.' " *The Arithmetic Teacher*, III (November, 1956), 210–211.

Fehr, Howard F., "A Philosophy of Arithmetic Instruction." *The Arithmetic Teacher*, II (April, 1955), 27–32.

Fehr, Howard F., "Note on Philosophy of Teaching Arithmetic." *The Arithmetic Teacher*, III (February, 1956), 31–32.

Fehr, Howard F., George McMeen, and Max Sobel, "Using Hand-Operated Computing Machines in Learning Arithmetic." *The Arithmetic Teacher*, III (October, 1956), 145–150.

Flagg, Elinor, "Developing Confident, Self-Reliant Learners in Arithmetic." *School Science and Mathematics*, LV (May, 1955), 381–388.

Flewelling, Robert W., "The Abacus as an Arithmetic Teaching Device." *The Arithmetic Teacher*, II (November, 1955), 107–111.

Flournoy, Frances, "The Controversy Regarding the Teaching of Higher-Decade Addition." *The Arithmetic Teacher*, III (October, 1956), 170–173.

Ford, Marie S., "Arithmetic—An Old Subject in New Apparel." *The Arithmetic Teacher*, III (October, 1956), 143–144.

Gaskill, A. R., "Stimulating the Better Arithmetic Pupil with Insight Producing Activities." *The Arithmetic Teacher*, IV (February, 1957), 33–34.

Gattegno, C., "New Developments in Arithmetic Teaching in Britain, Introducing the Concept of 'Set.' " *The Arithmetic Teacher*, III (April, 1956), 85–89.

Gibb, E. Glenadine, "A Selected Bibliography of Research in the Teaching of Arithmetic." *The Arithmetic Teacher*, I (April, 1954), 20–22.

Gibb, E. Glenadine, "Take-Away Is Not Enough!" *The Arithmetic Teacher*, I (April, 1954), 7–10.

Glazier, R. C., "Arithmetic via Television—Demonstration Lessons at Springfield." *The Arithmetic Teacher*, III (October, 1956), 168.

Goodrich, B. J., "The Day Camp and Arithmetic." *The Arithmetic Teacher*, IV (March, 1957), 77–78.

Greco, Anthony J., "Group Methods in Primary Grades." *The Arithmetic Teacher*, IV (February, 1957), 28–29.

Grime, Herschel E., "Adapting the Curriculum in Primary Arhtimetic to Abilities of Children." *The Mathematics Teacher*, XLIII (October, 1950), 242–244.

Grossnickle, Foster E., "Arithmetic for Those Who Excel." *The Arithmetic Teacher*, III (March, 1956), 41–48.

Grossnickle, Foster E., "Dilemmas Confronting the Teachers of Arithmetic." *The Arithmetic Teacher*, I (February, 1954), 12–15.

Grover, C. C., "The Rate of Progress of Pupils in Arithmetic in the Elementary School." *The Mathematics Teacher*, XLIV (January, 1951), 7–9.

Gunderson, Agnes G., "Arithmetic for Today's Six- and Seven-Year-Olds." *The Arithmetic Teacher*, II (November, 1955), 95–101.

Hall, Jack V., "A 'Self-Starter' Approach to Fractions." *The Mathematics Teacher*, XLIII (November, 1950), 331–333.

Hamilton, Jean, "Remedial Arithmetic in the Regular Classroom." *School Science and Mathematics*, LVI (March, 1956), 197–209.

Harmon, Norene, "Arithmetic Can Be Fun." *The Arithmetic Teacher*, IV (March, 1957), 82–83.

Hartung, Maurice L., "Estimating the Quotient in Division." *The Arithmetic Teacher*, IV (April, 1957), 100–111.

Hauck, Eldon, "Concrete Materials for Teaching Percentage." *The Arithmetic Teacher*, I (December, 1954), 9–12.

Hausdoerffer, William H., "Introducing Our Numbering System in the Primary Grades." *The Arithmetic Teacher*, IV (March, 1957), 61–63.

Hess, Adrien L., "A Bibliography of Mathematical Books for Elementary School Libraries." *The Arithmetic Teacher*, IV (February, 1957), 15–20.

Hibbard, Wilbur, "An Approach to Per Cents." *The Arithmetic Teacher*, II (November, 1955), 128.

Hickerson, J. Allen, "The Semantics and Grammar of Arithmetic Language." *The Arithmetic Teacher*, II (February, 1955), 12–16.

Hickerson, J. Allen, "Why 'Indent' in Multiplication?" *The Arithmetic Teacher*, III (December, 1956), 236–241.

Hickey, William S., "Who Counts?" *The Arithmetic Teacher*, II (November, 1955), 111–112.

Hildreth, Gertrude, "Principles of Learning Applied to Arithmetic." *The Arithmetic Teacher*, I (October, 1954), 1–5.

Holder, Lorena W., "A Place-Value Game." *The Arithmetic Teacher*, III (December, 1956), 248–249.

Holder, Lorena W., "Measurements—A Skit by Eighth Graders and Their Teacher." *The Arithmetic Teacher*, II (October, 1955), 86–90.

Hooper, Barbara, "An Experiment with Hand-Tally Counters." *The Arithmetic Teacher*, II (November, 1955), 119–120.

Hughson, Arthur, "Implementing a Mathematics Program." *The Arithmetic Teacher*, II (November, 1955), 102–103.

Hutcheson, Ruth, Edna Mantor, and Marjorie B. Holmberg, "The Elementary School Mathematics Library." *The Arithmetic Teacher*, III (February, 1956), 8–16.

Instebo, Esther, "How Many Children Are Here Today?" *The Arithmetic Teacher*, II (December, 1955), 161–162.

Jack, Dorothy, and Amanda Hebeler, "Arithmetic Experiences in Grade One." *The Arithmetic Teacher*, II (October, 1955), 70–71.

Janicki, George, "A Game of Squares." *The Arithmetic Teacher*, III (November, 1956), 211.

Janicki, George, "Bizz-Buzz Game in Arithmetic." *The Arithmetic Teacher*, III (February, 1956), 28.

Janicki, George, "Cross Figure Puzzle—Measures." *The Arithmetic Teacher*, III (February, 1956), 16.

Janicki, George, "The Try-Angle Puzzle." *The Arithmetic Teacher*, III (November, 1956), 220.

Jarolimek, John, "Teaching Quantitative Relationships in the Social Studies." *The Arithmetic Teacher*, IV (March, 1957), 70–74.

Jenkins, Jen, "A Plan for Teaching Arithmetic Shorthand." *The Arithmetic Teacher*, III (November, 1956), 207–209.

Jenkins, Jen, "Teaching the Concept of Cubic Measure Through the Use of Manipulative Aids." *The Mathematics Teacher*, XLIX (October, 1956), 489–490.

Jenkins, Jen, "Teaching the Concept of Perimeter Through the Use of Manipulative Aids." *The Mathematics Teacher*, L (April, 1957), 309–310.

Jenkins, Jen, "Teaching the Formula for Circle Area." *The Mathematics Teacher*, XLIX (November, 1956), 548–549.

Jenkins, Orville, "Larry and the Abacus." *The Arithmetic Teacher*, I (October, 1954), 21–24.

Johnson, Charles E., "Grouping Children for Arithmetic Instruction." *The Arithmetic Teacher*, I (February, 1954), 16–20.

Johnson, Donovan A., "Attitudes in the Mathematics Classroom." *School Science and Mathematics*, LVII (February, 1957), 113–120.

Johnson, J. T., "Decimal Versus Common Fractions." *The Arithmetic Teacher*, III (November, 1956), 201–203.

Johnson, Mary T., "Science and Arithmetic in the Fifth Grade." *School Science and Mathematics*, LIV (December, 1954), 742–747.

Junge, Charlotte, "The Arithmetic Curriculum—1954." *The Arithmetic Teacher*, I (April, 1954), 1–6.

Karau, Earl A., "Arithmetic Football." *The Arithmetic Teacher*, III (November, 1956), 212–213.

Kidd, Kenneth P., "Class Participation in a Relay Game." *The Arithmetic Teacher*, I (December, 1954), 27–28.

Kingston, J. Maurice, "Formulas Can Be Fun." *The Mathematics Teacher*, L (January, 1957), 35–37.

Lansdown, Brenda C., "From Cake to Cancellation." *The Arithmetic Teacher*, IV (April, 1957), 136–137.

Latino, Joseph J., "Take the Folly Out of Fractions." *The Arithmetic Teacher*, II (November, 1955), 113–118.

Layne, Fay, "We Took the Class Census." *The Mathematics Teacher*, XLV (March, 1952), 168–172.

Lentz, Donald W., "Mental Arithmetic." *The Arithmetic Teacher*, IV (April, 1957), 132.

Lyvers, Donald B., "A Fraction Circle." *The Arithmetic Teacher*, III (April, 1956), 119–121.

McDaid, Elmer W., "Implications of a Guidance and Counseling Program." *The Arithmetic Teacher*, III (March, 1956), 49–54.

McKeen, Gene, "Measures Make Arithmetic Meaningful." *The Arithmetic Teacher*, III (December, 1956), 247–248.

Maloney, John P., "Arithmetic at the Primary Level." *The Arithmetic Teacher*, IV (April, 1957), 112–118.

Manheimer, Wallace, "A Modest Proposal to the Teachers of Developmental Arithmetic for Solving the Many Problems that Beset Their Subject." *The Arithmetic Teacher*, III (March, 1956), 71–73.

Mayer, Louise A., "The Scarbacus or Scarsdale Abacus." *The Arithmetic Teacher*, II (December, 1955), 159.

Miller, G. H., "How Effective Is the Meaning Method?" *The Arithmetic Teacher*, IV (March, 1957), 45–49.

Moore, Tabbie Mae, "More About Casting Out Nines." *The Arithmetic Teacher*, III (November, 1956), 204–206.

Moser, Harold E., "Can We Teach Pupils to Distinguish the Measurement and Partition Ideas in Division?" *The Mathematics Teacher*, XLV (February, 1952), 94–97.

Moser, Harold E., "Levels of Learning—Planning in Depth." *The Arithmetic Teacher*, III (December, 1956), 221–225.

Moyer, Haverly O., "Testing the Attainment of the Broader Objectives of Arithmetic." *The Arithmetic Teacher*, III (March, 1956), 66–70.

Nadelman, Goldie, and Elsie B. Paskins, "The Role of Experiences in Arithmetic." *The Arithmetic Teacher*, II (November, 1955), 104–106.

Nadelman, Goldie, and Elsie B. Paskins, "The Role of Experiences in Arithmetic." *The Arithmetic Teacher*, IV (February, 1957), 30–32.

Nelson, Theodora, "Results of General Mathematics Tests." *The Arithmetic Teacher*, III (February, 1956), 21–26.

Neureiter, Paul R., "Strike Up Your Arithmetic Band, The Use of Rhythm in the Teaching of Arithmetic." *The Arithmetic Teacher*, IV (March, 1957), 64–69.

Newell, Laura, "The Role of a Principal in Teaching Arithmetic." *The Arithmetic Teacher*, II (April, 1955), 55–56.

Nies, Ruth H., "Classroom Experiences with Recreational Arithmetic." *The Arithmetic Teacher*, III (April, 1956), 90–93.

Norton, Monte S., "Enrichment as a Provision for the Gifted in Mathematics." *School Science and Mathematics*, LVII (May, 1957), 339–345.

Norton, Monte S., "What Are Some of the Important Factors to Consider in a Program of Identifying the Gifted Pupil in Mathematics and Science?" *School Science and Mathematics*, LVII (February, 1957), 103–108.

Oliver, Nina, "Flying Saucers—A Project in Circles." *The Mathematics Teacher*, XLIV (November, 1951), 455–457.

Osborn, Jesse, "The Hundred Board." *The Arithmetic Teacher*, III (March, 1956), 54–55.

Osborn, Jesse, "Watching the License Numbers." *The Arithmetic Teacher*, III (November, 1956), 182.

Osborn, Jesse, "Whither in Arithmetic Teaching—A Perceptive Perspective View." *The Arithmetic Teacher*, III (December, 1956), 226–228.

Peeler, Harry, "Teaching Verbal Problems in Arithmetic." *The Arithmetic Teacher*, III (December, 1956), 244–246.

Peoples, John A., "A Meaningful Approach to Cancellation." *The Arithmetic Teacher*, III (February, 1956), 29–30.

Petty, Olan, "Non-Pencil-and-Paper Solution of Problems." *The Arithmetic Teacher*, III (December, 1956), 229–235.

Petty, Olan, "Requiring Proof of Understanding." *The Arithmetic Teacher*, II (November, 1955), 121–123.

Pikal, Frances, "Review of Research Related to the Teaching of Arithmetic in the Upper Elementary Grades." *School Science and Mathematics*, LVII (January, 1957), 41–47.

Plank, Emma N., "Observations on Attitudes of Young Children Toward Mathematics." *The Mathematics Teacher*, XLIII (October, 1950), 252–263.

Poffenberger, Thomas, and Donald A. Norton, "Factors Determining Attitudes Toward Arithmetic and Mathematics." *The Arithmetic Teacher*, III (April, 1956), 113–116.

Priore, Angela, "Achievement of Pupils Entering the First Grade." *The Arithmetic Teacher*, IV (March, 1957), 55–60.

Ratanakul, Suchart, "Learning Arithmetic from Kindergarten to Grade 6." *The Arithmetic Teacher*, II (November, 1955), 129.

Reckzeh, John, "Addition and Subtraction Situations." *The Arithmetic Teacher*, III (April, 1956), 94–97.

Reed, Calvin H., "Developing Creative Thinking in Mathematics." *The Arithmetic Teacher*, IV (February, 1957), 10–12.

Rheins, Gladys B., and Joel J. Rheins, "A Comparison of Two Methods of Compound Subtraction." *The Arithmetic Teacher*, II (October, 1955), 63–69.

Riess, Anita P., "Pre-First Grade Arithmetic." *The Arithmetic Teacher*, IV (March, 1957), 50–54.

Risden, Gladys, "Better Arithmetic." *The Mathematics Teacher*, XLIII (December, 1950), 392–393.

Risden, Gladys, "Meaning Is the Key." *The Arithmetic Teacher*, III (November, 1956), 183–186.

Risden, Gladys, "What Is Wrong with School Arithmetic?" *The Mathematics Teacher*, XLVI (October, 1953), 407–410.

Roudebush, Elizabeth, "An Arithmetic Bulletin for Parents." *The Mathematics Teacher*, XLIV (May, 1951), 289–292.

Roys, William B., "The Fracto-Percenter." *The Arithmetic Teacher*, II (December, 1955), 162.

Ruderman, Harry D., "The Game of Tick-Tack-Toe." *The Mathematics Teacher*, XLIV (May, 1951), 344–347.

Sanford, Vera, "Computers; Computing If You Can Count to Five." *The Mathematics Teacher*, XLIII (November, 1950), 368–370.

Sanford, Vera, "Hindu-Arabic Numerals." *The Arithmetic Teacher*, II (December, 1955), 156–158.

Sauble, Irene, "Development of Ability to Estimate and to Compute Mentally." *The Arithmetic Teacher*, II (April, 1955), 33–39.

Schaaf, William L., "Scales of Notation—A Bibliography." *The Mathematics Teacher*, XLVII (October, 1954), 415–417.

Schaaf, William L., "The Miracle of Arithmetic." *The Mathematics Teacher*, XLVI (December, 1953), 591–593.

Schaughency, Mildred D., "Teaching Arithmetic with Calculators." *The Arithmetic Teacher*, II (February, 1955), 21–22.

Schiff, Herbert J., "Let Them Measure." *School Science and Mathematics*, LVII (April 1957), 291–292.

Schott, Andrew F., "Johnny Can Learn Arithmetic—The Report of an Arithmetic Contest." *The Arithmetic Teacher*, IV (March, 1957), 75–76.

Seegar, Raymond J., "Teaching the Three A's in Elementary Mathematics." *The Arithmetic Teacher*, IV (February, 1957), 24–27.

Shuster, Carl N., "Teaching the Digit Zero." *The Arithmetic Teacher*, IV (February, 1957), 13–14.

Smith, Linda C., "Concept of Money via Experience." *The Arithmetic Teacher*, II (February, 1955), 17–20.

Smith, Rolland R., "The Tens-Tens Counting Frame." *The Arithmetic Teacher*, III (November, 1956), 197–200.

Snader, Daniel, "Mathematical Background for Teachers of Arithmetic." *The Arithmetic Teacher*, III (March, 1956), 59–64.

Spears, Margaret, "Five Ways to Improve Arithmetic Instruction." *The Arithmetic Teacher*, III (February, 1956), 30.

Spitzer, Herbert F., and Frances Flournoy, "Developing Facility in Solving Verbal Problems." *The Arithmetic Teacher*, III (November, 1956), 177–182.

Stephens, Harold W., "They Love Arithmetic!" *The Arithmetic Teacher*, II (April, 1955), 60–61.

Streby, George W., "Reading in Mathematics." *The Arithmetic Teacher*, IV (March, 1957), 79–81.

Strueve, Helen K., "Arithmetic via Television—A Report of the Pittsburgh Experiment." *The Arithmetic Teacher*, III (October, 1956), 162–164.

Sueltz, Ben, "An Arithmetic Spell Down." *The Arithmetic Teacher*, III (November, 1956), 219.

Sueltz, Ben, "Counting Devices and Their Uses." *The Arithmetic Teacher*, I (February, 1954), 25–30.

Sueltz, Ben, "Often the Numbers Are Missing—A Test." *The Arithmetic Teacher*, III (March, 1956), 75–76.

Sueltz, Ben, "These Things We Believe." *The Mathematics Teacher*, XLIX (January, 1956), 19–21.

Sueltz, Ben, "Twenty-Five Questions on Arithmetic." *The Arithmetic Teacher*, III (December, 1956), 250–251.

Swenson, Esther, "An Ounce of Prevention." *The Arithmetic Teacher*, III (February, 1956), 1–7.

Swenson, Esther, "The How and Why of Discovery in Arithmetic." *The Arithmetic Teacher*, I (April, 1954), 15–19.

Thiele, C. L., "Fostering Discovery with Children." *The Arithmetic Teacher*, I (February, 1954), 6–11.

Thomson, Alice P., "Evaluation by Observation—Grade 3." *The Arithmetic Teacher*, III (April, 1956), 104–108.

Tuttle, Ruth Hodges, "What's in a Rhyme?" *The Arithmetic Teacher*, III (December, 1956), 242–243.

Ullrich, Anna, "Labeling Answers to Arithmetic Problems." *The Arithmetic Teacher*, II (December, 1955), 148–153.

Ulrich, Louis E., Sr., "Casting Out Nines—Our Decimal Number System." *The Arithmetic Teacher*, II (October, 1955), 77–79.

University of Illinois Committee on School Mathematics, "Arithmetic with Frames." *The Arithmetic Teacher*, IV (April, 1957), 119–124.

Urbancek, Joseph J., "Arithmetic in the Child's Future." *The Arithmetic Teacher*, III (November, 1956), 214–216.

Van Engen, H., "One, Two, Button My Shoe." *The Arithmetic Teacher*, I (October, 1954), 18–20.

Van Engen, H., "The Child's Introduction to Arithmetic Reasoning." *School Science and Mathematics*, LV (May, 1955), 358-362.

Van Engen, H., "Which Way Arithmetic?" *The Arithmetic Teacher*, II (December, 1955), 131–140.

Vincent, Lois, "Peter Is a Slow Learner." *The Arithmetic Teacher*, I (December, 1954), 24–26.

Weaver, J. Fred, "Big Dividends from Little Interviews." *The Arithmetic Teacher*, II (April, 1955), 40–47.

Weaver, J. Fred, "Misconceptions About Rationalization in Arithmetic." *The Mathematics Teacher*, XLIV (October, 1951), 377-381.

Weaver, J. Fred, "Six Years of Research on Arithmetic Instruction: 1951–1956." *The Arithmetic Teacher*, IV (April, 1957), 89–99.

Weaver, J. Fred, "Whither Research on Compound Subtraction?" *The Arithmetic Teacher*, III (February, 1956), 17–20.

Wheat, Harry G., "Unifying Ideas in Arithmetic." *The Arithmetic Teacher*, I (December, 1954), 1–8.

Willerding, Margaret, "A Cross Number Puzzle for Flag Day." *The Arithmetic Teacher*, IV (April, 1957), 118.

Willerding, Margaret, "A Cross Number Puzzle for St. Patrick's Day." *The Arithmetic Teacher*, IV (March, 1957), 74.

Willerding, Margaret, "A Cross Number Puzzle for Valentine's Day." *The Arithmetic Teacher*, IV (February, 1957), 9.

Willerding, Margaret, "Codes for Boys and Girls." *The Arithmetic Teacher*, II (February, 1955), 23–24.

Willerding, Margaret, "History of Mathematics in Teaching Arithmetic." *The Arithmetic Teacher*, I (April, 1954), 24–25.

Willerding, Margaret, "Units on Four States." *The Mathematics Teacher*, XLVII (January, 1954), 25–27.

Williams, Catherine M., "The Function of Charts in the Arithmetic Program." *The Arithmetic Teacher*, II (October, 1955), 72–76.

Wilson, Guy M., "Toward Perfect Scores in Arithmetic Fundamentals." *The Arithmetic Teacher*, I (December, 1954), 13–17.

Wisely, Edna, "An Approach to Problem Solving." *The Arithmetic Teacher*, IV (April, 1957), 125–128.

Woodby, Lauren G., "How Big Is a Billion?" *The Arithmetic Teacher*, II (December, 1955), 160.

Wrightstone, J. Wayne, "Constructing Tests of Mathematical Concepts for Young Children." *The Arithmetic Teacher*, III (April, 1956), 81–84.

Yi-Yun, Yen, "The Chinese Abacus." *The Mathematics Teacher*, XLIII (December, 1950), 402–404.

Young, William E., "Language Aspects of Arithmetic." *School Science and Mathematics*, LVII (March, 1957), 171–174.

Index